Design and Analysis

HOUGHTON MIFFLIN COMPANY

OF EXPERIMENTS IN

PSYCHOLOGY AND EDUCATION

E. F. Lindquist · STATE UNIVERSITY OF IOWA

HOUGHTON MIFFLIN COMPANY · BOSTON

The Riverside Press Cambridge

1956 IMPRESSION

Preface

This book is designed primarily as a teaching instrument and learning aid. Its purpose is to help students and research workers in psychology and education learn how to select or devise appropriate designs for the experiments they may have occasion to perform, and to analyze and interpret properly the results obtained through the use of those designs.

Either of two contrasting procedures could be followed in the preparation of a text with this purpose. One is to present a number of "standard" designs, selected for maximum usefulness in these fields, and to provide for each a worked example of its application to a specific problem, together with step-by-step directions for the computational work involved, with general rules for the interpretation of results, and with suggestions concerning the types of problems with which the designs may be employed. Under this procedure, the student would be asked to take the underlying theory for granted, and only a minimum demand would be made on his mathematical skills and abilities. This might be described as a "cook book" type of text — consisting of "recipes" for the use of a few basic designs — or as a "follow the leader" type of text, implying that the user follows blindly the examples set for him, without understanding the reasons for what he does.

The other possibility is to attempt to develop in the student a genuine *understanding* of the *basic principles* of experimental design and analysis, so that he may be capable of devising for himself the particular design needed in any specific situation, or of modifying or combining the commonly used or "standard" designs and analytical procedures and of qualifying the inferences drawn as specific conditions may demand.

The limitations and dangers of the first of these procedures in the training of research workers are fairly evident. The specific designs needed in psychological research in general are so many and so varied that it is quite impracticable in a single text to provide fully developed specific illustrations or "model solutions" for more than a small proportion of the total number

needed. The student trained under the first of these procedures will tend
to use only those designs for which "model" examples have been provided,
to select the one of these designs for which the illustrative problem "seems
most like" the particular problem with which he is concerned, and to analyze
and interpret the results exactly as in the illustrative problem. Lacking any
genuine understanding of the principles involved, or any adequate appreciation of underlying assumptions, he will fail to recognize important differences between his own situation and the "model" situation, and will therefore frequently select inappropriate designs or draw wrong inferences from
the results obtained. A large proportion of the many mistakes that have
been made in educational and psychological research in the past have thus
been due to attempts to apply intact to a new field or problem a design or
technique which has been successfully used in or with another, without
recognizing the many subtle but fundamental differences in the situations
involved.

For these reasons, the latter of these two procedures will be that followed
in this text. With very few exceptions, the rule will be observed of presenting *all* of the essential mathematical and logical basis of the designs and
analytical procedures considered, but of presenting this basis in a form that
will place it well within the grasp of the typical student and research worker
in these fields. Specifically, it will be assumed that the typical student
using this text will have had only a single introductory course in applied
statistics — including the binomial, normal, and t distributions as applied
in sampling error theory to simple random samples and simple (product
moment) correlation theory — and that his formal training in mathematics
may not have gone beyond a year's course in high school algebra, or does
not include calculus. Because of these limitations, it will of course be necessary to make some exceptions to the rule just stated. It will be necessary
to ask the student to take for granted, without proof, the derivations of the
basic sampling distributions (such as the χ^2 and F-distributions) and the
probability tables based on these distributions. Occasionally, to save time
and space, proofs will also be omitted for some of the less important and incidental techniques employed, even though relatively simple proofs for these
techniques could be presented.

Because of the student's background, it will be necessary in most cases
to employ proofs that are considerably more cumbersome and indirect, and in
some instances less rigorous, than those that the mathematical statistician
would prefer. For the purpose of insuring that the student will later make
most intelligent *use* of these designs, however, the important considerations
are that the proofs employed be essentially sound, that they stress all of
the important assumptions necessary in the most rigorous proofs, that they
be meaningful to the student, and that they be convincing or "intuitively"
acceptable to him. Again, in consideration of the student's background, the

explanations and discussions accompanying the mathematical derivations may at times seem somewhat verbose to the trained reader who may employ this text for reference purposes. The author has no apologies to offer for this feature. On the contrary, experience has shown that the student very frequently needs and appreciates considerable repetition or restatement of important concepts and explanations.

A special effort will be made in this text to develop in the student a keen awareness and thorough understanding of the assumptions underlying the various tests of significance and of the consequences of failure to satisfy these assumptions, with specific reference to the situations in and materials with which the educational and psychological research worker must contend. A special effort will also be made to clarify to the student the considerations involved in the selection of valid "error" terms and in the use of "pooled" error terms. These are matters which have often been seriously neglected in discussions of experimental design, and this neglect has in large part accounted for the frequent use of inappropriate designs and the drawing of wrong inferences from experimental results.

A special feature of this text is the reliance placed upon the study exercises at the end of each chapter. These are intended to develop in the student a genuinely functional understanding of the designs and techniques presented, and to induce him to take an aggressive rather than a passive learning attitude. It is common practice in the writing of textbooks of this kind to introduce concrete illustrations into the discussions as early as possible, and to present most of the logic in specific terms of these illustrations. This often has the advantage of making the ideas initially easier to grasp, but also often has the disadvantage of associating the ideas presented too closely with the particular illustration employed, so that the student has difficulty later in generalizing the concepts gained, or of divorcing them from the unique textbook illustrations and, of "translating" them into the terms of new applications. In this text, the policy will be followed of presenting each design and procedure initially in rather highly generalized terms, and of then leaving it to the student himself to make these generalizations more specific and meaningful in terms of the concrete illustrations suggested in the study exercises. Care will be taken in these exercises to provide a sufficient number of leading questions that the student should meet with no inordinate difficulties in making the applications. The instructor is of course free to select those exercises that are most closely related to the peculiar interests of his students, or to devise similar exercises that will be more satisfactory in this respect.

Because of the policy of employing highly generalized and logical initial presentations, instead of relying upon specific illustrations introduced early or in a cook book fashion, this text will prove relatively difficult to read, particularly upon *first* reading or before consideration of the study exercises. It has been the author's experience, however, that the *total* difficulty for the student of securing a genuine understanding of experimental design and analysis is reduced rather than increased by this type of presentation. It should be emphasized that the study exercises are intended to constitute an integral part of the total presentation, and that the textual part of this text cannot fairly be evaluated alone apart from the manner in which it is to be used with the study exercises in instruction and learning.

An effort has been made to base the study exercises, wherever possible, upon actual applications reported in the research literature. In many instances, however, it was necessary to modify the reported descriptions or data so as to adapt them more specifically to the purposes of the study exercises. The study exercises, therefore are not to be regarded as containing any implications concerning the validity or adequacy of the research studies cited.

The content of this text follows a close, logical organization. Each new step taken in the logical development rests upon those taken earlier. It is especially important, therefore, that the student master thoroughly the logic of the simpler designs considered in the early chapters, particularly Chapters 3–9. Some of the simpler designs find relatively few practical applications, but all are essential for developmental purposes. The student is warned that until he feels that he has acquired a complete understanding of these simpler designs, he can hardly expect to comprehend at all the more complex designs and perhaps more practical designs which follow. He is assured, however, that once he has a genuine understanding of the basic principles presented in these earlier chapters, he will find that he can move ahead with surprising ease through the later chapters in the text.

This text has been developed through the use and revision of three successive multilithed editions with the author's classes. The help the author received from his students in the revision and improvement of these materials was of inestimable value. Special acknowledgement for such help is due to Dr. Dorothy Sherman, for her most exceptional thoroughness in detecting typographical errors, slips, and inadequacies in presentation, and to Rita Senf for her help in eliminating many infelicities in style and diction.

The entire manuscript (excluding the study exercises) was read for the publishers by W. G. Cochran, of Johns Hopkins University, and by David Grant, of the University of Wisconsin, and both made their comments available to the writer in time for a final revision of the manuscript before publication. Both readers read the manuscript with unusual care, and the author was enabled to make many important improvements in presentation as well as to correct several errors in theory on the basis of these comments. The author gratefully acknowledges the very valuable help thus secured from the publishers and their readers.

Major acknowledgement is due to two of the author's students and research assistants, Dee W. Norton and Leonard Feldt.   Dee Norton made a very time-consuming and painstaking search of the research literature in psychology and education for illustrative applications of the various designs, and was primarily responsible for the construction of the study exercises based on these illustrations.   Dr. Norton's study of the effects upon the F-distribution of non-normality and heterogeneity of variance (pages 79–90) constitutes a real contribution to better understanding of the techniques considered in this text. Leonard Feldt took full responsibility for reading galley and page proof, and for compilation of the index.

The author is indebted to Professor Sir Ronald A. Fisher, Cambridge, to Dr. Frank Yates, Rothamsted, and to Messrs. Oliver and Boyd Limited, Edinburgh, for permission to reprint Tables 1 and 2, the Appendix Table, and part of Table 3, from their books *Statistical Tables for Biological, Agricultural, and Medical Research* and *Statistical Methods for Research Workers.*

E. F. Lindquist

Contents

6 The Treatments × Subjects Design   156

7 The Groups-Within-Treatments Design   172

Contents

Tables

1

Introduction: Fundamental Concepts and

Basic Designs

The Nature and Purpose of Educational and Psychological

Experiments in General

The major purpose of psychological experiments is to describe the effect of certain experimental "treatments" upon some characteristic of a particular population, or to test some hypothesis about this effect. The term "treatment" will be used throughout this text to refer in general to any induced or selected variation in the experimental procedures or conditions whose effect is to be observed and evaluated. In a given experiment the "treatments" may be methods of teaching a particular school subject; they may be interpolated experiences in a learning series; specific amounts of practice in performing a certain task; induced states of anxiety; the taking of certain types of achievement tests; specified dosages of certain drugs; etc. If the treatments represent different amounts or degrees of a single variable, that variable will be referred to as the "experimental variable." For example, the treatments may represent different amounts of practice in the same task, or differing intensities of a certain auditory stimulus, etc. In many experiments, however, there is no single "experimental variable," or no *single* respect in which the various treatments differ from one another. That is, the treatments may represent complex combinations of variations in a large number of factors which may not be specifically identified — as when the treatment consists of a complex method of teaching a given school subject, and there are many respects, instead of only one, in which the various treatments differ from one another.

In most experiments, the observed "effect" is described in terms of changes or differences in the *mean* value of a certain "criterion" variable. For example, the effects of different experimental conditions under which a certain task is performed may be measured in terms of the *mean* time of completing the task. In other experiments, the effects may be measured in terms of variances,

1

treatment is an independent variable

ranks, correlation coefficients, regression coefficients, proportions, etc. A single complex experiment may be concerned with more than one experimental variable (or more than one treatment classification), and also with the possible effects of the treatments on more than one criterion variable. However, the general purpose of the experiment may usually be analyzed into more specific purposes, each concerned with the effect of a single factor on a single criterion variable.

The Importance of Measures of Precision

In general, the experimental results differ from subject to subject, and are influenced by accidental or unintentional variations in many extraneous factors. Accordingly, the "effect" observed in a single experiment must always be regarded as an *estimate* of the corresponding "true" effect, that is, the effect that would have been obtained in a perfectly controlled experiment involving all members of the specified population. The usefulness or value of the experiment therefore depends upon two major characteristics of the "estimate" obtained: (1) its freedom from bias, and (2) its precision. An estimate may be said to be free from bias to the degree that its *average* value for an increasing number of similar experiments tends to approach the "true" value. The *precision* of the estimate depends upon the variability of such estimates for such a series of experiments — the less variable the estimates, the more precise is any single estimate.

In any experiment, it is just as important to know *how precise* the estimate is as to have the estimate itself. If no description whatever of the precision of the estimate is available, anyone may successfully contend that the observed effect is due entirely to "error" — to fluctuations in random sampling or to unintentional variations in extraneous factors. The estimate is therefore worthless, no matter how precise it may be in fact. This does not mean that the precision of the estimate must always be objectively described in quantitative terms, such as in terms of the *standard error* of the estimate. But unless *some* description of its precision is available, even though subjective, unreliable, and non-quantitative, it is impossible to know what inferences may safely be drawn from the estimate, or within what limits one may rely upon those inferences. It is extremely important, therefore, that the experiment be planned so as to provide a dependable description of precision with each estimate obtained.

Unfortunately, in the planning of many experiments, consideration is originally given only to the problem of how to measure or describe the desired *effect*, that is, to the problem of estimation. The problem of how to describe the precision of the estimate or how to test its significance frequently receives no consideration whatever until the experiment is concluded and all results are in. At this point, unfortunately, it is frequently found that the experimental design does not permit the valid use of any known test of significance, whereas a change could easily have been made in the original design to make this possible. It should therefore be a maxim of experimental research that in the original planning of the experiment provision should be made *both* for an unbiased estimate of the desired effect and for a valid quantitative description or estimate of the precision of the estimated effect. The latter description will be referred to as the "error estimate." Not a single step should be taken in the administration of the experiment until the problem of how to analyze and evaluate the results has been thought through and solved in complete detail.

In attempting to *improve* a contemplated experimental design, then, any provision for *increased* precision in the estimate of the treatment effect must be accompanied by a corresponding revision in the estimate of error. In fact, no efforts to increase the precision of an experiment will be of much avail unless one can also dependably describe the increased *degree* of precision attained. On the contrary, if by some device one eliminates a certain source of error, yet continues to employ an error estimate allowing for errors from that source, the experiment may appear *less* conclusive than before, even though it is actually more precise. Suppose, for example, that in order to control chance differences among the treatment groups in a learning experiment, these groups are "matched" with reference to intelligence test scores, but that nevertheless the test of significance appropriate for random (unmatched) samples is still used. In this case, the observed differences in the learning criterion among the various treatment groups may actually become smaller (since the differences may no longer be inflated by this particular source of error); but this fact will only make the available estimates of error appear *larger* in relation to the reduced differences. It should therefore also be a maxim of experimental design that if a given source of error cannot be eliminated both from the experimental results and from the estimates of error, it had usually better not be eliminated at all. In other words, it may sometimes be desirable to select an experimental design resulting in lower precision than another, if the first design permits a valid estimate of error and the second does not.

In general, the variations in the criterion measures among all of the subjects involved in an experiment (the "total" variance) may be attributed to a variety of different factors, or may arise from a number of different sources. If the experiment has been properly designed, it will be possible to analyze the total variance into a number of independent components, each of which may be identified with one of these sources of variation. One part of the total variance will be due to the experimental treatments. Other parts will be due to extraneous factors which have been *controlled* in the experiment, so that their effects on the various treatment groups are the same. Still other parts of the total variance will be due to *uncontrolled* sources, that is, to "error." The test of the significance of the treatment effects consists essentially in a comparison of the "treatments" variance with the "error" variance, in order to determine whether or not the observed differences among the treatment means may be attributed to these uncontrolled sources. Suppose, for example, that in a learning experiment in which the various treatment groups have been matched with reference to intelligence test scores, a single distribution of the criterion measures is made for all subjects in all treatment groups. The variance of this distribution (the total variance) is presumably due in part to differences among the treatments. It is also due in part to differences from subject to subject in whatever is measured by an intelligence test, a source of variation which in this case is *controlled* by the matching of subjects. Finally, it is due in part to *random* (uncontrolled) variations in the many other factors affecting learning, such as nature and amount of previous training, age, sex, motivation, etc. The test of significance of the treatment effect consists essentially in a comparison of the treatments variance with the error variance.

Sometimes, as has been suggested earlier, the mistake is made of failing to isolate that part of the total variance which is due to *controlled* sources, and an "error" variance is employed which is really a composite due both to controlled and uncontrolled sources. In matched group experiments like that just described, for example, the mistake has been made of failing to "take out" of the error variance that part of the total variance due to the controlled (matched) variable, and of still using the error estimate appropriate for independent (unmatched) random samples. The result, of course, is to make the so-called "error" variance unduly large and to make the experiment seem less precise than it really is.

We can now understand why the technique of analysis employed with many experimental designs is known as the method of *analysis of variance*. In these terms, the aim of the experimenter is to employ a design that will control or equalize the effect of as many important extraneous variables as feasible, that will *randomize* the effects of all uncontrolled factors, and that will permit analysis of the total variance into independent components which may be identified respectively with the treatments, the controlled sources of variation, and the "error" variations. The "error" variance will then constitute an accurate and unbiased estimate of the *precision* of the experiment, in terms of which the treatments effect may be properly evaluated.

Complete freedom from bias and perfect precision in an experiment are, of course, both impossible and unnecessary. How unbiased or how precise an estimate need be depends upon the broader purposes of the experiment. Some experiments are intended to determine only whether an effect exists at all, or whether there is *any* relationship between the experimental and criterion variables. In that case, if the true effect is considerable, or if the true relationship is pronounced, even a very crude experiment may reveal the *presence* of the effect or relationship. In other experiments the *presence* of some relationship between the experimental and criterion variables may be taken for granted; the purpose of the experiment may be to describe the *magnitude* or the nature of that relationship, and the effects to be described may be known or expected to be of relatively small magnitude. In such an experiment, obviously, a relatively high degree of precision is essential.

In designing the experiment, therefore, the aim of the experimenter should usually be, not to provide for the highest possible degree of precision in the estimate, but rather to secure, *with the minimum expenditure of his resources*, whatever degree of precision and freedom from bias is *sufficient* for his purposes. His objective, in other words, is to design an experiment that will serve the specified purposes with maximum *efficiency*. No attempt will be made here to provide an exact definition of the "efficiency" of an experiment.[1] Its efficiency may be roughly described as its "precision per unit of cost," but what is involved in "cost," or in what units it may be measured, is often very difficult to say. The true cost of an experiment may seldom be satisfactorily described simply in terms of dollars expended. Whenever human subjects are employed, the time, convenience, comfort, and motivation of the subjects are often more important than the time and convenience of the experimenter, but as elements of cost these factors are very difficult to assess or describe quantitatively. It should be clear, however, that the more precise of two experimental designs is not always the one to be preferred. The "cost" at which this precision is obtained is always an extremely important consideration in the choice. Unfortunately, in practice, the purposes of the experiment are often too vaguely defined or too complex to permit any exact statement of the degree of precision *required*, and the cost may be very difficult to assess. Hence, the practical aim of the designer frequently becomes only that, in effect, of securing the highest precision in the estimates that his own resources will permit. In other words, the factor of efficiency is often neglected.

Testing Hypotheses

The ultimate objective of psychological and educational research in general is to develop a more complete *theory* — of learning, of mental organization, of school organization, etc. It is therefore useful, in most experiments, to view the major purpose as that, not only of *describing* the effects of the treatments, but of testing some specific hypothesis concerning the true effects. In accord with the law of parsimony, we usually begin by testing the simplest possible hypothesis that will explain the observed effects. We will entertain more complex hypotheses only if we are forced to reject the simpler ones. Accordingly, we most often begin with the hypothesis that the true effect is *nil*, or that there is *no* true difference among the experimental treatments so far as the criterion is concerned. The specific purpose of most experiments is thus to test a "null" hypothesis. If we are forced to reject this hypothesis, we may then consider more complex hypotheses and plan further experiments to test these hypotheses more fully. For example, having shown by an initial experiment that there is *some* relationship between the criterion and the experimental variable, we may then plan a further experiment to test the hypothesis that this relationship is *linear*. If this hypothesis must be rejected,

---

[1] The term is used here in a somewhat different meaning than is usual in the mathematical theory of statistics.

we may next test the hypothesis that the relationship is parabolic, etc. Before going on to more complex hypotheses, however, we want to make very sure that the simple hypotheses are false, and that we are not following a "blind lead" in our subsequent experiments.

We know that, even though the hypothesis to be tested is true, we cannot expect the observed effect in an experiment to agree exactly with the hypothetical true effect. Noting the discrepancy between the observed effect and the hypothetical true effect, we ask, is this discrepancy too large to be reasonably attributed to "error," — too large to enable us to retain the hypothesis? If so, just how confident may we be that the hypothesis is false? If the experiment has been properly designed, we can supply objective and quantitative answers to these questions. Thus *a major objective of the design of an experiment is to make such answers possible.*

The Essential Characteristics of a Good Experimental Design

The essential characteristics of a good experimental design may now be summarized as follows:

1) It will insure that the observed treatment effects are *unbiased* estimates of the true effects.

2) It will permit a quantitative description of the precision of the observed treatment effects regarded as estimates of the "true" effects.

3) It will insure that the observed treatment effects will have whatever degree of precision is required by the broader purposes of the experiment.

4) It will make possible an objective test of a specific hypothesis concerning the true effects; that is, it will permit the computation of the relative frequency with which the observed discrepancy between observation and hypothesis would be exceeded if the hypothesis were true.

5) It will be *efficient;* that is, it will satisfy these requirements at the minimum "cost," broadly conceived.

These are not the only essential characteristics of a good experiment. The usefulness or worthwhileness of an experiment is primarily dependent upon a great many other factors, which can be no more than barely identified in a book of this kind. In the earliest stages of planning any experiment, the problem to be investigated is usually stated in relatively indefinite and general terms. As the planning proceeds, the problem is modified and restated repeatedly, always more definitely and specifically, or always in a form more amenable to experimental attack — especially in view of the subjects, equipment, materials, and other resources available to the experimenter. Indeed, the final step in the planning is often to restate the problem once more so as to make it fit the particular experimental design that seems feasible, rather than to make a final modification of the design to fit a final statement of the problem.

The important decisions to be made in planning the experiment are concerned with: (1) the definition of the "treatments," (2) the selection or exact definition of the population to be investigated, (3) the selection of a criterion, (4) the identification of the factors to be controlled and the level or levels at which each is to be controlled, (5) the final restatement of the problem, and (6) the selection of a specific experimental design. These decisions are interdependent. A decision made at a particular stage in the planning may require modifications in previous tentative decisions, which may in turn affect other previous decisions, etc. The selection of the experimental design is usually the last step taken, but, as already noted, even it may suggest desirable modifications in other decisions previously made.

Basic Experimental Designs

The majority of educational and psychological experiments in general are intended to determine the effects of certain treatments upon the *mean* value of a certain criterion variable for a specified population. It is with the designs employed in such experiments that this book is primarily concerned.

Nearly all complex designs that are employed in experiments of this type may be regarded as variations or combinations of a small number of *basic* designs. It is possible, by selecting relatively simple and restricted examples, to illustrate concretely the application of each of these basic designs in terms of elementary statistical concepts already familiar to the student. This will be done in the remaining sections of this chapter, in order to give the student some advance appreciation of the nature and content of the text as a whole. *The student is not expected to make any intensive study of these basic designs at this point;* a brief consideration of them is all that is needed for these introductory purposes. The purpose of most of the remaining chapters will then be to generalize the application of these basic designs to less restricted situations and show how they may be combined and modified to suit various experimental conditions and types of problems. The basic designs are as follows:

1) *Simple-Randomized Designs:* Those in which each treatment is independently administered to a different sample of subjects, all samples independently drawn at random from the same parent population.

2) *Treatments × Levels Designs* (read "treatments *by* levels"): Those in which the various treatments are administered to samples "matched" with reference to a variable or variables related to the criterion and therefore more alike in response to the treatments than simple random samples would be.

3) *Treatments × Subjects Designs* (read "treatments *by* subjects"): Those in which all treatments are successively administered to the same subjects.

4) *Random Replications Designs:* Those in which the same basic experiment (of the simple-randomized type) is "replicated" (repeated) with independent samples of subjects. The subjects for the various "replications" may be drawn from the same population, or the experiment as a whole may be concerned with a population consisting of a large number of subpopulations, and the subjects for each replication may be drawn at random from a different and *randomly selected* subpopulation. In either case, the "replications" represented in the experiment may be regarded as a random sample from a larger number of possible replications.

5) *Factorial Designs:* Those in which there are two or more *cross*-classifications of treatments, or in which the effects and interactions of two or more experimental variables are simultaneously observed.

6) *Groups-Within-Treatments Designs:* Those in which the population to be investigated consists of a large number of finite groups, and in which each treatment is administered to an independent random sample of intact groups.

The essential nature of each of these designs will later be further clarified and the reasons for the names given them made more apparent by concrete illustrations.

Basic Types of Error

The observed differences among the treatment means in any experiment are due only partly to actual differences in the effectiveness of the treatments. They are also partly due to *errors* of various kinds, that is, to the effects of extraneous variables or factors. Some errors may vary from experiment to experiment; others may be constant over all experiments concerning the same treatments. The variable errors may be classed into three categories according to the experimental units with which they are associated: *subjects*, treatment *groups*, and *replications*. Errors which are constant for all replications or throughout the experiment cannot be taken into consideration in any error analysis, their effects being inextricably intermingled with or inseparable from the treatments effect.

It may be worth while to illustrate these three types of variable errors by referring to a concrete experiment. Suppose an experiment to determine the relative effectiveness of two methods (A_1 and A_2) of teaching fourth-grade arithmetic is performed in a certain school. For the purposes of the experiment, the pupils are divided into two groups; one is to receive Treatment or Method A_1, the other Treatment A_2. One teacher is assigned to teach one group by one method, another to teach the other group by the other method. The "treatments effect" is measured by the difference in the mean scores for the two groups on a criterion achievement test administered at the close of the experiment.

Suppose that essentially the same experiment is performed independently in several different schools, the same treatments being administered under as nearly as possible the same conditions in each school. Suppose, also, that these schools are drawn from a certain population of schools, such as all public graded elementary schools in Iowa. Suppose, finally, that the object of these experiments individually and collectively is to estimate the difference in treatment means for the entire population of schools from which these particular schools are drawn, and to test the hypothesis that this difference is zero. In this situation, we may now illustrate the various types of error as follows:

Type S Errors: In any single replication of such an experiment, it is usually left to chance to determine which treatment each subject is to receive. If the subjects are assigned at random to the treatment groups, the group assigned to A_1 may by chance contain a larger proportion of the more intelligent pupils, or of those who like arithmetic, or of the more industrious pupils, or of the pupils who received superior instruction during the year preceding, etc., etc. Accordingly, the mean criterion score may be higher for A_1 than for A_2, even though the treatments are on the average equally effective for all pupils in general in the particular school involved. That part of an observed treatment effect which is thus due solely to the assignment of subjects to treatment groups will, for convenience in the subsequent discussion, be referred to as a "Type S" error. Type S errors are those which characterize simple random sampling.

Type G Errors: In any single replication of an experiment, substantial differences would be found in the criterion means for the various treatments, even though no Type S errors were present, and even though the methods or treatments were on the average equally effective for the population sampled. Such differences may result from countless extraneous factors which tend to have the same effect on all members of any one treatment group but a different constant effect on the members of any other treatment group, and which thus create systematic differences in the criterion means from group to group in the same replication. For example, in the illustration used, the group receiving Treatment A_1 may have been assigned a better teacher, or a better classroom, or a more favorable hour of the day for instruction, than the A_2 group. Again, the pupils receiving Treatment A_1 may inadvertently have been given more time on the criterion test than those receiving treatment A_2, or some other accidental failure to administer the experiment properly may favor one treatment at the expense of the other in the comparison of means. The effect of most such factors can and should be randomized with reference to treatments in each replication independently; those that arise during the experiment and cannot be randomized will in most cases be accidental and without bias. If this is the case, such errors will tend to cancel out in the long run (for a very large number of replications), but in any single replication they may have a pronounced effect on the observed differences in treatment means.

In general, these errors are associated with the administration of the experiment or with the experimenter, in the sense that they are subject to the experimenter's control, although many of them (such as teacher differences) are unavoidable and not the "fault" of the experimenter. As already noted, it is the experimenter's responsibility to reduce these errors to a minimum, and to randomize the effects of any factors that cannot be completely equalized. For example, in the illustration used, after having done his best to secure equally good teachers for both methods, the experimenter may then flip a coin to determine which teacher is to be assigned to Method A_1 and which to A_2.

It might be well to draw attention here to a very important source of error in educational and psychological experiments which has often gone unrecognized, or which, when recognized, has often been misclassified. In the illustrative situation, for example, suppose that among the pupils assigned to the experiment in this particular school, one pupil is a notorious troublemaker, seriously interfering with the effectiveness of instruction in his classes. A source of variation of this kind is certainly associated with an individual pupil, but it is not independent of all other pupils. On the contrary, it exerts an important systematic effect on all pupils in one treatment group, and is therefore a Type G rather than a Type S error. The presence of a "natural leader" who exerts a beneficial influence on the members of his group, or the "esprit de corps" developing from the subtle influences of the pupils upon one another, also illustrate Type G errors. The importance of such factors in "group dynamics" is often overlooked in experiments where the treatments are administered on a group basis, or the assumption is wrongly made that the effects of such factors are taken into consideration by tests of significance based upon Type S errors only.

Errors of the type here illustrated will, for convenience in the following discussion, be referred to as "Type G" errors. Type G errors may be defined as those due to the operation of extraneous factors which tend to have the same effect on all members of any given treatment group, but different effects on different treatment groups in any single replication.

Type R Errors: In the illustrative situation, it is quite possible that Treatment A_1 may actually be better than A_2 for certain schools in the given population, but that A_1 may really be inferior to A_2 for certain other schools. This could result from differences in curriculum, or in the administrative organization of the schools, or in school plant and equipment; or it could be due to any other conditions in the school or community making one method really more appropriate or effective than the other for that particular school or community. The observed effect of a treatment in any particular school could then be free from error so far as that school alone is concerned, yet be considerably in error as an estimate of the average treatment effect for all schools in the given population of schools.

There are many experiments in education and psychology which thus consist of a number of independent replications, each performed with samples drawn at random from a different sub-population in the total population with which the experiment as a whole is concerned. Variations in treatment effects from replication to replication, due neither to Type S nor Type G errors, but genuinely characteristic of the individual replications or sub-populations, will be referred to in this discussion as "Type R" errors.[1]

The Principle of Randomization

It is never possible to eliminate or to equalize completely the effects of any type of error, but under certain circumstances any *bias* in the treatment effect resulting from uncontrolled error variations may be successfully eliminated by *randomizing* the error variations with reference to the treatments. In the illustration just used, for example, a strictly random procedure may be followed in assigning the pupils to the treatment groups. While certain group differences (Type G errors) may be unavoidable, their effects may nevertheless be randomized. For example, it may not be possible or practicable to secure equally good teachers or to use the same teacher for both treatments; but it may be possible to leave entirely to chance the assignment of teachers to treatments. Similarly, the assignment of classrooms, periods, equipment, etc., may be done on a strictly random basis. Finally, if the experiment is to be replicated in several different schools, care may be taken to select a strictly random sample of schools from the population of schools involved, so that there will be no systematic tendency to select a disproportionately large number of schools in which one treatment is actually superior to the other.

There is, however, a still more important reason for randomizing error variations with reference to treatments in each replication. All tests of statistical significance and all standard error formulas are based on the fundamental laws of probability. Cognizance can be taken of a certain source of error in a statistical test of significance only if it has been left *entirely to chance* which treatment will benefit from this source in any single comparison of the treatments. Furthermore, a *number* of such comparisons must be made, in each of which the effect of the given source of error has been independently randomized with reference to the treatments. The usual "error estimate" is an estimate of the population *variance* of errors due to certain sources, and at least two observations, of course, are essential to the computation of a variance estimate. One of the most important and

---

[1] In later chapters these Type R errors will often be referred to as "interaction" effects, or, more specifically, as the *intrinsic* treatments × replications interaction effects (see pages 193–194). The *extrinsic* treatments × replications interaction effects constitute the Type G errors.

basic of all principles of experimental design is thus the *principle of randomization*. Briefly restated, this is the principle that *a given type of error can be eliminated as a source of bias and can be taken into consideration in an error estimate or a test of significance only if a number of independent observations of the effect of this type of error have been obtained, and only if these observations may be regarded as a random sample from all such observations possible.*

It should be noted that each of the three basic types of error must be randomized in an experiment if each is to be taken into consideration in a valid test of significance. Subjects must be randomly assigned to the treatment groups; Type G errors must be independently randomized for each replication; and the subpopulations with which the individual replications are performed must be selected at random from all subpopulations constituting the population involved. With some designs, as we shall see, it is possible to randomize certain but not all of these basic types of error. Thus the combination of error types for which the error estimate or test of significance is valid may differ from one design to another. Sometimes it is possible to randomize both the Type S and the Type G errors but not Type R errors. In other situations, it may be possible to randomize some of the Type G errors but not others. Whenever possible, of course, the experimenter should use a design permitting a test of significance that will be valid for all types of error affecting the observed result. That is, the experimenter should know how the treatment effects would fluctuate in similar experiments as the result of the *combined* effect of *all* sources of error. The sampling distribution involved in the test of significance should be the *joint* error distribution.

Illustrative Applications of Basic Designs

In terms of principles and concepts thus far considered, we are now ready to consider a specific illustration of each of the basic experimental designs listed on pages 7 and 8. Again it should be emphasized that the student is not expected at this point to make an intensive or exhaustive study of these designs. Two or three careful readings of these descriptions should suffice for the introductory purposes intended.

Simple-Randomized Designs: Consider again an experiment like that already described, in which the "treatments" are two methods of teaching a given unit of school instruction in arithmetic. The population involved consists of "all fourth-grade pupils in the public schools of Iowa"; the criterion is the score on an objective achievement test designed for the given unit of instruction. Suppose that, in a certain school, 60 pupils are available for the experiment, and that these may be regarded as a random sample from all pupils who might be taught fourth-grade arithmetic in that school. Suppose that these pupils are randomly assigned, 30 to one group and 30 to another; that all administrative arrangements are made for these groups, including the assignment of teachers, classrooms, periods, etc.; and that as a final step in the arrangement, a coin is flipped to determine which group is to be taught by Method A_1 and which by Method A_2. At the close of the period of instruction, both groups are given the criterion test, and the mean scores $(M_{A_1}$ and $M_{A_2})$ of the two groups are computed and compared. The estimated standard error of the difference in these means is computed by the formula

$$\text{est'd}\,\sigma_{(M_{A_1}-M_{A_2})} = \sqrt{\left(\frac{\Sigma d_{A_1}^2 + \Sigma d_{A_2}^2}{n_{A_1} + n_{A_2} - 2}\right)\left(\frac{1}{n_{A_1}} + \frac{1}{n_{A_2}}\right)}$$

in which d_{A_1} and d_{A_2} represent individual deviations from M_{A_1} and M_{A_2} respectively, and n_{A_1} and n_{A_2} represent the corresponding numbers of cases.

The significance of the difference is then tested by

$$t = \frac{M_{A_1} - M_{A_2}}{\text{est'd}\,\sigma_{(M_{A_1} - M_{A_2})}}$$

for which the number of degrees of freedom is $(n_{A_1} + n_{A_2} - 2)$.

It is immediately apparent that this test of significance takes into consideration Type S errors only. Most of the irrelevant factors resulting in Type G errors (such as teachers, classrooms, etc.) may have been randomized in the assignment of treatments to groups, but since we have only one observation of a difference in group means (that is, since we have only one observation containing a Type G error) we cannot estimate the variability of such errors. For the same reason we cannot estimate the variability from replication to replication (school to school) of treatment differences which are genuinely characteristic of the replications. That is, we cannot take Type R errors into consideration in the test of significance. Furthermore, this design only *randomizes*, but does not *control* or equalize, subject variations, except insofar as they are equalized by the random assignment of subjects to groups. Since the subjects involved in educational and psychological experiments are typically characterized by very large individual differences, it is necessary when using this design to employ relatively large samples in order to secure the desired degree of precision. For these reasons, the simple-randomized design finds relatively few applications in educational and psychological research, except as a unit in more complex designs.

The illustration of the simple-randomized design just presented involves only two treatments. When comparisons are to be made simultaneously among several treatments, a different analytical procedure and a different test of significance must be employed, but the possibilities and limitations of the design are otherwise unchanged. The manner in which the more generalized case is handled will be considered in Chapter 3.

Treatments × Levels Designs: The treatments × levels design provides for direct control of inter-subject variations. In this design, the treatments are administered to samples that have been "matched" with reference to a "control" variable or variables. Consider again the experiment in teaching fourth-grade arithmetic. Suppose that, on the basis of their achievement in *third*-grade arithmetic, the pupils had previously been rated as "superior," "average," or "inferior." Suppose then that the pupils from each of these three subgroups are independently assigned at random to the two experimental treatments. The two treatment groups would then be "matched" with reference to third-grade achievement, in that each treatment group contains the same proportion of subjects at each level.

This illustrative experiment may be diagrammed as follows:

Level	*Treatment*	
	A_1	A_2
L_1: Superior	$n = 10$ $M_{A_1 L_1}$	$n = 10$ $M_{A_2 L_1}$
L_2: Average	$n = 10$ $M_{A_1 L_2}$	$n = 10$ $M_{A_2 L_2}$
L_3: Inferior	$n = 10$ $M_{A_1 L_3}$	$n = 10$ $M_{A_2 L_3}$
	M_{A_1}	M_{A_2}

[handwritten margin notes: $M_{A_1 L_1} - M_{A_2 L_1}$ simple effect of treatment at superior level.]

[handwritten note below table: $M_{A_1} - M_{A_2}$ main effect of treatment]

For the sake of simplicity of illustration, we have let the number of cases ($n = 10$) be the same in each of the six subgroups. Accordingly, the over-all mean for Treatment A_1 is

$$M_{A_1} = \tfrac{1}{3}(M_{A_1 L_1} + M_{A_1 L_2} + M_{A_1 L_3}).$$

Now we know from elementary statistics [1] that the variance of the sum of a number of unrelated variables is equal to the sum of their variances, and that the variance of k times a given variable is equal to k^2 times the variance of that variable. From this it follows that the estimated error variance of M_{A_1} (k being equal to $\tfrac{1}{3}$) is

$$\text{est'd } \sigma^2_{M_{A_1}} = \frac{1}{9}\left(\text{est'd } \sigma^2_{M_{A_1 L_1}} + \text{est'd } \sigma^2_{M_{A_1 L_2}} + \text{est'd } \sigma^2_{M_{A_1 L_3}}\right)$$

$$= \frac{1}{9}\left(\frac{\Sigma d^2_{A_1 L_1}}{10 \times 9} + \frac{\Sigma d^2_{A_1 L_2}}{10 \times 9} + \frac{\Sigma d^2_{A_1 L_3}}{10 \times 9}\right) = \frac{1}{810}\left(\Sigma d^2_{A_1 L_1} + \Sigma d^2_{A_1 L_2} + \Sigma d^2_{A_1 L_3}\right)$$

in which $d_{A_1 L_1}$ is a deviation from $M_{A_1 L_1}$ (in the superior group for A_1), and $d_{A_1 L_2}$ and $d_{A_1 L_3}$ have similar meanings. The estimated error variance of M_{A_2} may be similarly computed. Accordingly, the estimated error variance for the difference in over-all treatment means is

$$\text{est'd } \sigma^2_{(M_{A_1} - M_{A_2})} = \text{est'd } \sigma^2_{M_{A_1}} + \text{est'd } \sigma^2_{M_{A_2}}$$

and the test of the significance of this difference is

---

[1] See Peters and Van Voorhis, *Statistical Procedures and Their Mathematical Bases* (New York: McGraw-Hill Book Company, Inc., 1940), pp. 77, 177.

$$t = \frac{M_{A_1} - M_{A_2}}{\text{est'd } \sigma_{(M_{A_1} - M_{A_2})}}$$

for which the number of degrees of freedom is 54, there being 9 degrees of freedom for the error variance of the mean of each of the six groups involved. (If the concept of degrees of freedom is not already understood by the student, he may postpone any consideration of it to Chapter 2. For present purposes, the indicated degrees of freedom may be taken for granted.)

The principal advantage of this design over the simple-randomized design is that it provides a direct control of Type S errors. If there is a substantial correlation between the control and the criterion variables, the treatment groups, having been made closely alike with reference to the control variable, will be much more alike with reference to the criterion variable than simple random samples would be. Differences in the criterion means due to random assignment of subjects to treatment groups will thus be considerably reduced, depending upon the degree of correlation between the control and the criterion variables.

Another advantage of the treatments × levels design is that it permits a separate study of the treatment effects at different levels of the control variable. In the illustrative experiment, for example, Treatment A_1 might be shown to be superior to A_2 for pupils of superior ability, but inferior to A_2 for pupils of inferior ability. To test the hypothesis that the treatments are *equally* effective at the upper and lower levels, one could use the t-test

$$t = \frac{(M_{A_1 L_1} - M_{A_2 L_1}) - (M_{A_1 L_3} - M_{A_2 L_3})}{\sqrt{\text{est'd } \sigma^2_{(M_{A_1 L_1} - M_{A_2 L_1})} + \text{est'd } \sigma^2_{(M_{A_1 L_3} - M_{A_2 L_3})}}}$$

in which

$$\text{est'd } \sigma^2_{(M_{A_1 L_1} - M_{A_2 L_1})} = \text{est'd } \sigma^2_{M_{A_1 L_1}} + \text{est'd } \sigma^2_{M_{A_2 L_1}},$$

and for which the degrees of freedom is the sum of the degrees of freedom for the standard errors of the means involved.

It is conceivable that Treatment A_1 is superior to A_2 at the upper level and inferior to A_2 at the lower level, but that for the upper and lower levels combined the two treatments are on the average equally effective. In that case, the t for $(M_{A_1} - M_{A_2})$ might prove non-significant and that for $[(M_{A_1 L_1} - M_{A_2 L_1}) - (M_{A_1 L_3} - M_{A_2 L_3})]$ significant. The reverse could also be true; that is, one treatment might be superior to the other but equally so at both levels.

The treatments effect for a given level of the control variable is known as the "simple" effect of the treatments at that level. The weighted average of the simple effects for *all* levels of the control variable is known as the "main" effect of the treatments. In the illustration, the simple effect of the treatments for the top level of the control variable is measured by

$M_{A_1 L_1} - M_{A_2 L_1}$; the main effect is measured by $M_{A_1} - M_{A_2}$, which in this case is the simple average of the simple effects.

If the second of the preceding t's proves significant, that is, if the simple effect is shown to differ from one level to another, we would conclude that there is an "interaction" between treatments and levels, or that the relative effectiveness of the treatments depends upon the level at which they are used. Such information could obviously be more valuable than that obtained from the test of the significance of the over-all difference.

For the sake of simplicity, only three levels were used in this illustration. In actual practice, a larger number of levels would ordinarily be employed to insure a closer matching of the treatment groups. In many instances, the matching would be based on quantitative measures, such as test scores, rather than on categorical ratings. The distribution of such scores could of course be divided into any desired number of intervals or levels, and the number of cases might differ from one level to another. In the general case, there would also be more than two treatments. In the special case here considered, it is possible to evaluate the results quite satisfactorily with simple t-tests, although the second t-test is concerned with only two levels, whereas a test of interaction should properly involve all levels. Other analytical procedures and tests of significance are required for the general case, and these will be presented later (Chapter 5). The basic limitations and possibilities of the general design, however, are adequately exemplified in this illustration.

In using this design, the different "levels" need not correspond to different scale intervals for a single continuous variable. The levels might correspond to non-ordered categories in any classification applicable to the members of the population involved, such as sex, religious preference, nationality, geographical location, etc. The subjects would then be randomized with reference to treatments for each level independently, but the treatments would be administered on a group basis to all levels simultaneously.

The name treatments × levels is ordinarily applied to a design only if the levels have been introduced in order to increase the precision of the experiment and for no other reason. However, essentially the same design can be employed even though the introduction of levels results in no appreciable increase in precision, the purpose being to permit a study of the simple effects and the differences among them (interaction) as well as of the main effects of the treatments. In this case, as we shall see later, the design would be termed a "factorial" design. The treatment × levels design is sometimes difficult to distinguish from a factorial design; the problem of this distinction will be considered later in the discussion of factorial designs.

Aside from the advantages here considered, the advantages and disadvantages of the treatments × levels design are the same as those of the simple-randomized design. In both designs, Type G and Type R (if any) errors are confused with the true treatment effects, and the available test of significance takes into consideration Type S errors only.

Treatments × *Subjects Designs:* If the treatments are such that all can be administered in sequence to the same subjects, and if the effects of each treatment are uninfluenced by the fact that other treatments have previously been administered to the same subjects, it is possible to eliminate entirely the influence of inter-subject differences upon the treatments effect. Suppose that an experiment is intended to determine the effect of the administration of two drugs (A_1 and A_2) on the time required to perform a certain task, such as the time required to cross out every letter "e" on a given printed page. Suppose that each of a group of n subjects, selected at random from a specified population, performs this task twice, once under the influence of Drug A_1 and once under the influence of Drug A_2. We will assume that the task has previously been performed often enough by the subjects so that there is no further improvement due to practice, and that the influence of Drug A_1 has dissipated entirely before Drug A_2 is administered. For each subject, a difference can be found between the two obtained times, a difference in favor of Drug A_1 being considered as positive and one in favor of A_2 as negative. The mean (M) and standard deviation (s) of the distribution of these differences can then be computed, and a simple t-test can be employed to test the hypothesis that the population value of the mean difference is zero, as follows:

$$t = \frac{M}{\text{est'd } \sigma_M} = \frac{M}{s/\sqrt{n-1}}$$

Since exactly the same subjects take both treatments, no part of the difference in treatment means can be attributed to differences among the subjects (inter-subject differences), although chance errors of measurement (intra-subject differences) might still favor one treatment or the other. Because inter-subject differences are usually a major source of error in educational and psychological experiments, the treatments × subjects design is usually far more precise than the simple-randomized or the treatments × levels design, granting that a fairly reliable criterion measure is employed. However, the usefulness of this design is severely limited by the fact that the effect of a given treatment is usually not independent of or unaffected by the previous administration of another treatment to the same subjects. (More complex designs will be considered later in which the effects of order and sequence of treatments are counter-balanced.) Furthermore, the use of this design usually requires that equivalent forms of a criterion test be available, so as to eliminate or render negligible the practice effect of taking the same test more than once.

Aside from the advantages and disadvantages just noted, the treatments × subjects design has all the limitations of the simple-randomized and treatments × levels designs. In none of these designs does the test of significance take into consideration Type G or Type R errors.

The Random Replications Design: We have seen that all the designs thus far considered have the common limitation that the available test of significance does not take Type G or Type R errors into consideration. Thus it is impossible to tell to what extent the observed treatment effect is due to such errors and to what extent to real differences among the treatments in the entire population considered.

We shall consider first a design which takes Type G (but not Type R) errors into consideration. To accomplish this, a number of different observations must be made of the treatment effects, Type G errors having been independently randomized for each observation. Suppose, for instance, that a methods experiment in arithmetic is to be performed with the pupils in a given school, and that 150 pupils are available for the experiment. (It is important to note that these 150 pupils must, for the purposes of this design, be regarded as a random sample from a hypothetical larger population of all pupils who might take fourth-grade arithmetic in this school under the general conditions now prevailing in this school.) Suppose then, that instead of conducting a single experiment with two random samples of, say, 15 pupils each, *five* separate experiments or replications are performed, the pupils having been randomly assigned to ten different groups for the purpose. Type G errors are *independently* randomized in each replication, and each is independently administered under as nearly as possible the same conditions. This experiment can be diagrammed as follows:

Treatments

	A_1	A_2	
Replication #1	$M_{A_1 R_1}$	$M_{A_2 R_1}$	$D_1 = (M_{A_1 R_1} - M_{A_2 R_1})$
Replication #2	$M_{A_1 R_2}$	$M_{A_2 R_2}$	D_2
Replication #3	$M_{A_1 R_3}$	$M_{A_2 R_3}$	D_3
Replication #4	$M_{A_1 R_4}$	$M_{A_2 R_4}$	D_4
Replication #5	$M_{A_1 R_5}$	$M_{A_2 R_5}$	D_5
	M_{A_1}	M_{A_2}	$\bar{D} = (M_{A_1} - M_{A_2})$

Since Type G errors have been independently randomized for each replication, we now have five observations of treatment effects (five D's) containing such errors. These five replications may be regarded as randomly selected from all possible replications of this kind in the hypothetical population referred to earlier. Accordingly, the Type G errors contained in these five observations may be regarded as a simple random sample from a hypothetical population of such errors for an indefinite number of such replications. The five observed D's, then, are a *simple random* sample from a hypothetical population of such D's. Accordingly, the estimated error variance of the mean difference ($\bar{D}$) is given by

$$\text{est'd } \sigma_{\bar{D}}^2 = \frac{\sum_{i=1}^{n}(D_i - \bar{D})^2}{n(n-1)}$$

in which, in this case, $n = 5$.

To test the hypothesis that the *true* mean of these differences (that for the hypothetical population described) is zero, we may use the simple *t*-test

$$t = \frac{\bar{D}}{\text{est'd } \sigma_{\bar{D}}}$$

for which the number of degrees of freedom is $n-1$ (in this case, 4).

If the purpose of this experiment is to determine the relative effectiveness of the methods for this particular school only, then there is no Type R error present, since all replications are performed with samples drawn at random from the same population. The *t*-test of significance just described is then valid for *all types of errors that have been randomized* for the various replications.

However, if the purpose of this illustrative experiment is to establish the relative effectiveness of the methods for a population of schools of which this school is a member, then of course a Type R error may be present. However, it will be constant for all replications within this school, and therefore will not be taken into consideration in the test of significance.

If the various replications are thus performed for random samples drawn from the *same* population, in which case there are no Type R errors present, the design will be referred to as a "simple" random replications design.

The random replications design in general differs from the "simple" random replications design in that, in the general case, the experiment as a whole is concerned with a total population consisting of a large number of subpopulations, and that each replication is performed for a different subpopulation, selected at random from the total population. In each replication independently (as in the case of simple replications), *all* systematic differences among the treatment groups, whether due to differences among subjects or to differences in experimental conditions, are randomized with reference to the treatments.

To illustrate the general case of random replications, suppose that a methods experiment in arithmetic is intended to determine the relative effectiveness of the methods for "all graded public elementary schools in Iowa," and that five of these schools are selected at random. Suppose that within each of these schools 30 pupils are selected at random from all fourth-grade pupils, and that 15 of these pupils are assigned, either arbitrarily or at random, to one of two treatment groups. Suppose also, that after all administrative arrangements have been made for these treatment groups, the treatments are finally assigned at random to these groups. This experiment may then be diagrammed exactly as in the preceding illustration, and the test of significance similarly computed and applied.

In the design just illustrated, all three of the basic types of error may be taken into consideration in the test of significance. In this case, there would be a different Type R error in each replication, and the five errors of this type represented in the five replications could be regarded as a simple random sample from the population of such errors for all schools in the given population. Thus, the variance of the distribution of five differences would

be due in part to the variance of errors due to subject differences, in part
to the variance of Type G errors, and in part to the variance of Type R
errors. Since in every case these errors are a random sample from a hypothetical population of such errors, the test of significance takes all types of
errors into consideration simultaneously. The only errors which are *not* taken
into consideration in this test are those which have not been randomized
independently in each replication, or which are constant for all replications.

Since Type G and Type R errors may be relatively very important in many
educational and psychological experiments, it is apparent that the random
replications design represents a very marked improvement over the designs
considered earlier.

Factorial Designs: Traditionally, the "ideal" experiment has been regarded
as one concerned with only a single experimental variable, and one in which
an attempt is made to "hold constant" the effects of all concomitant or
extraneous variables. We have already seen, however, that instead of hold-
ing a concomitant variable constant at only one level, it might be better
to replicate the experiment at several different levels of that variable. This
is desirable, not only in order to increase the precision of the experiment,
but also in order that the *interaction* (if any) between treatments and levels
may be studied, and in order that the relative effectiveness of the treatments
at each of a number of different levels may be determined simultaneously in
a single experiment. We have seen, also, that the "levels" involved in the
treatments × levels design need not correspond to different degrees or amounts
of a single continuous variable, but may represent different non-ordered
categories in any classification of the subjects. The interest might conceivably be greater in the interaction effect than in the main effect of the treatments. From this it is only a small step to the design in which two or more
experimental variables may be studied simultaneously in the same experiment, or in which comparisons may be made simultaneously within each of
a number of (cross) classifications of treatments. Suppose, for example,
that an investigation is being made to identify the factors which determine
the *rate* of reading a certain type of material at a certain level of comprehension. Traditionally, the procedure would have been to plan a number of
independent experiments of the single variable type, one concerned only with
size of type, another with *style* of type, another with *length of line* (width of
column), etc. In the size-of-type experiment, the factors of style of type
and length of line would be held constant; in the style-of-type experiment
the factors of size of type and length of line would be held constant, etc.

A much better procedure, however, might be to vary *all* these factors in
a single experiment so as not only to accomplish the purposes of the afore-
mentioned single-variable experiments, but also to study the possible interactions among the various factors. Let us consider a specific illustration
of such an experiment, in which, for the sake of simplicity, only two factors
(*size* and *style* of type) are involved and only two levels of each factor: Roman
vs. Clarendon styles and eight-point vs. twelve-point sizes of type. We will

let A represent the style factor and B the size factor. A_1 will represent Roman type, A_2 Clarendon type, B_1 eight-point and B_2 twelve-point type. Thus treatment A_1B_2 represents twelve-point Roman and A_2B_1 represents eight-point Clarendon, etc. Suppose that the same rate-of-reading test is printed in four editions: eight-point Roman, twelve-point Roman, eight-point Clarendon, twelve-point Clarendon. The experiment would thus be concerned with four treatments, corresponding to these four size-style combinations. The available subjects, say 100, may then be randomly divided into four equal treatment groups, each taking a different one of these four editions of the rate-of-reading test. To insure that all are tested under the same conditions, the test might be simultaneously administered to all subjects in a single group, one-fourth taking one edition, another fourth taking another edition, etc. The experiment might then be diagrammed as follows:

$$
\begin{array}{c}
\textit{Style} \\
\begin{array}{cc}
A_1 & A_2
\end{array}
\end{array}
$$

$$
\textit{Size} \quad
\begin{array}{c}
B_1 \\ \\ B_2
\end{array}
\begin{array}{|c|c|}
\hline
M_{A_1B_1} & M_{A_2B_1} \\
\hline
M_{A_1B_2} & M_{A_2B_2} \\
\hline
\end{array}
\quad
\begin{array}{l}
M_{B_1}\left(=\dfrac{M_{A_1B_1}+M_{A_2B_1}}{2}\right) \\ \\
M_{B_2}
\end{array}
$$

$$
M_{A_1} \quad M_{A_2}
$$

The "main" effect of *style*, that is, its average effect for both *sizes* of type, would be measured by $(M_{A_1} - M_{A_2})$, and the "main" effect of *size* by $(M_{B_1} - M_{B_2})$. The "simple" effects of *style* (the effects for each *size* separately) would then be measured by $(M_{A_1B_1} - M_{A_2B_1})$ and $(M_{A_1B_2} - M_{A_2B_2})$, and the "simple" effects of *size* would similarly be measured by $(M_{A_1B_1} - M_{A_1B_2})$ and $(M_{A_2B_1} - M_{A_2B_2})$. Finally, the "interaction" effect of *size* $\times$ *style* (read "size by style") would be measured by

$$[(M_{A_1B_1} - M_{A_2B_1}) - (M_{A_1B_2} - M_{A_2B_2})].$$

In this restricted example, a simple t-test could be used to test the significance of any of these "effects." For instance, the main effect of *size* would be tested by

$$
t = \frac{M_{B_1} - M_{B_2}}{\sqrt{\text{est'd } \sigma^2_{M_{B_1}} + \text{est'd } \sigma^2_{M_{B_2}}}}
$$

$$
= \frac{M_{B_1} - M_{B_2}}{\frac{1}{2}\sqrt{\left(\text{est'd } \sigma^2_{M_{A_1B_1}} + \text{est'd } \sigma^2_{M_{A_2B_1}}\right) + \left(\text{est'd } \sigma^2_{M_{A_1B_2}} + \text{est'd } \sigma^2_{M_{A_2B_2}}\right)}}
$$

in which $\sigma^2_{M_{A_1B_1}}$, $\sigma^2_{M_{A_2B_1}}$, etc., would be estimated as the error variance for the mean of any simple random sample.

Similarly, the simple effect of *style* for the eight-point *size* would be tested by

$$
t = \frac{M_{A_1B_1} - M_{A_2B_1}}{\sqrt{\text{est'd } \sigma^2_{M_{A_1B_1}} + \text{est'd } \sigma^2_{M_{A_2B_1}}}}
$$

and the interaction effect would be tested by

$$t = \frac{(M_{A_1B_1} - M_{A_2B_1}) - (M_{A_1B_2} - M_{A_2B_2})}{\sqrt{\text{est'd } \sigma^2_{M_{A_1B_1}} + \text{est'd } \sigma^2_{M_{A_2B_1}} + \text{est'd } \sigma^2_{M_{A_1B_2}} + \text{est'd } \sigma^2_{M_{A_2B_2}}}}$$

The problem of the numbers of degrees of freedom for these t's will be considered in later chapters. If the samples are large enough to provide 30 or more degrees of freedom for the t's, the normal probability table may be used to evaluate them.

If the interaction effect proved to be non-significant, one could proceed with the analysis on the assumption that there is no true interaction between *size* and *style;* that is, that for the whole population the effect of style is the same for both sizes, or that the effect of size is the same for both styles. In that case, the comparison of the main effect of style ($M_{A_1} - M_{A_2}$) would be just as precise and would serve the same purpose as if the same size of type had been used with all subjects, and the evaluation of the main effect of size — the comparison ($M_{B_1} - M_{B_2}$) — would be as precise and would serve the same purpose as if the same style of type had been used with all subjects. That is, a single experiment with 100 subjects would serve the same purposes as two single-variable experiments, each employing 100 subjects. Furthermore, the fact would have been established that the hypothesis of "no interaction" is tenable. This could not have been learned from either of the single-variable experiments, or from both independently considered.

If, on the other hand, the interaction effect proved to be significant, one would have to conclude that the effect of style is different for different sizes of type or that the effect of size is different for different styles. In that case, there would be little interest in the "main" effects; the attention would be centered instead on the "simple" effects. This experiment, it will be noted, consists essentially of two single-variable experiments with style of type, in each of which size is held constant. It may also be regarded as consisting of two single-variable experiments with size of type, in which style of type is held constant at different levels. The whole experiment may thus be regarded as consisting of *four* single-variable experiments, each involving 50 subjects. The precision of any one of these experiments, of course, is not as high as that of a single-variable experiment involving 100 subjects. However, the information secured from four single-variable experiments of 50 subjects each may well be regarded as more valuable or worth while than the information from one single-variable experiment involving 100 subjects. Furthermore, the experiment employing the factorial design would have demonstrated that there *is* an interaction, which again could not have been learned even from two single-variable experiments of 100 subjects each, if one were concerned only with size and the other only with style.

It should be clear, then, that this "factorial" design yields far more information than could be obtained from a single-variable experiment with 100 subjects but concerned with either size or style alone. It yields even more information than could be obtained from two such experiments together, using twice as many subjects. It should therefore be apparent why the factorial design and the method of analysis appropriate to it, which are due to R. A. Fisher, have often been described as among the most important contributions to experimental technique in recent decades.

The illustration here used was restricted to two levels of each of two factors, in order that simple t-tests might be employed to evaluate the results. In the general case, the factorial design involves several factors or treatment classifications, and the number of subjects may differ from one level to another of the same factor. In this general case, the analysis is considerably more complex, and simple t-tests of significance are no longer adequate. The general case of the factorial design will be considered in detail in Chapter 9.

We have noted earlier that the treatments × levels and the factorial designs have many features in common, and that it is sometimes difficult to decide under which of these types a particular design should be classified. If one variable or factor is introduced into the design primarily to make possible a more precise estimate of the "main" effect of the other factor, and if the interaction effect is of only incidental or secondary interest, the design may be clearly classified as a treatment × levels design. In this case, it is presumably known in advance that the control variable is related to the criterion variable. Hence, there would be no point in testing the significance of the main effect of the control factor. On the other hand, if the second variable is introduced primarily in order to study and evaluate its main effect along with that of the first factor, and/or to study the interaction between the two factors, then the design is clearly of the factorial type. In this case, it is presumably not known in advance whether the second factor is related to the criterion; hence the purpose of introducing the second factor is not to increase the precision of the experiment so far as the evaluation of the first factor is concerned. It seems worth while, for the purpose of the following discussions, to distinguish between these two designs wherever possible. However, if in some instances the purposes of the experiment are so mixed that one cannot readily decide how to classify the design, this is of little practical consequence so long as the results are properly analyzed and interpreted.

The "Groups-Within-Treatments" Design: When the purpose of an experiment is to establish generalizations about a population consisting of a large number of subpopulations, it is sometimes not possible to replicate the experiment, or to make all possible treatment comparisons, for each of a number of randomly selected subpopulations (as in the random replications design). For example, in a methods experiment in arithmetic, the methods may be such that if both are employed simultaneously in the same school, the pupils under one method may exchange information about the methods with those studying under another. The result may be that teachers and pupils who are intended to employ an unadulterated form of one method may, on their own initiative, introduce or make use of elements of the other method. Thus the results obtained for either treatment group may really be a mixture of the effects of both methods. In such cases, it might be better to administer only one method in one set of r_1 schools and only the other method in another random set of r_2 different schools. Such an experiment might be diagrammed as follows:

$$Treatment\ A_1$$

$$Schools: \quad \boxed{M_{A_1 S_1}} \quad \boxed{M_{A_1 S_2}} \quad \ldots \quad \boxed{M_{A_1 S_i}} \quad \ldots \quad \boxed{M_{A_1 S_{r_1}}}$$

$$M_{A_1} = \frac{1}{r_1}(M_{A_1 S_1} + M_{A_1 S_2} + \ldots + M_{A_1 S_i} + \ldots + M_{A_1 S_{r_1}})$$

$$Treatment\ A_2$$

$$\boxed{M_{A_2 S_1}} \quad \boxed{M_{A_2 S_2}} \quad \ldots\ldots\ldots\ldots \quad \boxed{M_{A_2 S_{r_2}}}$$

like split plot design

$$M_{A_2} = \frac{1}{r_2}(M_{A_2 S_1} + \ldots + M_{A_2 S_{r_2}})$$

(Note that the school whose mean is $M_{A_1 S_i}$ is not the same as the school whose mean is $M_{A_2 S_i}$.)

The appropriate test of the significance of the treatment effect would then be

$$t = \frac{M_{A_1} - M_{A_2}}{\sqrt{\text{est'd } \sigma^2_{M_{A_1}} + \text{est'd } \sigma^2_{M_{A_2}}}}$$

in which

$$\text{est'd } \sigma^2_{M_{A_1}} = \frac{\sum_{i=1}^{r_1}(M_{A_1 S_i} - M_{A_1})^2}{r_1(r_1 - 1)} \quad \text{and est'd } \sigma^2{}_{M_{A_2}} = \frac{\sum_{i=1}^{r_2}(M_{A_2 S_i} - M_{A_2})^2}{r_2(r_2 - 1)}.$$

This test of significance involves the assumptions that the number of cases (n) is the same in all schools and that the experimental subjects used in each school are a random sample of all pupils who might be given the same treatment in that school. It also regards each general treatment mean as the mean of a random sample of r *means* rather than as the mean of a sample of *rn subjects*. Since the schools employing either method are a simple random sample of all schools in the population, the Type S or Type G or Type R errors in the means for those schools may be regarded as a simple random sample from the distribution of such errors that would be found for all schools if all used the same method. (If any "extraneous" factor tends to operate systematically in favor of a certain method, it would presumably operate in the same fashion if this method were widely used in practice; hence, the "extraneous" factor might properly be regarded as an integral part of the method itself.) Thus the test of significance is valid for all types of variable errors affecting the criterion means in the various schools. This design is much less precise than other designs employing the same number of subjects, but since it eliminates any possibility of contamination of one treatment by another, it is sometimes preferable to other designs in spite of its lack of precision.

Combinations of Basic Designs: Some of the specific designs used in the preceding illustrations are rarely used in exactly the same form in actual research. Each illustration represents a highly restricted special case of a more generalized design in which there may be more than two categories in each treatment classification, and in which the number of subjects may vary from category to category within the same treatment classification, or from one level to another. Even in their generalized forms, however, these basic designs account only for some of the designs used in practice. Most designs actually employed in research represent rather complex *combinations* of these basic designs, or of the elements or principles contained in or represented by these basic designs. Just one illustration of these complex designs will be presented here. This design provides for two experimental variables, A and B, with three levels of A and two of B or with six different treatments representing the various combinations of A and B. Every subject takes all levels of A; half the subjects do so in combination with B_1 and half in combination with B_2. That is, half the subjects take three of the six treatments, the other half take the remaining three treatments. One purpose of the design is to counter-balance the effect of the rank order (O) in which the various treatments are administered to the same subjects. The design is diagrammatically represented below:

		A_1B_1	A_2B_1	A_3B_1			A_1B_2	A_2B_2	A_3B_2
	O_1	G_1	G_2	G_3		O_1	G_4	G_5	G_6
Level 1	O_2	G_3	G_1	G_2		O_2	G_6	G_4	G_5
	O_3	G_2	G_3	G_1		O_3	G_5	G_6	G_4

		A_1B_1	A_2B_1	A_3B_1			A_1B_2	A_2B_2	A_3B_2
	O_1	G_7	G_8	G_9		O_1	G_{10}	G_{11}	G_{12}
Level 2	O_2	G_9	G_7	G_8		O_2	G_{12}	G_{10}	G_{11}
	O_3	G_8	G_9	G_7		O_3	G_{11}	G_{12}	G_{10}

Level 3
etc.

The experiment is performed at seven different levels of a control variable L. The number of subjects at each level is a multiple of 6. Within each level the subjects are divided at random into six equal groups. Group 1 (G_1) takes treatments A_1B_1, A_2B_1, and A_3B_1, in that order. Group 2 (G_2) takes the same treatments in the following order; A_2B_1, A_3B_1, and A_1B_1; while Group 3 takes them in the order A_3B_1, A_1B_1, and A_2B_1. A similar pattern is followed with the subjects taking the various A-treatments in combination with B_2.

No attempt will be made here to attach more meaning to this design, or to indicate how the results might be analyzed and evaluated. The purpose of the example is simply to illustrate, in one instance, the fact that the ideas represented in the simple designs thus far considered can be combined to form much more complex designs. This particular illustration contains elements of the simple treatments $\times$ levels design, the simple treatments $\times$ subjects design, and the simple factorial design.

There is an almost unlimited number of ways in which more complex designs can be devised to fit specific experimental problems and situations. If the student is to develop the ability to select or devise for himself the designs most appropriate to his own particular problems, facilities, and resources, it is essential that he master *thoroughly* each of the basic designs as presented in more highly generalized form in succeeding chapters.

In concluding this chapter, it may be well to remind the student again that he is not expected to have acquired at this point any thorough understanding of the basic designs just presented. They have been presented here for introductory purposes only, to provide the student with a brief preview of what is to follow, to give him some advance inkling of the many interesting possibilities in experimental design. Each of these basic designs will be presented again in a more highly generalized form in the chapters which follow, and will there be accorded much more intensive consideration. Many questions which may have occurred to the student in reading this introductory chapter had therefore best be left unanswered until these later chapters.

2

The Chi-Square, t, and F Distributions

Introduction

As has been pointed out in Chapter 1, the purpose of most psychological experiments is to test some hypothesis concerning some characteristics (parameters) of the populations from which the experimental observations may be regarded as random samples. To test any such hypothesis, it is usually necessary to know the sampling distributions of estimates of these parameters derived from the experimental data. For the experimental designs considered in this text, the sampling distributions involved in the tests of significance are almost always of the type known as "F-distributions." Before giving any consideration to the tests of significance employed with these designs, therefore, it is necessary to acquaint the student with or to remind him of the important characteristics of the F-distribution and of the Chi-Square distribution in terms of which F is defined.

The Chi-Square Distribution

If a very large number of samples of the same size are independently drawn at random from a normal population, if each measure is expressed as a deviation from the population mean in units of the standard deviation of the population, and if the sum of the squares of these deviations is obtained for each sample, these sums will show a characteristic form of distribution which is known as the Chi-Square distribution. The definition of Chi-Square (χ^2) is given by

$$\chi^2 = \frac{\sum_{}^{n}(X - \mu)^2}{\sigma^2} \tag{1}$$

in which X is any measure in a sample of n cases drawn at random from a normal population, μ is the population mean, and σ^2 is the population variance. This distribution differs for samples of different sizes, ranging from distributions sharply skewed to the right for small samples to very nearly bell-shaped distribution for large samples. Figure 1 on page 28 indicates very roughly

27

the form of the χ^2-distribution for certain sizes of samples. There is a different χ^2-distribution for each possible value of n. For reasons to be explained later, the n of (1) is called the number of "degrees of freedom" for the corresponding χ^2-distribution.

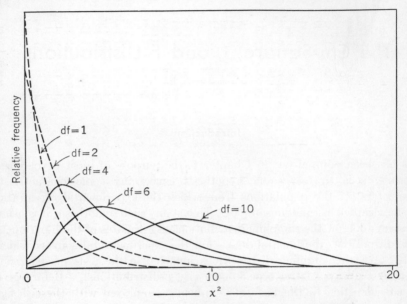

FIGURE 1. *Approximate forms of χ^2-distribution for certain degrees of freedom*

The mean of any χ^2-distribution is always equal to the number of degrees of freedom (df), and the mode of the distribution (except when $df = 1$) is at $df - 2$. As the number of degrees of freedom increases, the χ^2-distributions become more and more nearly the same in form; for $df > 30$, the χ^2-distributions may, for most practical purposes, be regarded as having the same form. (The mean and variance of the distribution, of course, continue to increase with further increases in degrees of freedom.) For $df > 30$, the distribution of $\sqrt{2\chi^2}$ is essentially normal, and has a mean of $\sqrt{2df - 1}$ and a standard deviation of 1.00.

The probability distribution function [1] for χ^2 has been determined and tables have been prepared showing the values of χ^2 exceeded by various proportions of the individual χ^2's in each of the χ^2-distributions for $df = 1$ to $df = 30$.

A table of χ^2 for $df = 1$ to $df = 30$ is given on page 29. Table 1 tells us, for example, that in the distribution of χ^2 with one degree of freedom the median value of χ^2 is .455, and that a value of 2.706 is exceeded by 10%

---

[1] $y = y_0 e^{-\frac{1}{2}\chi^2} (\chi^2)^{\frac{df-2}{2}}$

TABLE 1. Table of χ²

Probability

df	.99	.98	.95	.90	.80	.70	.50	.30	.20	.10	.05	.02	.01	.001
1	$.0^3157$	$.0^3628$	.00393	.0158	.0642	.148	.455	1.074	1.642	2.706	3.841	5.412	6.635	10.827
2	.0201	.0404	.103	.211	.446	.713	1.386	2.408	3.219	4.605	5.991	7.824	9.210	13.815
3	.115	.185	.352	.584	1.005	1.424	2.366	3.665	4.642	6.251	7.815	9.837	11.345	16.268
4	.297	.429	.711	1.064	1.649	2.195	3.357	4.878	5.989	7.779	9.488	11.668	13.277	18.465
5	.554	.752	1.145	1.610	2.343	3.000	4.351	6.064	7.289	9.236	11.070	13.388	15.086	20.517
6	.872	1.134	1.635	2.204	3.070	3.828	5.348	7.231	8.558	10.645	12.592	15.033	16.812	22.457
7	1.239	1.564	2.167	2.833	3.822	4.671	6.346	8.383	9.803	12.017	14.067	16.622	18.475	24.322
8	1.646	2.032	2.733	3.490	4.594	5.527	7.344	9.524	11.030	13.362	15.507	18.168	20.090	26.125
9	2.088	2.532	3.325	4.168	5.380	6.393	8.343	10.656	12.242	14.684	16.919	19.679	21.666	27.877
10	2.558	3.059	3.940	4.865	6.179	7.267	9.342	11.781	13.442	15.987	18.307	21.161	23.209	29.588
11	3.053	3.609	4.575	5.578	6.989	8.148	10.341	12.899	14.631	17.275	19.675	22.618	24.725	31.264
12	3.571	4.178	5.226	6.304	7.807	9.034	11.340	14.011	15.812	18.549	21.026	24.054	26.217	32.909
13	4.107	4.765	5.892	7.042	8.634	9.926	12.340	15.119	16.985	19.812	22.362	25.472	27.688	34.528
14	4.660	5.368	6.571	7.790	9.467	10.821	13.339	16.222	18.151	21.064	23.685	26.873	29.141	36.123
15	5.229	5.985	7.261	8.547	10.307	11.721	14.339	17.322	19.311	22.307	24.996	28.259	30.578	37.697
16	5.812	6.614	7.962	9.312	11.152	12.624	15.338	18.418	20.465	23.542	26.296	29.633	32.000	39.252
17	6.408	7.255	8.672	10.085	12.002	13.531	16.338	19.511	21.615	24.769	27.587	30.995	33.409	40.790
18	7.015	7.906	9.390	10.865	12.857	14.440	17.338	20.601	22.760	25.989	28.869	32.346	34.805	42.312
19	7.633	8.567	10.117	11.651	13.716	15.352	18.338	21.689	23.900	27.204	30.144	33.687	36.191	43.820
20	8.260	9.237	10.851	12.443	14.578	16.266	19.337	22.775	25.038	28.412	31.410	35.020	37.566	45.315
21	8.897	9.915	11.591	13.240	15.445	17.182	20.337	23.858	26.171	29.615	32.671	36.343	38.932	46.797
22	9.542	10.600	12.338	14.041	16.314	18.101	21.337	24.939	27.301	30.813	33.924	37.659	40.289	48.268
23	10.196	11.293	13.091	14.848	17.187	19.021	22.337	26.018	28.429	32.007	35.172	38.968	41.638	49.728
24	10.856	11.992	13.848	15.659	18.062	19.943	23.337	27.096	29.553	33.196	36.415	40.270	42.980	51.179
25	11.524	12.697	14.611	16.473	18.940	20.867	24.337	28.172	30.675	34.382	37.652	41.566	44.314	52.620
26	12.198	13.409	15.379	17.292	19.820	21.792	25.336	29.246	31.795	35.563	38.885	42.856	45.642	54.052
27	12.879	14.125	16.151	18.114	20.703	22.719	26.336	30.319	32.912	36.741	40.113	44.140	46.963	55.476
28	13.565	14.847	16.928	18.939	21.588	23.647	27.336	31.391	34.027	37.916	41.337	45.419	48.278	56.893
29	14.256	15.574	17.708	19.768	22.475	24.577	28.336	32.461	35.139	39.087	42.557	46.693	49.588	58.302
30	14.953	16.306	18.493	20.599	23.364	25.508	29.336	33.530	36.250	40.256	43.773	47.962	50.892	59.703

For larger values of n, the expression $\sqrt{2\chi^2} - \sqrt{2n-1}$ may be used as a normal deviate with unit variance, remembering that the probability for χ^2 corresponds with that of a single tail of the normal curve. (Table reprinted from Table III of R. A. Fisher, *Statistical Methods for Research Workers*, published by Oliver and Boyd Ltd by permission of the author and publishers.)

of the χ^2's in this distribution. The table shows that for a χ^2 with 6 degrees of freedom, the probability is .80 that a randomly selected value of χ^2 will exceed 3.07. Again, the chances are 2 in 100 that the χ^2 will exceed 15.033.

For values of df larger than 30, the normal distribution of $\sqrt{2\chi^2}$ may be used in lieu of the χ^2-distribution.

From the definition of χ^2, it follows axiomatically that *the sum of two independent χ^2's is itself distributed as χ^2 with degrees of freedom equal to the sum of the degrees of freedom for the χ^2's added.* To illustrate, if the value of χ^2, computed by (1), is obtained for one random sample of 10 cases and another independent random sample of 5 cases, the sum of these two values of χ^2 must, of course, be the same as the χ^2, computed by (1), for the combined sample of 15 cases. This is an extremely important rule in statistical applications of χ^2.

According to this rule, if B and C are independent of one another and both are distributed as χ^2 with b and c degrees of freedom, respectively, then $A = B + C$ is also distributed as χ^2 with $a = b + c$ degrees of freedom. The converse of this rule is also true. If A and B are each distributed as χ^2 with a and b degrees of freedom, respectively, and if $A = B + C$ and C is independent of B, then $C = A - B$ is also distributed as χ^2 with $c = a - b$ degrees of freedom.

By means of this converse of the rule of sums, it may be shown that if a random sample of n cases is drawn from a normal population, but each measure is expressed as a deviation from the *sample* mean instead of from the population mean, again in terms of the *population* σ, the sum of the squared deviations will again be distributed as χ^2, but now with $n-1$ degrees of freedom. That is, the distribution of $\dfrac{\overset{n}{\Sigma}(X - M)^2}{\sigma^2}$ for random samples of n cases each is exactly the same as that of $\dfrac{\overset{n}{\Sigma}(X - \mu)^2}{\sigma^2}$ for samples of $n-1$ cases each, M and μ being the sample and population means, respectively.

To prove this, we may first, for any single measure (X), write as an identity,

$$(X - \mu) = (X - M) + (M - \mu).$$

Squaring both sides of this expression, we have

$$(X - \mu)^2 = (X - M)^2 + 2(X - M)(M - \mu) + (M - \mu)^2.$$

Summing these expressions for the n measures in the sample

$$\overset{n}{\Sigma}(X - \mu)^2 = \overset{n}{\Sigma}(X - M)^2 + 2(M - \mu)\overset{n}{\Sigma}(X - M) + n(M - \mu)^2.$$

Dividing each side by the population variance (σ^2) and noting that $\overset{n}{\Sigma}(X - M) = 0$, we have

$$\frac{\overset{n}{\Sigma}(X - \mu)^2}{\sigma^2} = \frac{\overset{n}{\Sigma}(X - M)^2}{\sigma^2} + \frac{n(M - \mu)^2}{\sigma^2}. \tag{2}$$

We now note that the second right-hand term of (2) may be written

$$\frac{n(M - \mu)^2}{\sigma^2} = \frac{(M - \mu)^2}{\sigma^2/n} = \frac{(M - \mu)^2}{\sigma_M^2}$$

which, according to (1), conforms to the definition of χ^2, the degrees of free-dom for this χ^2 being 1. We note also that the left-hand term of (2) is, according to (1), also distributed as χ^2, with n degrees of freedom. Granting that the right-hand terms are independent of one another, it then follows by the converse of the rule of sums that the first right-hand term must also be distributed as χ^2, with degrees of freedom equal to the difference between the degrees of freedom for the left-hand and the second right-hand terms, namely $(n-1)$. Accordingly, granting independence, we may write

$$\chi^2 = \frac{\sum_{}^{n}(X - M)^2}{\sigma^2}, \, df = n - 1 \cdot \tag{3}$$

According to the rule of sums stated earlier, the sum of a number of χ^2's obtained by means of (3) is also distributed as χ^2, the number of degrees of freedom for this χ^2 being determined by that rule. Suppose again that we have a sample of 30 cases drawn at random from a normal population, and that we divide it at random into sub-samples of 5, 10, and 15 cases. Suppose we then compute a χ^2 for each sub-sample according to (3). The sum of these χ^2's will then have 27 df, although it is based on 30 cases. To find the frequency with which this χ^2 is exceeded by chance, one must enter the χ^2 table with $df = 27$, even though the number of cases in the sample is 30.

Proof of the Independence of the Mean and Variance of Random Samples Drawn from a Normal Population

We have not yet proved that the right-hand terms of (2) are independent of one another. Before doing so, it will be well to define more exactly the meaning of "independence." Two variates may be said to be independent in the probability sense if the distribution of the first is exactly the same for all values of the second, and *vice versa*. Given the paired variates X and Y, X may be said to be independent of Y if the distribution of X is the same for all values of Y, or if that of Y is the same for all values of X. From this definition, it is axiomatic that if X is independent of Y, then aX is also independent of Y, a being a constant; and $X - a$ and X^a are each also independent of Y.

Proof that the right-hand terms of (2) are independent rests on the more fundamental proposition that the mean and variance of random samples drawn from a normal population are independent. Obviously, if the mean (M) is independent of the variance $[\Sigma(X - M)^2/n]$, then, by the axioms stated above, $n(M - \mu)^2$ in (2) must be independent of $\Sigma(X - M)^2$.

The proof of the independence of the mean and variance is somewhat involved, and some students may prefer to take this proof on faith. In that case, they may skip the rest of this section and go on to the section on "Degrees of Freedom." However, the proof provided here involves no mathematics beyond that taught in high school algebra, and with a little perserverance most students should be able to understand it completely.

To prove that the mean and variance of random samples drawn from a normal population are independent, we must first demonstrate the independence of the *sum* and *difference* of two measures independently drawn at random from the same normal population. For simplicity, we will express each measure as a deviation $\left(z = \dfrac{X - \mu}{\sigma} \right)$ from the population mean in terms of the population standard deviation. Suppose, then that we draw a very large number of pairs of measures at random from the same normal population, letting z' represent the first measure drawn and z the second drawn in each pair. Suppose we then plot each pair of measures on a scattergram (see Figure 2), and for each (extremely small) unit of area on the scattergram we erect a perpendicular proportional to the number of pairs of measures plotted

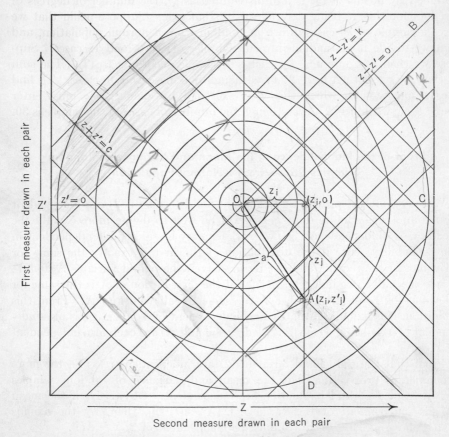

First measure drawn in each pair

Second measure drawn in each pair

FIGURE 2. *Scattergram for Pairs of Measures Drawn at Random from a Normal Population*

in that unit of area. If we then let the number of pairs drawn approach infinity, and also let the unit of area become infinitesimally small, the upper ends of these perpendiculars will describe a smooth bell-shaped surface, which we will call the correlation surface.

If z and z' are independent, the distribution of z for any given value of z', or of z' for any given value of z, is the same normal distribution as that which characterizes the entire population. Accordingly, the distribution of z along the line $z' = 0$ (Line C in the figure) will be described by the normal curve $y = y_0 e^{\frac{-z^2}{2}}$, y_0 representing the ordinate at the mean of this curve.

Accordingly, the ordinate of this curve at the point $(z_i, 0)$ is $y_0 e^{\frac{-z_i^2}{2}}$. The distribution of z' along the line $z = z_i$ (Line D in the figure) is likewise a normal distribution whose mean ordinate we have just shown to be $y_0 e^{\frac{-z_i^2}{2}}$. Accordingly the ordinate of this latter curve at the point (z_i, z_j) is $y_0 e^{\frac{-z_i^2}{2}} e^{\frac{-z_j^2}{2}} = y_0 e^{\frac{-(z_i^2+z_j^2)}{2}}$. From this it is evident that the points on the scattergram for which the frequency (ordinate) is a constant are the points for which $z_i^2 + z_j^2$ is a constant, that is, for which $z_i^2 + z_j^2 = a^2$. From the fact that the square on the hypotenuse of a right angle triangle is equal to the sum of the squares on the legs of the triangle, it is apparent that these points of equal frequency would lie along the circle whose radius is a and whose center is at 0.

We have now shown that the lines of equal frequency on the scattergram are concentric circles with centers at 0, as is indicated in the figure. This means that the correlation surface is completely symmetrical about 0, or that the line of intersection of the correlation surface with any plane through 0 perpendicular to the scattergram will always describe the same normal curve. It means also that the line of intersection with the correlation surface of *any* plane perpendicular to the scattergram is a normal curve with the same variance as that which characterizes the entire population.

We may next note that all points for which the *sum* of z and z' is a constant lie on a straight line ($z + z' = c$) with a slope of -1.00. The sloping line passing through the point A in the diagram, and all lines parallel to it, are such lines. It is obvious that the closer one of these lines comes to the lower left corner of the figure, the lower is the value of the sum of the measures. The closer the line comes to the upper right corner, the higher is the value of the sum.

It is likewise apparent that all pairs of measures for which the *difference* is a constant will fall along a line ($z - z' = k$), with a slope equal to $+1.00$, such as line B and all lines parallel to it in the figure. For every pair of measures represented by a point on line B (which passes through the means of the z and z' distributions), the value of z is equal to the value of z'; hence their difference is equal to zero. All points along any line parallel to B represent pairs for which the difference is constant. The farther this line from B, the larger is the value of the difference. It is now apparent that for all lines of constant sums, the distribution of $(z - z')$ is a normal distribution with exactly the same mean and variance. In other words, $(z + z')$ is *independent* of $(z - z')$, or the sum of two measures selected at random from a normal distribution is independent of their difference.

We may next note that for any sample of size n, the sum of the squared deviations from the sample mean, $\Sigma(X - M)^2$, is equal to $1/n$ times the sum of the squares of the differences for all possible pairs of measures. That is, $\Sigma(X - M)^2 = \dfrac{1}{n} \displaystyle\sum_{i=1}^{n-1} \sum_{j=2}^{n} (X_i - X_j)^2$ when i takes all values up to $n - 1$ and j all values from 2 to n. A general proof of this would be quite cumbersome so it will be demonstrated below only for the case in which $n = 3$. If he wishes, the student can readily provide similar proofs for $n = 4$ and $n = 5$, at which point he will be ready to recognize that the relationship holds for any value of n.

For $n = 3$

$$\Sigma(X - M)^2 = \left(X_1 - \frac{X_1 + X_2 + X_3}{3}\right)^2 + \left(X_2 - \frac{X_1 + X_2 + X_3}{3}\right)^2$$
$$+ \left(X_3 - \frac{X_1 + X_2 + X_3}{3}\right)^2$$

$$= \tfrac{1}{9}[(2X_1 - X_2 - X_3)^2 + (2X_2 - X_1 - X_3)^2 + (2X_3 - X_1 - X_2)^2]$$

$$= \tfrac{1}{9}[4X_1^2 + X_2^2 + X_3^2 - 4X_1X_2 - 4X_1X_3 + 2X_2X_3$$

$$+ 4X_2^2 + X_1^2 + X_3^2 - 4X_1X_2 - 4X_2X_3 + 2X_1X_3$$

$$+ 4X_3^2 + X_1^2 + X_2^2 - 4X_1X_3 - 4X_2X_3 + 2X_1X_2]$$

$$= \tfrac{1}{3}(2X_1^2 + 2X_2^2 + 2X_3^2 - 2X_1X_2 - 2X_1X_3 - 2X_2X_3)$$

$$= \tfrac{1}{3}[(X_1 - X_2)^2 + (X_1 - X_3)^2 + (X_2 - X_3)^2]$$

$$= \frac{1}{n} \sum_{i=1}^{n-1} \sum_{j=2}^{n} (X_i - X_j)^2.$$

Now it is axiomatic that if a certain variate is independent of each of a number of other variates, then that variate must also be independent of their sum. We know that $X_3, X_4, \ldots X_n$ are all independent of $(X_1 - X_2)$. Hence, according to the axiom, $(X_3 + X_4 + \ldots + X_n)$ is independent of $(X_1 - X_2)$. We have already shown that $(X_1 + X_2)$ is independent of $(X_1 - X_2)$. Therefore, according to the axiom, $T = (X_1 + X_2 + X_3 \ldots + X_n)$ is independent of $(X_1 - X_2)$. In the same way, it may be shown that T is independent of the difference between any other two measures. Hence,

T must be also independent of the square $(X_i - X_j)^2$ of any of the differences, and finally, of the sum $\sum_{i=1}^{n-1} \sum_{j=2}^{n} (X_i - X_j)^2$ of the squared differences for all possible pairs of measures. From this it follows that the mean of the sample is independent of the variance.

Degrees of Freedom

We have seen that the number with which we enter the table represents the number of cases in a sample only when χ^2 is computed by (1). In practice, nearly all χ^2's are computed in other ways, so that the number with which the χ^2 table is entered is only rarely the number of cases in a sample.

We see now why it is convenient to call the number with which we enter the χ^2 table by some name that suggests its general nature, and we can begin to understand the reason for the name "degrees of freedom." When each measure in a random sample is expressed as a deviation from the *population* mean, any measure selected is free to take any value. Thus, in a sample of n cases, there are n "degrees of freedom," one corresponding to each observation. When each measure is expressed as a deviation from the *sample* mean, the value of the "last" measure drawn is already determined by the values of the other measures, or by the restriction that the sum of the deviations must be zero. For example, in a sample of four cases, we can specify any value we wish for three of the deviations, such as -4.0, 2.3, and -1.7, but if the sum of the deviations is to equal zero, the fourth deviation must be 3.4. We say, then, that the value of χ^2 for this sample has three degrees of freedom ($df = 3$).

We may state as a general rule that the number of degrees of freedom for a χ^2 computed from a number of observations is equal to the number of observations minus the number of algebraically independent *linear restrictions* placed upon them. That is, if we have computed a χ^2 from N observations on which r linear restrictions have been placed, the degrees of freedom for the χ^2 is $N - r$. In general, a linear restriction takes the form of a first degree or linear equation specifying a relationship existing among the observations. In all the applications of χ^2 represented in this text, the linear restrictions represent only simple restrictions upon *sums* of the measures involved. In (3), for example, we have specified that the sum of the deviations must be equal to zero, or that the sum of the measures is nM. Accordingly, the degrees of freedom for a χ^2 computed by (3) is one less than for a χ^2 computed from the same sample by (1).

Any one of a number of linear restrictions is *algebraically independent* of the others if it is not already determined by or is not related to the others. Suppose, for instance, that in the case of a sample of 4 measures, A, B, C and D, we specify that $A + B = 3$, $C + D = 7$, $A + C = 4$, and $B + D = 6$.

We have thus imposed four linear restrictions, but only three of them are algebraically independent, since, if any three of these relations hold, the remaining one is bound to hold also. That is, any one of the four restrictions may be derived from the other three, or may be regarded as already determined by them.

Suppose that we have a random sample of $N = nr$ cases drawn from a normal population and that this sample is divided at random into r sub-samples of n cases each. The number of degrees of freedom for the χ^2 computed by (3) for any sub-sample is $n - 1$. Accordingly, the number of degrees of freedom for the χ^2 represented by the sum of these χ^2's for all sub-samples is $r(n - 1) = N - r$. For example, if there are four sub-samples in a sample of 40 cases, $N - r = 40 - 4 = 36$. We may regard the four sub-sample *means* as constituting a random sample of four cases. If each of these means is expressed as a deviation from the sample mean, we may compute from them by (3) a χ^2 with three degrees of freedom. If the sample mean is expressed as a deviation from the population mean, we can compute from it by (1) a χ^2 with one degree of freedom. Thus the χ^2 with 40 degrees of freedom which could be computed by (1) from the total sample has been partitioned into one χ^2 with 36 degrees of freedom, another χ^2 with 3 degrees of freedom, and another χ^2 with one degree of freedom, all 40 degrees of freedom thus being accounted for.

Just as a number of independent χ^2's can be combined into a single χ^2, so can the χ^2 for a sample be divided, by a process similar to that just illustrated, into a number of constituent χ^2's. In the analysis of all the designs considered in this text, the total sum of squared deviations from the general mean $[\overset{n}{\Sigma}(X - M)^2]$ is analyzed into components corresponding to different sets of subgroups into which the total sample is divided, or to the different sources of variation; the total df is also correspondingly partitioned. We will see that with any sample we can, if we wish, identify a component of the total sum of squared deviations from the general mean with each *individual degree of freedom* for that total. Under appropriate hypotheses, a χ^2 can be computed on the basis of each component of the total sum of squared deviations. This kind of analysis, which has been termed "analysis of variance," is basic in all the designs considered in this text. It is therefore extremely important that the student master thoroughly the χ^2-distribution and the concept of degrees of freedom.

It should be noted that the *general* concept of degrees of freedom is broader than the meanings attached to it here. The rule for determining the degrees of freedom for a sample in terms of restrictions upon the means of subgroups, for instance, is adequate for the purposes of this text, but would not serve in determining the degrees of freedom for χ^2 in a test of goodness of fit of a hypothetical frequency distribution to an observed one. However, for the sake of simplicity of presentation, it seems desirable here to attach only as many meanings to this term as the purposes of this text demand.

The t-Distribution

The t-ratio may be defined as the ratio between a randomly selected normal deviate expressed in units of the population σ, and the square root of a randomly selected χ^2 divided by its degrees of freedom. Suppose that X is normally distributed for a population whose mean is μ and whose variance is σ^2 and that $z = \dfrac{X - \mu}{\sigma}$. If we select a z at random from this population and independently select a χ^2 at random from the χ^2-distribution for k degrees of freedom, we may form a t-ratio as follows:

$$ t = \frac{z}{\sqrt{\dfrac{\chi^2}{k}}}. $$

This ratio has a characteristic distribution for each of the possible values of k. Its distribution is much like the normal distribution but is more peaked than the normal distribution for small values of k. For $k = \infty$, t is normally distributed. For $k > 30$, the t-distribution may, for most practical purposes, be regarded as normally distributed with zero mean and unit variance.

Suppose now that we draw a random sample of n cases from a normal distribution of X's, compute the sample mean (M), and estimate its standard error (σ_M). The ratio $\dfrac{M - \mu}{\text{est'd } \sigma_M}$ is then distributed as t with $(n - 1)$ degrees of freedom. This is evident if we divide both numerator and denominator of the ratio by $\sigma_M = \sigma/\sqrt{n}$, having substituted for est'd σ_M its value $\sqrt{\dfrac{\Sigma(X - M)^2}{n(n - 1)}}$. The independence of numerator and denominator follows from the independence of the mean and variance of a random sample from a normal population. The ratio $\dfrac{M_1 - M_2}{\text{est'd } \sigma_{(M_1 - M_2)}}$, in which M_1 and M_2 are the means of independent random samples of n_1 and n_2 cases, respectively, and est'd $\sigma_{(M_1 - M_2)} = \sqrt{\dfrac{\Sigma(X - M_1)^2 + \Sigma(X - M_2)^2}{n_1 + n_2 - 2}\left(\dfrac{1}{n_1} + \dfrac{1}{n_2}\right)}$, may similarly be shown to be distributed as t with $(n_1 + n_2 - 2)$ degrees of freedom. It is assumed that the student using this text is familiar with the applications of these t-ratios in testing hypotheses concerning population means and differences in population means.

Table 2 on page 38 presents the relative frequencies with which various *absolute* values of t are exceeded for $df = 1$ to $df = 30$. For example, in the t-distribution for 2 degrees of freedom, $|t| > .289$ 80% of the time, $|t| > 9.925$ 1% of the time, etc.

The F-Distribution

Suppose now that we have two independent χ^2-distributions, one for df_1 degrees of freedom, and the other for df_2 degrees of freedom. Suppose that

TABLE 2. Table of t

df	P = .9	.8	.7	.6	.5	.4	.3	.2	.1	.05	.02	.01
1	.158	.325	.510	.727	1.000	1.376	1.963	3.078	6.314	12.706	31.821	63.657
2	.142	.289	.445	.617	.816	1.061	1.386	1.886	2.920	4.303	6.965	9.925
3	.137	.277	.424	.584	.765	.978	1.250	1.638	2.353	3.182	4.541	5.841
4	.134	.271	.414	.569	.741	.941	1.190	1.533	2.132	2.776	3.747	4.604
5	.132	.267	.408	.559	.727	.920	1.156	1.476	2.015	2.571	3.365	4.032
6	.131	.265	.404	.553	.718	.906	1.134	1.440	1.943	2.447	3.143	3.707
7	.130	.263	.402	.549	.711	.896	1.119	1.415	1.895	2.365	2.998	3.499
8	.130	.262	.399	.546	.706	.889	1.108	1.397	1.860	2.306	2.896	3.355
9	.129	.261	.398	.543	.703	.883	1.100	1.383	1.833	2.262	2.821	3.250
10	.129	.260	.397	.542	.700	.879	1.093	1.372	1.812	2.228	2.764	3.169
11	.129	.260	.396	.540	.697	.876	1.088	1.363	1.796	2.201	2.718	3.106
12	.128	.259	.395	.539	.695	.873	1.083	1.356	1.782	2.179	2.681	3.055
13	.128	.259	.394	.538	.694	.870	1.079	1.350	1.771	2.160	2.650	3.012
14	.128	.258	.393	.537	.692	.868	1.076	1.345	1.761	2.145	2.624	2.977
15	.128	.258	.393	.536	.691	.866	1.074	1.341	1.753	2.131	2.602	2.947
16	.128	.258	.392	.535	.690	.865	1.071	1.337	1.746	2.120	2.583	2.921
17	.128	.257	.392	.534	.689	.863	1.069	1.333	1.740	2.110	2.567	2.898
18	.127	.257	.392	.534	.688	.862	1.067	1.330	1.734	2.101	2.552	2.878
19	.127	.257	.391	.533	.688	.861	1.066	1.328	1.729	2.093	2.539	2.861
20	.127	.257	.391	.533	.687	.860	1.064	1.325	1.725	2.086	2.528	2.845
21	.127	.257	.391	.532	.686	.859	1.063	1.323	1.721	2.080	2.518	2.831
22	.127	.256	.390	.532	.686	.858	1.061	1.321	1.717	2.074	2.508	2.819
23	.127	.256	.390	.532	.685	.858	1.060	1.319	1.714	2.069	2.500	2.807
24	.127	.256	.390	.531	.685	.857	1.059	1.318	1.711	2.064	2.492	2.797
25	.127	.256	.390	.531	.684	.856	1.058	1.316	1.708	2.060	2.485	2.787
26	.127	.256	.390	.531	.684	.856	1.058	1.315	1.706	2.056	2.479	2.779
27	.127	.256	.389	.531	.684	.855	1.057	1.314	1.703	2.052	2.473	2.771
28	.127	.256	.389	.530	.683	.855	1.056	1.313	1.701	2.048	2.467	2.763
29	.127	.256	.389	.530	.683	.854	1.055	1.311	1.699	2.045	2.462	2.756
30	.127	.256	.389	.530	.683	.854	1.055	1.310	1.697	2.042	2.457	2.750
∞	.12566	.25335	.38532	.52440	.67449	.84162	1.03643	1.28155	1.64485	1.95996	2.32634	2.57582

(Table Reprinted from Table IV of R.A.Fisher, *Statistical Methods for Research Workers*, published by Oliver and Boyd Ltd. by permission of the author and publishers.)

we select a value of χ^2 at random from each distribution, divide each χ^2 by its own number of degrees of freedom, and then form a ratio between the two quotients, as follows:

$$\frac{\chi_1^2/df_1}{\chi_2^2/df_2}.$$

Suppose we do this repeatedly until we have a very large number of such ratios. We will then find that this ratio takes a characteristic form of distribution. The form of this distribution differs for each possible combination of values for df_1 and df_2. The exact form of each of these distributions is known, and tables have been constructed showing what value of this ratio is exceeded certain proportions of the time for each of a large number of combinations of degrees of freedom. The determination of the form of this distribution is due to R. A. Fisher, and the ratio has been named the F-ratio in honor of Fisher by G. W. Snedecor. The F-ratio may be defined symbolically as

$$F = \frac{\chi_1^2/df_1}{\chi_2^2/df_2}. \qquad\qquad (4)$$

The F-distribution always has a median of 1.00 or less, but the values of F may range from zero to extremely large values, depending upon the number of degrees of freedom. It is important to note that the numerator and denominator of (4) must be *independent* of one another if the ratio is to be distributed as F. For example, if the χ^2 in the numerator were always a sum of the χ^2 in the denominator plus some other χ^2, that is, if the χ^2 in the numerator always contained the χ^2 in the denominator, the numerator and denominator would show a positive correlation for a series of such ratios. In that case the values of F would obviously cluster more closely around 1.00 than if the numerator and denominator were uncorrelated. In order, then, to show that a ratio like that in (4) is distributed as F, we must always establish the independence of the two χ^2's.

Table 3, pages 41–44, gives the 20%, 10%, 5%, 2.5%, 1%, 0.5% and 0.1% "points" in the F-distribution for each of various combinations of degrees of freedom. The "20% point" in an F-distribution represents the value of F exceeded 20% of the time in this distribution, or the point on the F-scale to the right of which 20% of the distribution lies. The other percent points are similarly defined. In Table 2 the 5% value of F for 2 and 6 degrees of freedom, for instance, is 5.14. This means that in the F-distribution for these degrees of freedom, 5% of the distribution lies to the right of 5.14.

Frequently the degrees of freedom of the F to be evaluated in an experiment do not correspond to any of the combinations of degrees of freedom for which F is tabled in Table 3. In that case, one may interpolate between the tabled values, but the common procedure in practice is to use the F for the nearest combination of *smaller* degrees of freedom than can be found in the table. For example, if the obtained F had 10 and 3 degrees of freedom one would use the value for 8 and 3 degrees of freedom, or if the obtained F had 17 and 48 degrees of freedom, one would use the F for 12 and 40 degrees of freedom.

If it is desired to know the value of F below or to the left of which a certain percent of the cases fall, this may be determined by simply substituting the reciprocal of F for the F read from Table 2 when the degrees of freedom are interchanged. For instance, the point *below* which 5% of the F's fall in the distribution for 2 and 6 degrees of freedom is $1/19.33 = .0517$, the denominator being the F for 6 and 2 degrees of freedom.

It is easy to show that for F for 1 and k degrees of freedom is distributed as t^2 for k degrees of freedom. Accordingly, the first column of the F-table constitutes a condensed t-table, giving the value of t^2 for the selected levels of significance for 40, 60, and 120 degrees of freedom, as well as for all values of numbers of degrees of freedom of 30 and below.

It should be apparent from the definition of F that the ratio between the estimates $[\Sigma(X - M)^2/(n - 1)]$ of the population variance derived from two random samples drawn from the same normal population is distributed as F. Accordingly, given the variance estimates obtained from random samples drawn from different populations, we may, on the assumption that the populations are normal, test the hypothesis that the populations have the same variance. [It should be noted that in this case, if the F-ratio is always formed by putting the larger estimate in the numerator, the F which is significant at the 2% level is that which exceeds the 1% point in the table, that which exceeds the 5% value in the table is significant at the 10% level, etc.]

The F-ratio, as we shall see, provides the basis for nearly all the tests of significance in the designs we shall consider later in this text; the logic just presented should therefore be thoroughly mastered by the student.

TABLE 3

Percent Points in the Distribution of F

df₂		df₁ = 1	2	3	4	5	6	8	12	24	∞
1	0.1%	405284	500000	540379	562500	576405	585937	598144	610667	623497	636619
	0.5%	16211	20000	21615	22500	23056	23437	23925	24426	24940	25465
	1 %	4052	4999	5403	5625	5764	5859	5981	6106	6234	6366
	2.5%	647.79	799.50	864.16	899.58	921.85	937.11	956.66	976.71	997.25	1018.30
	5 %	161.45	199.50	215.71	224.58	230.16	233.99	238.88	243.91	249.05	254.32
	10 %	39.86	49.50	53.59	55.83	57.24	58.20	59.44	60.70	62.00	63.33
	20 %	9.47	12.00	13.06	13.73	14.01	14.26	14.59	14.90	15.24	15.58
2	0.1	998.5	999.0	999.2	999.2	999.3	999.3	999.4	999.4	999.5	999.5
	0.5	198.50	199.00	199.17	199.25	199.30	199.33	199.37	199.42	199.46	199.51
	1	98.49	99.00	99.17	99.25	99.30	99.33	99.36	99.42	99.46	99.50
	2.5	38.51	39.00	39.17	39.25	39.30	39.33	39.37	39.42	39.46	39.50
	5	18.51	19.00	19.16	19.25	19.30	19.33	19.37	19.41	19.45	19.50
	10	8.53	9.00	9.16	9.24	9.29	9.33	9.37	9.41	9.45	9.49
	20	3.56	4.00	4.16	4.24	4.28	4.32	4.36	4.40	4.44	4.48
3	0.1	167.5	148.5	141.1	137.1	134.6	132.8	130.6	128.3	125.9	123.5
	0.5	55.55	49.80	47.47	46.20	45.39	44.84	44.13	43.39	42.62	41.83
	1	34.12	30.81	29.46	28.71	28.24	27.91	27.49	27.05	26.60	26.12
	2.5	17.44	16.04	15.44	15.10	14.89	14.74	14.54	14.34	14.12	13.90
	5	10.13	9.55	9.28	9.12	9.01	8.94	8.84	8.74	8.64	8.53
	10	5.54	5.46	5.39	5.34	5.31	5.28	5.25	5.22	5.18	5.13
	20	2.68	2.89	2.94	2.96	2.97	2.97	2.98	2.98	2.98	2.98
4	0.1	74.14	61.25	56.18	53.44	51.71	50.53	49.00	47.41	45.77	44.05
	0.5	31.33	26.28	24.26	23.16	22.46	21.98	21.35	20.71	20.03	19.33
	1	21.20	18.00	16.69	15.98	15.52	15.21	14.80	14.37	13.93	13.46
	2.5	12.22	10.65	9.98	9.60	9.36	9.20	8.98	8.75	8.51	8.26
	5	7.71	6.94	6.59	6.39	6.26	6.16	6.04	5.91	5.77	5.63
	10	4.54	4.32	4.19	4.11	4.05	4.01	3.95	3.90	3.83	3.76
	20	2.35	2.47	2.48	2.48	2.48	2.47	2.47	2.46	2.44	2.43
5	0.1	47.04	36.61	33.20	31.09	29.75	28.84	27.64	26.42	25.14	23.78
	0.5	22.79	18.31	16.53	15.56	14.94	14.51	13.96	13.38	12.78	12.14
	1	16.26	13.27	12.06	11.39	10.97	10.67	10.29	9.89	9.47	9.02
	2.5	10.01	8.43	7.76	7.39	7.15	6.98	6.76	6.52	6.28	6.02
	5	6.61	5.79	5.41	5.19	5.05	4.95	4.82	4.68	4.53	4.36
	10	4.06	3.78	3.62	3.52	3.45	3.40	3.34	3.27	3.19	3.10
	20	2.18	2.26	2.25	2.24	2.23	2.22	2.20	2.18	2.16	2.13
6	0.1	35.51	27.00	23.70	21.90	20.81	20.03	19.03	17.99	16.89	15.75
	0.5	18.64	14.54	12.92	12.03	11.46	11.07	10.57	10.03	9.47	8.88
	1	13.74	10.92	9.78	9.15	8.75	8.47	8.10	7.72	7.31	6.88
	2.5	8.81	7.26	6.60	6.23	5.99	5.82	5.60	5.37	5.12	4.85
	5	5.99	5.14	4.76	4.53	4.39	4.28	4.15	4.00	3.84	3.67
	10	3.78	3.46	3.29	3.18	3.11	3.05	2.98	2.90	2.82	2.72
	20	2.07	2.13	2.11	2.09	2.08	2.06	2.04	2.02	1.99	1.95
7	0.1	29.22	21.69	18.77	17.19	16.21	15.52	14.63	13.71	12.73	11.69
	0.5	16.24	12.40	10.88	10.05	9.52	9.16	8.68	8.18	7.65	7.08
	1	12.25	9.55	8.45	7.85	7.46	7.19	6.84	6.47	6.07	5.65
	2.5	8.07	6.54	5.89	5.52	5.29	5.12	4.90	4.67	4.42	4.14
	5	5.59	4.74	4.35	4.12	3.97	3.87	3.73	3.57	3.41	3.23
	10	3.59	3.26	3.07	2.96	2.88	2.83	2.75	2.67	2.58	2.47
	20	2.00	2.04	2.02	1.99	1.97	1.96	1.93	1.91	1.87	1.83
8	0.1	25.42	18.49	15.83	14.39	13.49	12.86	12.04	11.19	10.30	9.34
	0.5	14.69	11.04	9.60	8.81	8.30	7.95	7.50	7.01	6.50	5.95
	1	11.26	8.65	7.59	7.01	6.63	6.37	6.03	5.67	5.28	4.86
	2.5	7.57	6.06	5.42	5.05	4.82	4.65	4.43	4.20	3.95	3.67
	5	5.32	4.46	4.07	3.84	3.69	3.58	3.44	3.28	3.12	2.93
	10	3.46	3.11	2.92	2.81	2.73	2.67	2.59	2.50	2.40	2.29
	20	1.95	1.98	1.95	1.92	1.90	1.88	1.86	1.83	1.79	1.74
9	0.1	22.86	16.39	13.90	12.56	11.71	11.13	10.37	9.57	8.72	7.81
	0.5	13.61	10.11	8.72	7.96	7.47	7.13	6.69	6.23	5.73	5.19
	1	10.56	8.02	6.99	6.42	6.06	5.80	5.47	5.11	4.73	4.31
	2.5	7.21	5.71	5.08	4.72	4.48	4.32	4.10	3.87	3.61	3.33
	5	5.12	4.26	3.86	3.63	3.48	3.37	3.23	3.07	2.90	2.71
	10	3.36	3.01	2.81	2.69	2.61	2.55	2.47	2.38	2.28	2.16
	20	1.91	1.94	1.90	1.87	1.85	1.83	1.80	1.76	1.72	1.67

Table 3 is abridged from Table V of R. A. Fisher and F. Yates, *Statistical Tables for Biological, Agricultural, and Medical Research,* published by Oliver and Boyd Ltd. by permission of the authors and publishers. The 0.5% and 2.5% points are reprinted by permission from *Biometrika,* vol 33 (April, 1943), pp. 73–88 ("Tables of Percentage Points of the Inverted Beta (F) Distribution").

THE CHI–SQUARE, t, AND F DISTRIBUTIONS

TABLE 3 (cont.)

df_2		1	2	3	4	5	6	8	12	24	∞
10	0.1%	21.04	14.91	12.55	11.28	10.48	9.92	9.20	8.45	7.64	6.76
	0.5%	12.83	9.43	8.08	7.34	6.87	6.54	6.12	5.66	5.17	4.64
	1 %	10.04	7.56	6.55	5.99	5.64	5.39	5.06	4.71	4.33	3.91
	2.5%	6.94	5.46	4.83	4.47	4.24	4.07	3.85	3.62	3.37	3.08
	5 %	4.96	4.10	3.71	3.48	3.33	3.22	3.07	2.91	2.74	2.54
	10 %	3.28	2.92	2.73	2.61	2.52	2.46	2.38	2.28	2.18	2.06
	20 %	1.88	1.90	1.86	1.83	1.80	1.78	1.75	1.72	1.67	1.62
11	0.1	19.69	13.81	11.56	10.35	9.58	9.05	8.35	7.63	6.85	6.00
	0.5	12.23	8.91	7.60	6.88	6.42	6.10	5.68	5.24	4.76	4.23
	1	9.65	7.20	6.22	5.67	5.32	5.07	4.74	4.40	4.02	3.60
	2.5	6.72	5.26	4.63	4.28	4.04	3.88	3.66	3.43	3.17	2.88
	5	4.84	3.98	3.59	3.36	3.20	3.09	2.95	2.79	2.61	2.40
	10	3.23	2.86	2.66	2.54	2.45	2.39	2.30	2.21	2.10	1.97
	20	1.86	1.87	1.83	1.80	1.77	1.75	1.72	1.68	1.63	1.57
12	0.1	18.64	12.97	10.80	9.63	8.89	8.38	7.71	7.00	6.25	5.42
	0.5	11.75	8.51	7.23	6.52	6.07	5.76	5.35	4.91	4.43	3.90
	1	9.33	6.93	5.95	5.41	5.06	4.82	4.50	4.16	3.78	3.36
	2.5	6.55	5.10	4.47	4.12	3.89	3.73	3.51	3.28	3.02	2.72
	5	4.75	3.88	3.49	3.26	3.11	3.00	2.85	2.69	2.50	2.30
	10	3.18	2.81	2.61	2.48	2.39	2.33	2.24	2.15	2.04	1.90
	20	1.84	1.85	1.80	1.77	1.74	1.72	1.69	1.65	1.60	1.54
13	0.1	17.81	12.31	10.21	9.07	8.35	7.86	7.21	6.52	5.78	4.97
	0.5	11.37	8.19	6.93	6.23	5.79	5.48	5.08	4.64	4.17	3.65
	1	9.07	6.70	5.74	5.20	4.86	4.62	4.30	3.96	3.59	3.16
	2.5	6.41	4.97	4.35	4.00	3.77	3.60	3.39	3.15	2.89	2.60
	5	4.67	3.80	3.41	3.18	3.02	2.92	2.77	2.60	2.42	2.21
	10	3.14	2.76	2.56	2.43	2.35	2.28	2.20	2.10	1.98	1.85
	20	1.82	1.83	1.78	1.75	1.72	1.69	1.66	1.62	1.57	1.51
14	0.1	17.14	11.78	9.73	8.62	7.92	7.43	6.80	6.13	5.41	4.60
	0.5	11.06	7.92	6.68	6.00	5.56	5.26	4.86	4.43	3.96	3.44
	1	8.86	6.51	5.56	5.03	4.69	4.46	4.14	3.80	3.43	3.00
	2.5	6.30	4.86	4.24	3.89	3.66	3.50	3.29	3.05	2.79	2.49
	5	4.60	3.74	3.34	3.11	2.96	2.85	2.70	2.53	2.35	2.13
	10	3.10	2.73	2.52	2.39	2.31	2.24	2.15	2.05	1.94	1.80
	20	1.81	1.81	1.76	1.73	1.70	1.67	1.64	1.60	1.55	1.48
15	0.1	16.59	11.34	9.34	8.25	7.57	7.09	6.47	5.81	5.10	4.31
	0.5	10.80	7.70	6.48	5.80	5.37	5.07	4.67	4.25	3.79	3.26
	1	8.68	6.36	5.42	4.89	4.56	4.32	4.00	3.67	3.29	2.87
	2.5	6.20	4.77	4.15	3.80	3.58	3.41	3.20	2.96	2.70	2.40
	5	4.54	3.68	3.29	3.06	2.90	2.79	2.64	2.48	2.29	2.07
	10	3.07	2.70	2.49	2.36	2.27	2.21	2.12	2.02	1.90	1.76
	20	1.80	1.79	1.75	1.71	1.68	1.66	1.62	1.58	1.53	1.46
16	0.1	16.12	10.97	9.00	7.94	7.27	6.81	6.19	5.55	4.85	4.06
	0.5	10.58	7.51	6.30	5.64	5.21	4.91	4.52	4.10	3.64	3.11
	1	8.53	6.23	5.29	4.77	4.44	4.20	3.89	3.55	3.18	2.75
	2.5	6.12	4.69	4.08	3.73	3.50	3.34	3.12	2.89	2.63	2.32
	5	4.49	3.63	3.24	3.01	2.85	2.74	2.59	2.42	2.24	2.01
	10	3.05	2.67	2.46	2.33	2.24	2.18	2.09	1.99	1.87	1.72
	20	1.79	1.78	1.74	1.70	1.67	1.64	1.61	1.56	1.51	1.43
17	0.1	15.72	10.66	8.73	7.68	7.02	6.56	5.96	5.32	4.63	3.85
	0.5	10.38	7.35	6.16	5.50	5.07	4.78	4.39	3.97	3.51	2.98
	1	8.40	6.11	5.18	4.67	4.34	4.10	3.79	3.45	3.08	2.65
	2.5	6.04	4.62	4.01	3.66	3.44	3.28	3.06	2.82	2.56	2.25
	5	4.45	3.59	3.20	2.96	2.81	2.70	2.55	2.38	2.19	1.96
	10	3.03	2.64	2.44	2.31	2.22	2.15	2.06	1.96	1.84	1.69
	20	1.78	1.77	1.72	1.68	1.65	1.63	1.59	1.55	1.49	1.42
18	0.1	15.38	10.39	8.49	7.46	6.81	6.35	5.76	5.13	4.45	3.67
	0.5	10.22	7.21	6.03	5.37	4.96	4.66	4.28	3.86	3.40	2.87
	1	8.28	6.01	5.09	4.58	4.25	4.01	3.71	3.37	3.00	2.57
	2.5	5.98	4.56	3.95	3.61	3.38	3.22	3.01	2.77	2.50	2.19
	5	4.41	3.55	3.16	2.93	2.77	2.66	2.51	2.34	2.15	1.92
	10	3.01	2.62	2.42	2.29	2.20	2.13	2.04	1.93	1.81	1.66
	20	1.77	1.76	1.71	1.67	1.64	1.62	1.58	1.53	1.48	1.40
19	0.1	15.08	10.16	8.28	7.26	6.61	6.18	5.59	4.97	4.29	3.52
	0.5	10.07	7.09	5.92	5.27	4.85	4.56	4.18	3.76	3.31	2.78
	1	8.18	5.93	5.01	4.50	4.17	3.94	3.63	3.30	2.92	2.49
	2.5	5.92	4.51	3.90	3.56	3.33	3.17	2.96	2.72	2.45	2.13
	5	4.38	3.52	3.13	2.90	2.74	2.63	2.48	2.31	2.11	1.88
	10	2.99	2.61	2.40	2.27	2.18	2.11	2.02	1.91	1.79	1.63
	20	1.76	1.75	1.70	1.66	1.63	1.61	1.57	1.52	1.46	1.39

TABLE 3 (cont.)

df₁ df₂		1	2	3	4	5	6	8	12	24	∞
20	0.1%	14.82	9.95	8.10	7.10	6.46	6.02	5.44	4.82	4.15	3.38
	0.5%	9.94	6.99	5.82	5.17	4.76	4.47	4.09	3.68	3.22	2.69
	1 %	8.10	5.85	4.94	4.43	4.10	3.87	3.56	3.23	2.86	2.42
	2.5%	5.87	4.46	3.86	3.51	3.29	3.13	2.91	2.68	2.41	2.09
	5 %	4.35	3.49	3.10	2.87	2.71	2.60	2.45	2.28	2.08	1.84
	10 %	2.97	2.59	2.38	2.25	2.16	2.09	2.00	1.89	1.77	1.61
	20 %	1.76	1.75	1.70	1.65	1.62	1.60	1.56	1.51	1.45	1.37
21	0.1	14.59	9.77	7.94	6.95	6.32	5.88	5.31	4.70	4.03	3.26
	0.5	9.83	6.89	5.73	5.09	4.68	4.39	4.01	3.60	3.15	2.61
	1	8.02	5.78	4.87	4.37	4.04	3.81	3.51	3.17	2.80	2.36
	2.5	5.83	4.42	3.82	3.48	3.25	3.09	2.87	2.64	2.37	2.04
	5	4.32	3.47	3.07	2.84	2.68	2.57	2.42	2.25	2.05	1.81
	10	2.96	2.57	2.36	2.23	2.14	2.08	1.98	1.88	1.75	1.59
	20	1.75	1.74	1.69	1.65	1.61	1.59	1.55	1.50	1.44	1.36
22	0.1	14.38	9.61	7.80	6.81	6.19	5.76	5.19	4.58	3.92	3.15
	0.5	9.73	6.81	5.65	5.02	4.61	4.32	3.94	3.54	3.08	2.55
	1	7.94	5.72	4.82	4.31	3.99	3.76	3.45	3.12	2.75	2.31
	2.5	5.79	4.38	3.78	3.44	3.22	3.05	2.84	2.60	2.33	2.00
	5	4.30	3.44	3.05	2.82	2.66	2.55	2.40	2.23	2.03	1.78
	10	2.95	2.56	2.35	2.22	2.13	2.06	1.97	1.86	1.73	1.57
	20	1.75	1.73	1.68	1.64	1.61	1.58	1.54	1.49	1.43	1.35
23	0.1	14.19	9.47	7.67	6.69	6.08	5.65	5.09	4.48	3.82	3.05
	0.5	9.63	6.73	5.58	4.95	4.54	4.26	3.88	3.47	3.02	2.48
	1	7.88	5.66	4.76	4.26	3.94	3.71	3.41	3.07	2.70	2.26
	2.5	5.75	4.35	3.75	3.41	3.18	3.02	2.81	2.57	2.30	1.97
	5	4.28	3.42	3.03	2.80	2.64	2.53	2.38	2.20	2.00	1.76
	10	2.94	2.55	2.34	2.21	2.11	2.05	1.95	1.84	1.72	1.55
	20	1.74	1.73	1.68	1.63	1.60	1.57	1.53	1.49	1.42	1.34
24	0.1	14.03	9.34	7.55	6.59	5.98	5.55	4.99	4.39	3.74	2.97
	0.5	9.55	6.66	5.52	4.89	4.49	4.20	3.83	3.42	2.97	2.43
	1	7.82	5.61	4.72	4.22	3.90	3.67	3.36	3.03	2.66	2.21
	2.5	5.72	4.32	3.72	3.38	3.15	2.99	2.78	2.54	2.27	1.94
	5	4.26	3.40	3.01	2.78	2.62	2.51	2.36	2.18	1.98	1.73
	10	2.93	2.54	2.33	2.19	2.10	2.04	1.94	1.83	1.70	1.53
	20	1.74	1.72	1.67	1.63	1.59	1.57	1.53	1.48	1.42	1.33
25	0.1	13.88	9.22	7.45	6.49	5.88	5.46	4.91	4.31	3.66	2.89
	0.5	9.48	6.60	5.46	4.84	4.43	4.15	3.78	3.37	2.92	2.38
	1	7.77	5.57	4.68	4.18	3.86	3.63	3.32	2.99	2.62	2.17
	2.5	5.69	4.29	3.69	3.35	3.13	2.97	2.75	2.51	2.24	1.91
	5	4.24	3.38	2.99	2.76	2.60	2.49	2.34	2.16	1.96	1.71
	10	2.92	2.53	2.32	2.18	2.09	2.02	1.93	1.82	1.69	1.52
	20	1.73	1.72	1.66	1.62	1.59	1.56	1.52	1.47	1.41	1.32
26	0.1	13.74	9.12	7.36	6.41	5.80	5.38	4.83	4.24	3.59	2.82
	0.5	9.41	6.54	5.41	4.79	4.38	4.10	3.73	3.33	2.87	2.33
	1	7.72	5.53	4.64	4.14	3.82	3.59	3.29	2.96	2.58	2.13
	2.5	5.66	4.27	3.67	3.33	3.10	2.94	2.73	2.49	2.22	1.88
	5	4.22	3.37	2.98	2.74	2.59	2.47	2.32	2.15	1.95	1.69
	10	2.91	2.52	2.31	2.17	2.08	2.01	1.92	1.81	1.68	1.50
	20	1.73	1.71	1.66	1.62	1.58	1.56	1.52	1.47	1.40	1.31
27	0.1	13.61	9.02	7.27	6.33	5.73	5.31	4.76	4.17	3.52	2.75
	0.5	9.34	6.49	5.36	4.74	4.34	4.06	3.69	3.28	2.83	2.29
	1	7.68	5.49	4.60	4.11	3.78	3.56	3.26	2.93	2.55	2.10
	2.5	5.63	4.24	3.65	3.31	3.08	2.92	2.71	2.47	2.19	1.85
	5	4.21	3.35	2.96	2.73	2.57	2.46	2.30	2.13	1.93	1.67
	10	2.90	2.51	2.30	2.17	2.07	2.00	1.91	1.80	1.67	1.49
	20	1.73	1.71	1.66	1.61	1.58	1.55	1.51	1.46	1.40	1.30
28	0.1	13.50	8.93	7.19	6.25	5.66	5.24	4.69	4.11	3.46	2.70
	0.5	9.28	6.44	5.32	4.70	4.30	4.02	3.65	3.25	2.79	2.25
	1	7.64	5.45	4.57	4.07	3.75	3.53	3.23	2.90	2.52	2.06
	2.5	5.61	4.22	3.63	3.29	3.06	2.90	2.69	2.45	2.17	1.83
	5	4.20	3.34	2.95	2.71	2.56	2.44	2.29	2.12	1.91	1.65
	10	2.89	2.50	2.29	2.16	2.06	2.00	1.90	1.79	1.66	1.48
	20	1.72	1.71	1.65	1.61	1.57	1.55	1.51	1.46	1.39	1.30
29	0.1	13.39	8.85	7.12	6.19	5.59	5.18	4.64	4.05	3.41	2.64
	0.5	9.23	6.40	5.28	4.66	4.26	3.98	3.61	3.21	2.76	2.21
	1	7.60	5.42	4.54	4.04	3.73	3.50	3.20	2.87	2.49	2.03
	2.5	5.59	4.20	3.61	3.27	3.04	2.88	2.67	2.43	2.15	1.81
	5	4.18	3.33	2.93	2.70	2.54	2.43	2.28	2.10	1.90	1.64
	10	2.89	2.50	2.28	2.15	2.06	1.99	1.89	1.78	1.65	1.47
	20	1.72	1.70	1.65	1.60	1.57	1.54	1.50	1.45	1.39	1.29

TABLE 3 (cont.)

df$_2$	df$_1$	1	2	3	4	5	6	8	12	24	∞
30	0.1%	13.29	8.77	7.05	6.12	5.53	5.12	4.58	4.00	3.36	2.59
	0.5%	9.18	6.35	5.24	4.62	4.23	3.95	3.58	3.18	2.73	2.18
	1 %	7.56	5.39	4.51	4.02	3.70	3.47	3.17	2.84	2.47	2.01
	2.5%	5.57	4.18	3.59	3.25	3.03	2.87	2.65	2.41	2.14	1.79
	5 %	4.17	3.32	2.92	2.69	2.53	2.42	2.27	2.09	1.89	1.62
	10 %	2.88	2.49	2.28	2.14	2.05	1.98	1.88	1.77	1.64	1.46
	20 %	1.72	1.70	1.64	1.60	1.57	1.54	1.50	1.45	1.38	1.28
40	0.1	12.61	8.25	6.60	5.70	5.13	4.73	4.21	3.64	3.01	2.23
	0.5	8.83	6.07	4.98	4.37	3.99	3.71	3.35	2.95	2.50	1.93
	1	7.31	5.18	4.31	3.83	3.51	3.29	2.99	2.66	2.29	1.80
	2.5	5.42	4.05	3.46	3.13	2.90	2.74	2.53	2.29	2.01	1.64
	5	4.08	3.23	2.84	2.61	2.45	2.34	2.18	2.00	1.79	1.51
	10	2.84	2.44	2.23	2.09	2.00	1.93	1.83	1.71	1.57	1.38
	20	1.70	1.68	1.62	1.57	1.54	1.51	1.47	1.41	1.34	1.24
60	0.1	11.97	7.76	6.17	5.31	4.76	4.37	3.87	3.31	2.69	1.90
	0.5	8.49	5.80	4.73	4.14	3.76	3.49	3.13	2.74	2.29	1.69
	1	7.08	4.98	4.13	3.65	3.34	3.12	2.82	2.50	2.12	1.60
	2.5	5.29	3.93	3.34	3.01	2.79	2.63	2.41	2.17	1.88	1.48
	5	4.00	3.15	2.76	2.52	2.37	2.25	2.10	1.92	1.70	1.39
	10	2.79	2.39	2.18	2.04	1.95	1.87	1.77	1.66	1.51	1.29
	20	1.68	1.65	1.59	1.55	1.51	1.48	1.44	1.38	1.31	1.18
120	0.1	11.38	7.31	5.79	4.95	4.42	4.04	3.55	3.02	2.40	1.56
	0.5	8.18	5.54	4.50	3.92	3.55	3.28	2.93	2.54	·2.09	1.43
	1	6.85	4.79	3.95	3.48	3.17	2.96	2.66	2.34	1.95	1.38
	2.5	5.15	3.80	3.23	2.89	2.67	2.52	2.30	2.05	1.76	1.31
	5	3.92	3.07	2.68	2.45	2.29	2.17	2.02	1.83	1.61	1.25
	10	2.75	2.35	2.13	1.99	1.90	1.82	1.72	1.60	1.45	1.19
	20	1.66	1.63	1.57	1.52	1.48	1.45	1.41	1.35	1.27	1.12
∞	0.1	10.83	6.91	5.42	4.62	4.10	3.74	3.27	2.74	2.13	1.00
	0.5	7.88	5.30	4.28	3.72	3.35	3.09	2.74	2.36	1.90	1.00
	1	6.64	4.60	3.78	3.32	3.02	2.80	2.51	2.18	1.79	1.00
	2.5	5.02	3.69	3.12	2.79	2.57	2.41	2.19	1.94	1.64	1.00
	5	3.84	2.99	2.60	2.37	2.21	2.09	1.94	1.75	1.52	1.00
	10	2.71	2.30	2.08	1.94	1.85	1.77	1.67	1.55	1.38	1.00
	20	1.64	1.61	1.55	1.50	1.46	1.43	1.38	1.32	1.23	1.00

STUDY EXERCISES

1. The table below describes a normal population of z-scores. For any z-score in the body of the table, the corresponding numbers in the left and top margins represent the tens and units digits, respectively, in the percentile rank

	0	1	2	3	4	5	6	7	8	9
9	1.28	1.34	1.41	1.48	1.55	1.64	1.75	1.88	2.05	2.33
8	0.84	0.88	0.92	0.95	0.99	1.04	1.08	1.13	1.18	1.23
7	0.52	0.55	0.58	0.61	0.64	0.67	0.71	0.74	0.77	0.81
6	0.25	0.28	0.31	0.33	0.36	0.39	0.41	0.44	0.47	0.50
5	0.00	0.03	0.05	0.08	0.10	0.13	0.15	0.18	0.20	0.23
4	−0.25	−0.23	−0.20	−0.18	−0.15	−0.13	−0.10	−0.08	−0.05	−0.03
3	−0.52	−0.50	−0.47	−0.44	−0.41	−0.39	−0.36	−0.33	−0.31	−0.28
2	−0.84	−0.81	−0.77	−0.74	−0.71	−0.67	−0.64	−0.61	−0.58	−0.55
1	−1.28	−1.23	−1.18	−1.13	−1.08	−1.04	−0.99	−0.95	−0.92	−0.88
0		−2.33	−2.05	−1.88	−1.75	−1.64	−1.55	−1.48	−1.41	−1.34

of the z-score. For example, the z-score whose percentile rank is 72 in this normal population is $+0.58$. A random sample may be selected from this population through the use of a table of random numbers, as follows: Make a "blind" selection of a two-digit number from a table of random numbers (see Appendix). Regard this number as a percentile rank in the z-score distribution, then read the corresponding z-score from the table above. For example, if the random number is 33 the corresponding z-score is -0.44. Continue this process until a random sample of the desired size is drawn.

Following the procedure outlined above, draw a sample of four z-scores at random from the normal probability table.

a) Compute χ^2 for your sample,[1] using formula (1).

b) Compute χ^2 for your sample, using formula (3).

c) What is the probability, in any single instance of this kind, of obtaining a value of χ^2 larger than that obtained in (b) preceding?

2. The 12 z-scores in the upper part of the table below were selected at random from a table like the preceding in the manner described in Exercise 1 and were randomly assigned, three to each of four subsamples. The results of certain computations for each subsample are given below the z-scores ($\bar{z}$ represents the mean of the three z-scores in the subsample).

Subsamples

	1	2	3	4		
	-1.86	.46	-1.28	-1.91		
	$-.42$	$-.75$	2.28	-1.01		
	$-.59$	$-.06$	1.13	$-.79$		
Σz	-2.87	$-.35$	2.13	-3.71	$T = \overset{12}{\Sigma} z$	$= -4.80$
Σz^2	3.98	.78	8.11	5.29	$M = -4.80$	$= -.40$
$(\Sigma z)^2/3$	2.75	.04	1.51	4.59		12
$\Sigma(z - \bar{z})^2$	1.23	.74	6.60	.70		

a) For the total sample of 12 cases, the value of χ^2, taking deviations from the population mean [formula (1)], is $\chi_1^2 = 18.16$. If the deviations are taken from the mean of the 12 scores [formula (3)], $\chi_2^2 = 16.24$. What number of degrees of freedom is associated with each of these χ^2's? Are these χ^2's independent? Explain.

---

[1] A worth-while exercise for a class of N students is to have each student compute $100/N$ χ^2's in this fashion, all for samples of 4 cases each, and then to tabulate the distribution of these 100 χ^2's to show empirically what a χ^2 distribution means.

b) Compute a χ^2 for each subsample separately, taking deviations from the population mean. How many degrees of freedom for each? How are these subsample χ^2's related to χ_1^2?

c) Compute a χ^2 for each subsample separately, in each case taking deviations from the subsample mean. The sum of these χ^2's is distributed as χ^2 with how many degrees of freedom?

d) Regarding the four subsample *means* as a random sample from a population of such means (each based on three scores), obtain the χ^2 associated with the deviations of the subsample means from the population mean. Relate this χ^2 and the χ^2's obtained in (c) to χ_1^2.

e) Compute the χ^2 associated with the deviation of the subsample means from the sample mean (M). How does this relate to those already given or obtained?

f) Compute the χ^2 associated with the deviation of the sample mean (M) from the population mean, and relate it to the previous χ^2's.

3. In 2b we have obtained four independent values of χ^2. Form the ratio of the first to the second. Show that this is an "F" ratio. Determine the relative frequency with which this ratio would be exceeded in a very large number of pairs of independent samples of 3 cases each drawn at random from this population, if in every case the ratio were formed by placing the larger of the two χ^2's in the numerator.

4. How can an F-ratio be formed using the χ^2's obtained in 2c and 2e? How frequently is this result exceeded by chance?

5. A z-score is drawn at random from a normal population of such scores and its square is recorded. This process is repeated a very large number of times and a frequency distribution made of the resulting squared z-scores. What will be the mode of this distribution? What will be the median? How does the distribution relate to χ^2?

6. Show that F with 1 and k degrees of freedom is equal to the square of t with k degrees of freedom. Check the tables to verify this relationship.

$$t = \frac{z}{\sqrt{\dfrac{\chi^2}{k}}} = t^2 \quad \frac{\dfrac{(x-M)^2}{\sigma^2}}{\dfrac{\chi^2}{k}} = \frac{\dfrac{(x-M)^2}{\sigma}}{\dfrac{\chi^2}{k}} = \frac{\chi^2}{\dfrac{\chi^2}{k}} = 1/df$$

$$t = \frac{z^2}{\dfrac{\chi^2}{k}} \qquad + F = \frac{\chi_1^2/df_1}{\chi_2^2/df_2}$$

3

The Simple-Randomized Design

The Importance of the Simple-Randomized Design

The importance of the simple-randomized design in experimental work cannot be overemphasized. Not only is the design widely employed by itself, but it constitutes a basic unit in nearly all of the more complex designs employed in experimental research. The treatments × levels design, for example, may be regarded as consisting of a number of "replications" or repetitions of the simple-randomized design, one for each level of the control variable. The random replications design likewise consists of a number of simple-randomized experiments, one performed for each of a number of subpopulations randomly selected from all those constituting the parent population. A factorial experiment, again, may be regarded as consisting of a number of simple-randomized experiments concerning one of the factors, each experiment performed for a different level (or combination of levels) of the other factor (or factors).

It is therefore extremely important that the student achieve a thorough mastery of the simple-randomized design. Accordingly, a special effort has been made in this chapter to make all of the essential mathematical theory readily accessible to the student not trained in mathematics, to anticipate and to answer as many as possible of the questions that might occur to him, and to smooth out possible difficulties by liberal illustration and explanation. The chapter is to be regarded not as an independent discussion of a particular design, but as an essential introduction to the succeeding chapters. Until the student achieves a thorough understanding of this chapter, he cannot hope to grasp the full implications of the chapters to follow.

The Hypothesis to be Tested

The simple-randomized design is that in which each treatment is independently administered to a different group of subjects, all groups having been originally drawn at random from the same parent population. After the treatments have been administered these groups may be regarded as

47

random samples from a single population only if the treatments all have identical effects on the distribution of criterion measures for the population. Otherwise the group receiving Treatment A_1 may be regarded as a random sample from an imaginary or hypothetical population which is like the parent population except that all its members have now received Treatment A_1. The sample that received Treatment A_2 may, likewise, be regarded as a random sample from a population like the original, except that all members of this population have received A_2, etc. We must therefore think of a number (a) of different *hypothetical* populations, each of which may be regarded as generated from the parent population by administering the given treatment to all of its members. We will hereafter refer to these hypothetical populations as the "treatment populations." The hypothesis we wish to test is that the criterion means of these treatment populations are identical. In the subsequent discussion, we will refer to this hypothesis as the "over-all null hypothesis" to emphasize the fact that it is concerned simultaneously with *all* of the treatments, as contrasted with more specific null hypotheses concerned only with single *pairs* of treatments.

Limitations of the Simple t-Test

We have seen (page 13) that in a simple-randomized experiment involving only two treatments, a t-test can be employed to test the null hypothesis concerning the treatment population means. Suppose, however, that several treatments, say four, are involved. To simplify the illustration, we will suppose also that the number of cases is the same in each group. We are now interested in the over-all null hypothesis that all four treatments are equally effective, or in the possibility that all observed differences among treatment means are due to sampling fluctuations. It might seem that we could test this hypothesis by applying the t-test successively to each of the six possible differences between two treatment means. Presumably, if any one of these differences proved to be significant, the over-all null hypothesis would have to be rejected; if none proved to be significant, the hypothesis could be retained. Obviously, the one of the six differences most likely to be significant is the largest. The simplest way to test the over-all null hypothesis would then seem to be to select the largest observed difference and apply a simple t-test to it. This, however, is not a valid procedure.

In applying a simple t-test to a difference between the means of two independent random samples, we read from the table for t the probability that the observed value of t would be exceeded in any single randomly selected instance if the null hypothesis were true. The probability that a single randomly selected difference will exceed a given value, however, is by no means the same as the probability that the *largest* of a *number* of randomly selected differences will exceed this value. This should be obvious from a simple analogy. Suppose that a single card is selected at random from a

deck of playing cards.   The probability that the card selected will be an
ace is $\frac{1}{13}$ or .07+.   Now suppose that five cards are drawn at random, one
at a time, from the complete deck, each card being replaced before the next
is drawn.   The probability that at least one of these cards will be an ace
is of course very much higher than .07.   Actually it is .33—.

The correct probability is computed as follows: The probability that any
given card dealt will be an ace is $\frac{1}{13}$.   The probability that it will be *other*
than an ace is $\frac{12}{13}$.   The probability that both of two cards selected at random
will be other than an ace is $\frac{12}{13} \times \frac{12}{13}$.   This follows from the fundamental law
of probability which states that the probability that two independent events
will occur together is equal to the product of their separate probabilities.
Similarly, the probability that all the five cards selected at random will be
other than an ace is $(\frac{12}{13})^5 = .6702$.   Accordingly, the probability that one or
more of the cards *will* be an ace is $1 - .6702 = .3298$.

In any simple-randomized design, in order to use the t-ratio of the largest
observed difference among treatment means as a basis for testing the over-all
null hypothesis, we would need a special table for t showing the probability
that the *largest* difference among the means of the given number of random
samples of the given sizes would exceed the observed value.   Thus we would
need a different t-table for each of the almost countless combinations of number of treatments and size of sample, noting that in the general case, the
size of each treatment group may differ from that of every other.   Even
though we had such tables, however, this type of test would be unsatisfactory,
since it is concerned only with one (the largest) of the observed differences
and ignores the information contained in the other differences.   Fortunately,
this problem has a much better solution, which will be explained in the
following sections.

The Test of the Over-all Null Hypothesis

The Steps in Testing an Hypothesis: In testing an exact hypothesis about
a population on the basis of data obtained from random samples drawn from
that population, the generally accepted procedure is as follows: (1) Obtain a
measure of discrepancy between the hypothesis and the sample observations.
(2) Determine the sampling distribution this measure of discrepancy would
have if the hypothesis were true.   (3) Decide what risk we are willing to
take of rejecting a true hypothesis.   (4) In accordance with this decision,
mark off regions of rejection and acceptance in the hypothetical sampling
distribution.   (5) Either reject the hypothesis if the observed discrepancy
falls in the region of rejection or retain the hypothesis if the discrepancy
falls in the region of acceptance.   We shall now follow this procedure in
testing the over-all null hypothesis for a simple-randomized experiment.
(If the student is not already familiar with these steps, they should become
clear as he works through the following discussion.)

The Measure of Discrepancy: Before defining our measure of discrepancy, we may note that if all treatments have identical effects on the distribution of criterion measures for the parent population, that is, if the distribution of criterion measures is the same for all treatment populations, these populations may be regarded as just *one* population. In this case the various treatment groups may be all regarded as simple random samples from the *same* population, whose variance we shall denote as σ^2. We shall see that from the experimental data we can derive two independent and unbiased estimates of σ^2 — one estimate based on the differences among the observed treatment means, the other upon the variance of the measures within the individual treatment groups. We can then form the ratio of the first of these estimates to the second. If the treatments have identical effects, the first of these estimates will exceed the other only by chance. If the hypothesis is false, that is, if the treatments really differ in effectiveness, then the differences among the observed treatment means will be larger than they would otherwise be, as will the estimate of σ^2 derived from them, so that the ratio will then tend to be larger than 1.00. The greater the differences among the observed treatment means, the larger this ratio will be. Accordingly, we can use the ratio as a measure of the discrepancy between hypothesis and observation, and if we can discover the sampling distribution of this ratio, we can use it in a statistical test of the hypothesis.

Our first step will be to derive an estimate of σ^2 from the observed treatment means. We shall consider first the case in which the number of cases (n) is the same for all treatment groups. If the treatments have identical effects on the distribution of criterion measures for the parent population, the various treatment groups are all random samples from the same population, and the *means* of these treatment groups are a simple random sample of a cases from a population of such means. We shall denote the variance of this population distribution of means as σ_M^2. We can then secure an unbiased estimate of σ_M^2 as follows:

$$\text{est'd } \sigma_M^2 = \frac{\sum_{j=1}^{a}(M_j - M)^2}{a - 1},$$

in which M_j is the mean of the jth treatment group and M is the general mean for all groups $\left(M = \dfrac{\sum_{j=1}^{a} M_j}{a}\right)$. We know, however, that $\sigma_M^2 = \sigma^2/n$.

Hence, by substituting in the preceding expression, we get

$$\frac{\text{est'd } \sigma^2}{n} = \frac{\sum_{j=1}^{a}(M_j - M)^2}{a - 1}$$

or

$$\text{est}_1\, \sigma^2 = \frac{n\sum_{j=1}^{a}(M_j - M)^2}{a - 1}.$$

Thus we have a way of estimating σ^2 from the obtained *means* of the treatment groups. We shall denote this estimate as $\text{est}_1\,\sigma^2$, to distinguish it from the estimate next to be secured.

We next note again that if the treatments have identical effects on the criterion distribution, each treatment group is a simple random sample from the same population as any other, so that for any treatment group (j), we can secure an unbiased estimate of σ^2 as follows:

$$\text{est'd } \sigma^2 = \frac{\Sigma(X - M_j)^2}{n - 1}$$

However, we can secure a *better* estimate by *averaging* these estimates for all of the a treatment groups. That is,

$$\text{est}_2\,\sigma^2 = \frac{1}{a}\left[\frac{\Sigma(X - M_1)^2}{n - 1} + \frac{\Sigma(X - M_2)^2}{n - 1} + \cdots + \frac{\Sigma(X - M_a)^2}{n - 1}\right]$$

$$= \frac{\sum\limits_{j=1}^{a}\Sigma(X - M_j)^2}{a(n - 1)}.$$

We thus have two estimates of σ^2, one obtained from the treatment means, the other from the individual measures within the individual treatment groups. We can then form a ratio, $\text{est}_1\,\sigma^2/\text{est}_2\,\sigma^2$, between these two estimates. If the treatments have identical effects, we would expect this ratio to exceed 1.00 only by chance. If the null hypothesis is false, we would expect the ratio to be systematically larger than 1.00. Clearly, therefore, this ratio measures the discrepancy between our over-all null hypothesis and the experimental observations.

The Sampling Distribution of the Measure of Discrepancy: To determine the sampling distribution of this measure of discrepancy, we must first make certain basic assumptions. These are

1) The experimental treatment groups were originally drawn at random from the same parent population.[1]

_____

[1] On the basis of these three assumptions, we shall show that our measure of discrepancy is distributed as F (see pages 52–53) if the null hypothesis is true. Strictly, while these assumptions are together *sufficient*, the first is not entirely *necessary* for this purpose alone. That is, the measure of discrepancy is distributed as F if each treatment group is drawn at random from its own "treatment population" (and if assumptions 2 and 3 are satisfied also), whether or not the treatment groups are alike before administration of the treatments. Our real interest, however, is in the hypothesis of equal *treatment* effects, not just in the hypothesis of equal criterion means for the populations following administration of the treatments. Equal criterion means at the close of the experiment imply equal treatment effects only if we can assume that the populations were alike before the treatments were administered. Accordingly, we have specified more than is really necessary for an F-distribution alone, and shall follow a similar practice with the F-tests used in later designs.

We have noted that, after administration of the treatments, each group may be regarded as a simple random sample from a different "treatment population."

2) The variance (σ^2) of the distribution of criterion measures is the same for each of these treatment populations.

3) The form of each of these distributions is normal.

Our measure of discrepancy is

$F \text{ test}$

$$\frac{\text{est}_1 \sigma^2}{\text{est}_2 \sigma^2} = \frac{\dfrac{n\sum\limits_{j}^{a}(M_j - M)^2}{a - 1}}{\dfrac{\sum\limits_{j}^{a}\sum(X - M_j)^2}{N - a}}, \tag{5}$$

in which $N = na$ is the total number of cases.

The usefulness of this form of the ratio will become apparent later. If we divide both numerator and denominator of (5) by σ^2, we may rewrite it as follows:

$\text{an } F \text{ test}$

$$\frac{\text{est}_1 \sigma^2}{\text{est}_2 \sigma^2} = \frac{\left.\dfrac{\sum\limits_{j=1}^{a}(M_j - M)^2}{\sigma^2/n}\right/ (a - 1)}{\left.\sum\limits_{j=1}^{a}\dfrac{\Sigma(X - M_j)^2}{\sigma^2}\right/ (N - a)}. \tag{6}$$

We note that $\sum\limits_{j=1}^{a}(M_j - M)^2$ represents the sum of the squared deviations from the mean in a sample of a cases, each "case" in this instance being a *group* mean. We note also that if our hypothesis is true and our basic assumptions are satisfied, all a groups are drawn at random from the *same* population. In that case, σ^2/n is the population variance of these group means, since each group mean is the mean of a random sample of n measures. Ac-

cordingly, $\dfrac{\sum\limits_{j=1}^{a}(M_j - M)^2}{\sigma^2/n}$ is, on the assumption of normality and by the proposition (3) stated on page 31, distributed as χ^2 with $a - 1$ degrees of freedom.

In the denominator of this ratio, we note that by assumptions 1 and 3 the term $\dfrac{\Sigma(X - M_j)^2}{\sigma^2}$ is also distributed as χ^2, this time with $n - 1$ degrees of freedom. Accordingly, the sum, $\sum\limits_{j=1}^{a}\dfrac{\Sigma(X - M_j)^2}{\sigma^2}$, of a such terms must be distributed as χ^2 with $\sum\limits_{j=1}^{a}(n_j - 1) = a(n - 1) = N - a$ degrees of freedom. (It should be apparent that this is true whether n is variable or constant.)

Thus, if our hypothesis is true, the ratio between the two estimates of the population variance (6) may be regarded as a ratio between two values of χ^2, each divided by its own degrees of freedom. If we can show that these χ^2's are independent, it will follow that this ratio is distributed as F, again granting that the hypothesis is true.

We have already observed (page 35) that the mean and variance of a simple random sample drawn from a normal population are independent of one another. If our hypothesis is true, it follows from this, for any single treatment group, that $n(M_j - M)^2$ is independent of $\sum(X - M_j)^2$. The sums of these two expressions for all treatment groups must also be independent of one another. That is, $\sum\limits_{j}^{a} n(M_j - M)^2$ is independent of $\sum\limits_{j}^{a}\sum(X - M_j)^2$ and the χ^2 in the numerator of (6) is independent of that in the denominator. Accordingly, under a true hypothesis, our measure of discrepancy is distributed as F. That is, we may write

$$F = \frac{\dfrac{\sum\limits_{j=1}^{a} n(M_j - M)^2}{a - 1}}{\dfrac{\sum\limits_{j=1}^{a}\sum(X - M_j)^2}{N - a}}, \; df = (a - 1)/(N - a).$$

between groups

within groups

The preceding proof that under a true hypothesis the ratio of the two estimates of the population variance is distributed as F applies only when the number of cases is the same for all treatment groups. However, it may readily be shown [1] that this ratio is still distributed as F when n is not constant. In its more general form, the ratio is written

---

[1] To prove

$$\frac{\sum\limits_{j=1}^{a} n_j(M_j - M)^2}{\sigma^2} \text{ is distributed as } \chi^2 \text{ with } a - 1 \; df,$$

let μ = population mean, then

$$\frac{(M_j - \mu)^2}{\sigma^2/n_j} \text{ is distributed as } \chi^2 \text{ with } 1 \; df.$$

Hence,

$$\left[\frac{(M_1 - \mu)^2}{\sigma^2/n_1} + \frac{(M_2 - \mu)^2}{\sigma^2/n_2} + \ldots + \frac{(M_a - \mu)^2}{\sigma^2/n_a}\right] = \frac{\sum\limits_{j=1}^{a} n_j(M_j - \mu)^2}{\sigma^2}$$

is distributed as χ^2 with $a \; df$.

Now, if we impose the restriction on the preceding expression that the deviations be computed from the sample mean (M) rather than from the population mean (μ), one degree of freedom is lost, and

$$F = \frac{\dfrac{\displaystyle\sum_{j=1}^{a} n_j (M_j - M)^2}{a - 1}}{\dfrac{\displaystyle\sum_{j=1}^{a}\sum^{n_j} (X - M_j)^2}{N - a}}, \; df = (a - 1)/(N - a), \qquad (7)$$

in which n_j is variable.

The Measure of Discrepancy as a "Mean Square" Ratio

For convenience we shall henceforth let $\displaystyle\sum_{j=1}^{a}\sum^{n_j} (X - M_j)^2$ be represented by ss_w, and will refer to it as "the sum of squares for within-groups." This is an abbreviation for "the sum of the squared deviations of the individual measures from their respective group means." We shall similarly refer to $\displaystyle\sum_{j}^{a} n_j (M_j - M)^2 = ss_A$ as "the sum of squares for treatments," which stands for "the sum of the weighted squared deviations of the individual treatment means from the general mean." The degrees of freedom for ss_A and ss_w are $(a - 1)$ and $(N - a)$, respectively. For convenience also, we shall refer to the numerator of the ratio in (7) as the "mean square" for treatments (ms_A) and to the denominator as the "mean square" for within-groups (ms_w). This notation may be summarized as follows:

$$ss_A = \sum_{j=1}^{a} n_j (M_j - M)^2$$

$$ss_w = \sum_{j=1}^{a}\sum^{n_j} (X - M_j)^2$$

$$df_A = (a - 1)$$

$$df_w = (N - a)$$

$$ms_A = \frac{\displaystyle\sum_{j=1}^{a} n_j (M_j - M)^2}{a - 1} = \frac{ss_A}{df_A}$$

$$ms_w = \frac{\displaystyle\sum_{j=1}^{a}\sum^{n_j} (X - M_j)^2}{N - a} = \frac{ss_w}{df_w}.$$

$$\frac{\displaystyle\sum_{j=1}^{a} n_j (M_j - M)^2}{\sigma^2} \text{ is distributed as } \chi^2 \text{ with } a - 1 \; df.$$

The proof that $\dfrac{\displaystyle\sum_{j=1}^{a}\sum^{n_j} (X - M_j)^2}{\sigma^2}$ is distributed as χ^2 has already been given, hence the ratio in (7) is one between two χ^2's each divided by its degrees of freedom, and is distributed as F.

In terms of this notation, our measure of discrepancy is given by

$$F = \frac{ms_A}{ms_w}, \quad df = (a - 1)/(N - a),$$

and may be referred to as the "mean square ratio" for treatments and within-groups.

Computational Procedures: In order to apply this F-test in an actual experiment, we must compute ss_A and ss_w. We shall now derive more convenient formulas for the computation of these terms.

If we let the totals for a single group and for all groups collectively be represented by $T_j = \sum\limits^{n_j} X$ and $T = \sum\limits_{j=1}^{a} \sum\limits^{n_j} X$, respectively, we may write

$$ss_A = \sum_{j=1}^{a} n_j(M_j - M)^2 = \sum_{j=1}^{a} n_j\left(\frac{T_j}{n_j} - \frac{T}{N}\right)^2$$

$$= \sum_{j=1}^{a} n_j\left(\frac{T_j^2}{n_j^2} - 2\frac{T_j T}{n_j N} + \frac{T^2}{N^2}\right)$$

$$= \sum_{j=1}^{a} \frac{T_j^2}{n_j} - 2\frac{T}{N} \sum_{j=1}^{a} T_j + \frac{T^2}{N^2} \sum_{j=1}^{a} n_j.$$

This reduces to

$$ss_A = \sum_{j=1}^{a} \frac{T_j^2}{n_j} - \frac{T^2}{N}, \qquad (8)$$

which represents in general the most convenient way of computing ss_A.

To derive a computational formula (10) for ss_w, we note next that for a single measure in group j

$$(X - M) = (X - M_j) + (M_j - M).$$

Squaring both sides of this equality, we have

$$(X - M)^2 = (X - M_j)^2 + 2(X - M_j)(M_j - M) + (M_j - M)^2.$$

If we now sum such expressions for all the n_j measures in group j, we get

$$\sum^{n_j}(X - M)^2 = \sum^{n_j}(X - M_j)^2 + 2(M_j - M)\sum^{n_j}(X - M_j) + n_j(M_j - M)^2.$$

Since $\sum\limits^{n_j}(X - M_j) = 0$, this reduces to

$$\sum^{n_j}(X - M)^2 = \sum^{n_j}(X - M_j)^2 + n_j(M_j - M)^2.$$

Summing such expressions for all a groups, we get

$$\sum_{j=1}^{a}\sum^{n_j}(X - M)^2 = \sum_{j=1}^{a}\sum^{n_j}(X - M_j)^2 + \sum_{j=1}^{a}n_j(M_j - M)^2.$$

We will call $\sum\limits_{j=1}^{a}\sum\limits^{n_j}(X - M)^2$ the "total sum of squares," meaning "the sum of the squared deviations from the general mean of all measures in all groups," and will let it be represented by ss_T. We may then write $ss_T = ss_w + ss_A$.

Thus we see that the sum of the squared deviations of the individual measures from the general mean for all treatment groups may be analyzed into the two components needed in the two terms we wish to compute for our F-test.

It is much easier to compute ss_T directly by means of

$$ss_T = \sum_{j=1}^{a}\sum^{n_j}X^2 - \frac{T^2}{N} \tag{9}$$

than it is to compute ss_w directly. Hence, the easiest way to secure ss_w is first to compute ss_T and ss_A, and then to subtract the latter from the former. That is, ss_w is best computed as a residual by

$$ss_w = ss_T - ss_A. \tag{10}$$

The results of the computations may be summarized in a table as follows:

Summary Table

Source of Variation	df	Sum of Squares	Mean Square
Treatments (A)	$a-1$	$ss_A = \sum_{j=1}^{a} T_j^2/n_j - T^2/N$	$ms_A = ss_A/a - 1$
Within-groups (w)	$N-a$	$ss_w = ss_T - ss_A$	$ms_w = ss_w/N - a$
Total	$N-1$	$ss_T = \sum_{j=1}^{a}\sum^{n_j}X^2 - T^2/N$	

We begin the computation by first securing $\sum^{n_j}X = T_j$ and $\sum^{n_j}X^2$ for each individual treatment group. Given an adding machine and a table of squares, we can enter each X in turn on the left side of the keyboard, looking up the square of this value and entering it at the same time on the right side of the keyboard. Thus, $\sum^{n_j}X$ and $\sum^{n_j}X^2$ may be obtained simultaneously. (This can be done more conveniently, without the use of a table of squares, if an automatic calculating machine is available.) We then add the T_j's for the various groups to secure T. Each T_j is then squared and divided by its corresponding n_j; these values are summed and $\frac{T^2}{N}$ is subtracted from their sum to yield the sum of squares for treatments. The sums of the squared X's are then totalled for all treatment groups to give $\sum_{j=1}^{a}\sum^{n_j}X^2$, from which $\frac{T^2}{N}$ is subtracted to yield the total sum of squares. The sum of squares for within-groups is then secured as a residual. These steps will be made clearer by the worked example which follows.

A Worked Example: Suppose that a certain experiment involves four treatments, A_1, A_2, A_3, and A_4, administered to independent samples of 5, 4, 6 and 4 subjects, respectively. The criterion measures secured at the close of the experiment are given in the table below.

Computational Example

Criterion Scores

Treatment A_1	Treatment A_2	Treatment A_3	Treatment A_4
7	6	4	3
3	10	2	4
4	8	2	5
3	5	1	4
6		2	
		1	

n_j	5	4	6	4	$N = 19$
T_j	23	29	12	16	$T = 80$
$\sum^{n_j} X^2$	119	225	30	66	$\sum_{j=1}^{a} \sum^{n_j} X^2 = 440$
M_j	4.60	7.25	2.00	4.00	$M = 4.21$
T_j^2	529	841	144	256	
T_j^2/n_j	105.80	210.25	24.00	64.00	$\sum_{j=1}^{a} T_j^2/n_j = 404.05$

$$ss_A = \sum_{j=1}^{a} T_j^2/n_j - \frac{T^2}{N} = 404.05 - 336.84 = 67.21$$

$$ss_T = \sum_{j=1}^{a} \sum^{n_j} X^2 - \frac{T^2}{N} = 440 - 336.84 = 103.16$$

$$ss_w = ss_T - ss_A = 103.16 - 67.21 = 35.95$$

The results of the first computational steps are also given. It is not necessary to secure and record $\sum^{n_j} X^2$ separately for each treatment group, but ordinarily this is done since it is desirable to *check* the work in small units. Then if an error is found the computation need be repeated only for the particular group involved. The importance of checking each step carefully before going on to subsequent steps cannot be overemphasized. Formulas (8) and (9) are used to compute the sums of squares for treatments and for total, and the sum of squares for within-groups is then secured as a residual. The results are summarized in the table below:

Source of Variation	df	ss	ms
Treatments (A)	3	67.21	22.40
Within-groups (w)	15	35.95	2.40
Total	18	103.16	

$$F = \frac{22.40}{2.40} = 9.33$$

In this computational example, non-significant digits have at times been retained in the results. For instance, since $T_1 = 23$ contains only two significant digits, there can be only two significant digits in M_1, which strictly should be written 4.6 rather than 4.60. However, for simplicity in computations of this kind [based on formulas like (8) and (9)], the rule will be followed in this text of always carrying all intermediate results to two more decimal places than are significant in an individual observation. Final results used in the tests of significance — that is, the F's and t's — will be given only to two decimal places, to be consistent with the entries in Tables 1 and 2. This means, as in the example already presented, that non-significant digits will frequently be carried in the intermediate steps in the computation, and that sometimes not all digits in the F's or t's reported will be significant. However, this computational procedure is satisfactory for all practical purposes and is simple to employ.

The Expected Value of ms_w: We have thus far completed the first two of the steps involved in testing the null hypothesis. That is, we have defined (and shown how to compute) our measure of discrepancy and have determined its sampling distribution. Before going on to the remaining steps, we will consider certain important properties of the mean squares for treatments and within-groups. Specifically, we will demonstrate that ms_w is an unbiased estimate of the common variance (σ^2) of the treatment populations, or that the "expected" value of ms_w is σ^2. The "expected" value of a sample statistic is defined as its average value for an infinite number of similar (independent) samples. We will also derive an expression for the expected value of ms_A. These relationships will add considerably to the meaningfulness of our measure of discrepancy and of our test of significance, and will provide us later with a basis for estimating the standard errors of individual treatment means and for testing the significance of the differences for individual pairs of means.

The derivations in this section and that following are entirely algebraic in character and should be within the grasp of most students using this text. However, the student who is not adept at algebra can perhaps afford to skip these derivations and to take (11), (16) and (17) for granted. Most students, however, should read the interpretive comments following these derivations (pages 62–64).

We shall begin by showing that the expected value of ms_w is σ^2, or that for a single experiment, ms_w is an unbiased estimate of σ^2. This has already been shown (page 51) for the case in which $n_j = n$ is a constant, but we shall now prove it for the general case in which n_j is variable.

Suppose that a large number (k) of similar simple-randomized experiments have been performed with the same experimental treatments, each experiment having been performed under the same conditions with independent random samples drawn from the same population. As before, we will let M_j represent the observed mean for the jth treatment in a single experiment, M the weighted mean of the M_j's, μ_j the population mean for Treatment j, and μ the weighted mean of the μ_j's. For any measure (X) in the jth treatment group in a single experiment, we may then write the identity

$$(X - \mu_j) = (X - M_j) + (M_j - \mu_j).$$

Squaring both sides of this expression

$$(X - \mu_j)^2 = (X - M_j)^2 + 2(X - M_j)(M_j - \mu_j) + (M_j - \mu_j)^2.$$

Summing such expressions for the n_j measures in the treatment group,

$$\Sigma(X - \mu_j)^2 = \Sigma(X - M_j)^2 + 2(M_j - \mu_j)\Sigma(X - M_j) + n_j(M_j - \mu_j)^2.$$

Transposing, and noting that $\Sigma(X - M_j) = 0$,

$$\Sigma(X - M_j)^2 = \Sigma(X - \mu_j)^2 - n_j(M_j - \mu_j)^2.$$

Summing such expressions for the a treatment groups,

$$\sum_{j=1}^{a}\Sigma(X - M_j)^2 = \sum_{j=1}^{a}\Sigma(X - \mu_j)^2 - \sum_{j=1}^{a}n_j(M_j - \mu_j)^2.$$

Summing such expressions for all k experiments and dividing by k,

$$\frac{1}{k}\sum^{k}\sum_{j=1}^{a}\Sigma(X - M_j)^2 = \frac{1}{k}\sum^{k}\sum_{j=1}^{a}\Sigma(X - \mu_j)^2 - \frac{1}{k}\sum^{k}\sum_{j=1}^{a}n_j(M_j - \mu_j)^2$$

$$= \sum_{j=1}^{a}n_j\frac{\sum^{k}\Sigma\Sigma(X - \mu_j)^2}{kn_j} - \sum_{j=1}^{a}n_j\frac{\sum^{k}\Sigma(M_j - \mu_j)^2}{k}.$$

Since $\dfrac{1}{k}\sum^{k}$ symbolizes the process of finding the mean of k values, the preceding expression may be read

$$\text{"mean of } \sum_{j=1}^{a}\overset{n_j}{\Sigma}(X - M_j)^2 \text{ for } k \text{ experiments"}$$

$$= \sum_{j=1}^{a}n_j\frac{\sum^{k}\Sigma\Sigma(X - \mu_j)^2}{kn_j} - \sum_{j=1}^{a}n_j\frac{\sum^{k}\Sigma(M_j - \mu_j)^2}{k}.$$

Now, letting k become infinitely large ($k \to \infty$), this means that *in the long run* the

$$\text{mean of } \sum_{j=1}^{a}\sum^{n_j}(X - M_j)^2 = \sum_{j=1}^{a}n_j\sigma^2 - \sum_{j=1}^{a}n_j\frac{\sigma^2}{n_j}$$

$$= N\sigma^2 - a\sigma^2$$

$$= \sigma^2(N - a).$$

From this it follows that in the long run ($k \to \infty$) the

$$\text{mean of } \frac{\sum\limits_{j=1}^{a}\sum(X - M_j)^2}{N - a} \ (= ms_w) = \sigma^2,$$

which is equivalent to saying that ms_w is an unbiased estimate of σ^2. It is also equivalent to saying that the "expected" value of ms_w is σ^2. The symbol $E(= \frac{1}{k}\sum^{k}$ when $k \to \infty$) stands for "expected value of." Thus,

$$E(ms_w) = \sigma^2. \tag{11}$$

The Expected Value of ms_A: The expression for the expected value of ms_A will be derived only for the case in which $n_j = n$ is a constant. We first write, for a single treatment group in a single experiment,

$$(M_j - M) = (M_j - \mu) + (\mu - M)$$

$$= (M_j - \mu) - (M - \mu).$$

Squaring both sides of this identity,

$$(M_j - M)^2 = (M_j - \mu)^2 + (M - \mu)^2 - 2(M_j - \mu)(M - \mu).$$

Multiplying both sides by n_j, and summing for the a values of j, we get

$$\sum_{j=1}^{a}n_j(M_j - M)^2 = \sum_{j=1}^{a}n_j(M_j - \mu)^2 + \sum_{j=1}^{a}n_j(M - \mu)^2 - 2\sum_{j=1}^{a}n_j(M_j - \mu)(M - \mu),$$

in which, if we let $N = \sum_{j}^{a}n_j$,

$$\sum_{j=1}^{a}n_j(M - \mu)^2 = N(M - \mu)^2,$$

and

$$2\sum_{j=1}^{a}n_j(M_j - \mu)(M - \mu) = 2(M - \mu)\sum_{j=1}^{a}n_j(M_j - \mu)$$

$$= 2(M - \mu)(\sum_{j=1}^{a}n_jM_j - \sum_{j=1}^{a}n_j\mu)$$

$$= 2(M - \mu)(NM - N\mu)$$

$$= 2N(M - \mu)^2.$$

Hence,

$$\sum_{j=1}^{a}n_j(M_j - M)^2 = \sum_{j=1}^{a}n_j(M_j - \mu)^2 - N(M - \mu)^2.$$

Summing these expressions for the k experiments and dividing by k,

$$\frac{1}{k}\sum^{k}\sum^{a}_{j=1}n_j(M_j - M)^2 = \frac{1}{k}\sum^{k}\sum^{a}_{j=1}n_j(M_j - \mu)^2 - \frac{N\sum^{k}(M-\mu)^2}{k}. \quad (12)$$

Now, for a single treatment group in a single experiment

$$n_j(M_j - \mu)^2 = n_j[(M_j - \mu_j) + (\mu_j - \mu)]^2$$
$$= n_j[(M_j - \mu_j)^2 + (\mu_j - \mu)^2 + 2(M_j - \mu_j)(\mu_j - \mu)].$$

Summing these expressions for the k experiments and dividing by k,

$$\frac{1}{k}\sum^{k}n_j(M_j - \mu)^2 = \frac{1}{k}\sum^{k}n_j(M_j - \mu_j)^2 + n_j(\mu_j - \mu)^2 + 2(\mu_j - \mu)\frac{\sum^{k}n_j(M_j - \mu_j)}{k}.$$

If we let $k \to \infty$, we note that in the preceding expression

$$\frac{1}{k}\sum^{k}n_j(M_j - \mu_j)^2 = n_j\sigma^2_{M_j} = n_j\frac{\sigma^2}{n_j} = \sigma^2,$$

and

$$2(\mu_j - \mu)\frac{\sum^{k}n_j(M_j - \mu_j)}{k} = 2(\mu_j - \mu) \cdot 0 = 0.$$

Hence,

$$\frac{1}{k}\sum^{k}n_j(M_j - \mu)^2 = \sigma^2 + n_j(\mu_j - \mu)^2.$$

Accordingly, in (12), when $k \to \infty$

$$\frac{1}{k}\sum^{k}\sum^{a}_{j=1}n_j(M_j - \mu)^2 = \sum^{a}_{j=1}\frac{1}{k}\sum^{k}n_j(M_j - \mu)^2$$
$$= \sum^{a}_{j=1}[\sigma^2 + n_j(\mu_j - \mu)^2]$$
$$= a\sigma^2 + \sum^{a}_{j=1}n_j(\mu_j - \mu)^2 \quad (13)$$

and

$$\frac{N\sum^{k}(M - \mu)^2}{k} = N\sigma^2_M.$$

But if n_j is constant
$$M = \frac{1}{a}(M_1 + M_2 + \cdots + M_j + \cdots + M_a).$$

Hence,

$$\sigma^2_M = \frac{1}{a^2}(\sigma^2_{M_1} + \sigma^2_{M_2} + \ldots + \sigma^2_{M_a})$$
$$= \frac{1}{a^2} \cdot a\sigma^2_{M_j} = \frac{\sigma^2}{an} = \frac{\sigma^2}{N}$$

and

$$\frac{N\sum^{k}(M - \mu)^2}{k} = N\sigma^2_M = \frac{N\sigma^2}{N} = \sigma^2. \quad (14)$$

Hence, substituting from (13) and (14) in (12),

$$\frac{1}{k}\sum_{}^{k}\sum_{j=1}^{a} n_j(M_j - M)^2 = a\sigma^2 + \sum_{j=1}^{a} n_j(\mu_j - \mu)^2 - \sigma^2$$

$$= (a - 1)\sigma^2 + \sum_{j=1}^{a} n_j(\mu_j - \mu)^2.$$

Dividing both sides by $(a - 1)$,

$$\frac{1}{k}\sum_{}^{k}\sum_{j=1}^{a}\frac{n_j(M_j - M)^2}{a - 1} = \sigma^2 + \frac{\sum_{j=1}^{a} n_j(\mu_j - \mu)^2}{a - 1}. \tag{15}$$

Hence, the expected value of ms_A is

$$E(ms_A) = \sigma^2 + \frac{\sum_{j=1}^{a} n_j(\mu_j - \mu)^2}{a - 1}. \tag{16}$$

Interpretation of Expected Value of ms_A: It is difficult to attach a useful meaning to $\sum_{j=1}^{a} n_j(\mu_j - \mu)^2/(a - 1)$. It is neither a population variance nor an estimate of one, nor is it the variance of any actual distribution. Only if $n_j = n$ is a constant and the particular treatments involved in the experiment may be regarded as a random sample from a population of treatments does it have a clear meaning. In this case it is n times an unbiased estimate of the variance of a population consisting of the means of an infinite number of treatment populations. However, there are very few experiments in education and psychology in which it makes sense to regard the particular experimental treatments as a random sample from any real or hypothetical population of treatments.

If a single factor (A) underlies the treatment classification, so that the various "treatments" represent different amounts, or durations, or intensities, etc., of a single experimental variable, $\sum_{j=1}^{a} n_j(\mu_j - \mu)^2/(a - 1)$ may possibly be regarded as a "measure" of the "potency" of the experimental factor. It measures this potency in the sense that the higher the relationship between the experimental and criterion variables, the larger the differences $(\mu_j - \mu)$ will be. There is no satisfactory logical basis, however, for weighting the squared deviations by a variable n_j, since n_j is arbitrarily selected.

Even though $n_j = n$ is a constant, the meaning of $\sum_{j=1}^{a} n_j(\mu_j - \mu)^2/(a - 1)$ depends on another wholly arbitrary choice — namely, the choice of the particular amounts, or durations, etc., of the experimental variable represented in the experiment. For example, if the "treatments" represent varying amounts of practice in performing a certain task, $\sum_{j=1}^{a} n_j(\mu_j - \mu)^2/(a - 1)$ will obviously be quite different if the experimental comparisons are among 2, 3, and 4 hours of practice than if they are among 1, 3, and 5 days of practice, or among 1, 5, and 9 days of practice, etc.

All that one can safely say about $\sum_{j=1}^{a} n_j(\mu_j - \mu)^2/(a-1)$ is that its magnitude depends on the differences among the population means for the *particular* treatments selected for experimental comparison — noting carefully the wholly arbitrary manner in which these treatments may have been defined or selected and the weights (n_j) assigned. In this restricted sense, $\sum_{j=1}^{a} n_j(\mu_j - \mu)^2/(a-1)$ may be regarded as a measure of the potency of the "treatments effect," but even then it is best limited to the case in which $n_j = n$ is a constant.

The mistake [1] has frequently been made in experimental work of attempting to use the *mean square ratio* (ms_A/ms_w) as a measure of the *relative* potency of the experimental factor, that is, of its potency in comparison with that of the factors which give rise to differences among subjects within the same treatment groups. That this is not a valid interpretation of F is evident from (16) which, since $E(ms_w) = \sigma^2$, may in the case in which $n_j = n$ be written

$$E(ms_A) = E(ms_w) + \sum_{j=1}^{a} n_j(\mu_j - \mu)^2/(a-1). \tag{17}$$

Accordingly, if in a particular experiment ms_A and ms_w happened to be equal to their expected values, the mean square ratio would be

$$F = \frac{ms_A}{ms_w} = \frac{ms_w + \dfrac{\sum_{j=1}^{a} n_j(\mu_j - \mu)^2}{a-1}}{ms_w}. \tag{18}$$

From this it is apparent that F depends not only on the magnitude of the differences among the treatment population means, but also on the variability of the experimental material (as measured by ms_w), on the sizes of the experimental groups (n_j), and on the number of treatments (a). In other words, F depends not only on the real differences among the particular treatments involved, but on the precision of the experiment and the number of treatments as well. A high F does not necessarily mean that the treat-

---

[1] In particular, it has been argued (see Peters and Van Voorhis, *Statistical Procedures and Their Mathematical Bases*, McGraw-Hill Book Company, Inc., 1940, pp. 324–325) that ϵ^2, the unbiased correlation ratio (which is a function of F and the numbers of cases and treatments) is superior to F as a basis for testing the null hypotheses, since ϵ^2 may be interpreted as a measure of the "strength of the relationship" between the experimental and the criterion variables. This argument overlooks entirely the fact that in most applications of analysis of variance to experimental designs, the value of either F or ϵ^2 depends upon the arbitrary choice of categories in the treatment classifications, and hence is not meaningful as an index of strength of relationship.

ments differ greatly, nor does a low F necessarily mean that they are much alike.

In spite of the difficulty of interpreting $\sum_{j=1}^{a} n_j(\mu_j - \mu)^2/(a-1)$, we can draw some very useful inferences from (16). We may note first that if the null hypothesis is true, that is, if $\mu_1 = \mu_2 = \ldots = \mu_a = \mu$, then $\sum_{j=1}^{a} n_j(\mu_j - \mu)^2/(a-1)$ equals zero, and the expected value of ms_A is σ^2. This is the same as the expected value of ms_w under the null hypothesis. Accordingly, if the null hypothesis is true and both ms_A and ms_w have their expected values, the ratio between them is 1.00. However, if the null hypothesis is false and both ms_A and ms_w have their expected values, the ratio between them will be greater than 1.00. This confirms our choice of a measure of discrepancy, and has further implications which will be made clear in the following section.

The F-ratio as a Ratio of the Observed Variance of the Treatment Means to Their Expected Chance Variance: It will be useful for purposes of subsequent discussions to observe that the F-ratio of (5) may be regarded as the ratio of the observed variance of the a treatment means to the variance that they would be expected to have as a result only of chance fluctuations in simple random sampling. Let us note first that when $n_j = n$ is constant, our best estimate of the variance (σ^2) of the population from which the treatment groups are drawn is that denoted as $est_2\sigma^2$ on page 51. The variance in the means of an infinite number of random samples of n cases each drawn from a population whose variance is σ^2 is $\sigma_M^2 = \sigma^2/n$. Hence the best estimate of σ_M^2 that we can secure from the treatment groups is

$$\text{est'd } \sigma_M^2 = \frac{\text{est'd } \sigma^2}{n} = \frac{1}{an} \sum_{j=1}^{a}\sum (X - M_j)^2/(n-1).$$ We know that if a random sample of n cases is drawn from a population whose varance is σ^2, the average or expected variance of the sample is $\frac{(n-1)}{n}\sigma^2$. Accordingly, the expected chance variance of a sample of a means drawn from a population of means whose variance is σ_M^2 would be

$$\frac{(a-1)}{a} \text{ est } \sigma_M^2 = \frac{(a-1)}{a} \cdot \frac{1}{an} \cdot \sum_{j=1}^{a}\sum (X - M_j)^2/(n-1).$$

With these facts in mind, let us examine the F-ratio (5) when both numerator and denominator are multiplied by $(a-1)/an$. The result is

$$F = \frac{\dfrac{\Sigma(M_j - M)^2}{a}}{\dfrac{(a-1)}{a} \cdot \dfrac{1}{an} \cdot \sum\sum (X - M_j)^2/(n-1)}$$

$$= \frac{\text{observed variance of treatment means}}{\text{expected chance variance of these means}}.$$

Defining the Region of Rejection: We are now ready to go on with the remaining steps (page 49) in testing the null hypothesis. We shall postpone temporarily any consideration of Step 3, that of deciding what risk to take of rejecting a true hypothesis, and go on first to Step 4, that of marking off the region of rejection along the scale of possible values of the measure of discrepancy. We are interested, of course, in the possibility that the treatments really differ in their effectiveness, and that this has caused the observed variance of the means to be *larger* than it would be as the result of chance alone. In other words, we are interested only in the possibility that the ratio of observed to chance variance of treatment means is too *large* to be reasonably attributed to chance. If the obtained ratio turns out to be less than 1.00, we have no basis for rejecting the hypothesis. If the assumptions underlying the test are true, an F of less than 1.00 could be due *only* to chance. The only other possible explanation is that the assumption of random sampling is false in that the treatment groups are *more alike* than random samples would be. It is apparent, then, that the region of rejection should be entirely under the right tail of the distribution. That is, the test will be of the type known as a "one-tailed" test, as contrasted with one in which the region of rejection consists of two parts, one under the right tail and one under the left tail of the sampling distribution.

Suppose now that we have defined the region of rejection as that lying to the right of the 1% point in the F-distribution, and that our measure of discrepancy (the mean square ratio) has been found to lie in this region. If the basic assumptions have been satisfied, (pages 51–52), there are only two possible explanations for this event. One is that the null hypothesis is true, and that the ratio has fallen in the region of rejection only as a result of chance fluctuations in random sampling. We know that under a true null hypothesis this would happen only very rarely (one percent of the time). To retain the null hypothesis, then, we must contend that a rare event has actually "come off" in this instance. The other explanation is that the null hypothesis is false, or that the treatments really differ in effectiveness, and that the large ratio is due primarily to these real differences rather than to chance. If we choose this latter interpretation, we need not contend that a rare event has actually occurred, and hence, we prefer the second interpretation. We know, however, that under a true null hypothesis the mean square ratio *will* fall in this region of rejection one time out of every one hundred in the long run. In choosing the second interpretation, then, we run the risk that this is one of those times, and that we are rejecting a true null hypothesis. How large this risk is depends, in this one-tailed test, upon the "percent point" in the F distribution at which the region of rejection begins. If the region of rejection begins at the 5% point, we will in the long run reject an hypothesis, when it is true, five percent of the times it is tested. That is, we will be taking a 5% risk of rejecting a true null hypothesis, or will be making the test at the 5% level of significance. Generally, we wish to keep this risk small. It is common practice, therefore, to make the region of rejection begin at the 5%, the 1%, or sometimes even at the 0.1% point in the F-distribution. In other words, it is customary to make the test at a "high" level of significance — a high level being one corresponding to a small risk, and vice versa.

The F-table (Table 3, pages 41–44) has been constructed so that we may employ any one of seven convenient [1] levels of significance, corresponding to the 20%, 10%, 5%, 2.5%, 1%, 0.5% and 0.1% points in the F-distribution. For convenience in the discussion, we will refer to the corresponding values of F as the "20% value of F," the "10% value of F," etc.

An Example: Suppose that in an actual experiment, we have decided in advance to make the test of significance at the 5% level, or to reject the hypothesis if the mean square ratio exceeds the 5% value of F. For reasons to be considered later, this decision should always be made before examining the data. Suppose that the ratio turns out to be 13.27, and that the degrees of freedom for the ratio are 3 and 5. Turning to the table for F, we find that the 5% value for 3 and 5 degrees of freedom is 5.41. Accordingly, we reject the null hypothesis. We note that in this case we could have rejected the hypothesis had we made the test at the 1% level. However, we should not change the level of significance at which the test is to be made after seeing the experimental results. This would be much like changing the betting odds on a horse race after the race is over.

Type I and Type II Errors

It does not follow from the preceding discussion that it is always desirable to set a very high level of significance for the test of the null hypothesis. We must keep in mind that there are always two kinds of errors possible in testing any statistical hypothesis. One is the error (sometimes called a Type I error) of rejecting an hypothesis when it is true. The other is that (Type II) of retaining an hypothesis when it is false. The risk of making a Type I error is exactly determined when we establish our region of rejection (assuming, of course, that all the basic assumptions are exactly satisfied). The relative frequency with which a false hypothesis would be retained under the same circumstances, however, cannot be determined in practice. This frequency depends on *how far* the hypothesis departs from the truth. Suppose, for example, that the (null) hypothesis is *almost* true, or that the treatments are very nearly the same in effectiveness, and the treatment population means differ only very slightly. If a large number of similar experiments were independently performed with these treatments, the mean square ratios obtained would be only slightly larger than if the null hypothesis had been true. Let us remember again that the mean square

---

[1] There are ways of interpolating between these values (see C. J. Burke, "Computation of the Level of Significance in the F-test," *Psychological Bulletin*, vol. 48 (September, 1951) pp. 392–397); but there is hardly ever any practical need to employ them.

ratio is the same as the ratio of the observed variance of the treatment means to their chance variance. The effect of the small real differences among treatments would be to add a small and constant amount $\left[\sum_{j=1}^{a} n_j(\mu_j - \mu)^2/(a - 1) \right]$ to the numerator of each ratio [see (18), page 63], and this would affect the value of each ratio only slightly. Under these circumstances, the actual sampling distribution of the ratios might be that represented by Curve A in Figure 3, while Curve F might represent the sampling distribution that

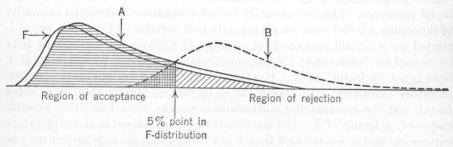

FIGURE 3. *Relation of possible actual distributions (A and B) of mean square ratios to the distribution (F) that would have been obtained had the null hypothesis been true*

would have been obtained had the null hypothesis been true. The diagonally ruled area represents 5% of the area in the F-distribution; the horizontally ruled area in the A-distribution represents the proportion of the times that the false null hypothesis is retained when this region of rejection is employed. In the situation represented by Curve A, the false null hypothesis would be retained almost 95% of the times it is tested.

Suppose, on the other hand, that the null hypothesis is far from true, or that the treatments differ markedly in effectiveness and that the population means for these treatments differ widely. If a series of similar experiments were performed with these treatments, large ratios of the observed to the expected variances of treatment means would nearly always be obtained. This is because the effect of adding a large constant $\left[\sum_{j=1}^{a} n_j(\mu_j - \mu)^2/(a - 1) \right]$ to the numerator of each ratio would be to increase the value of each ratio markedly, particularly of those that would otherwise be less than or only slightly larger than 1.00. In this case, the actual sampling distribution of these ratios might be very crudely represented by Curve B in Figure 3. The vertically ruled area in this distribution indicates the relative frequency with which the false null hypothesis would be accepted in this case. We see that the false null hypothesis would only rarely be retained, or that the risk of a Type II error would be quite small.

It should now be clear why it is not always desirable to set a very high level for the test of significance. From the preceding illustration, it is evident that, other things being equal, the higher the level of significance of the test, the greater is the danger of retaining a false hypothesis. If we try to reduce the risk of a Type I error, we increase the risk of a Type II error. Since the consequences of either type of error are unfortunate, we must set the level of significance of our test with both types of error in mind.

The Consequences of Type I and Type II Errors: The consequences of a Type II error are quite different in nature from those of a Type I error. To weigh the relative seriousness of these consequences, it will be useful to regard psychological and educational experiments as classifiable into two broad categories. The first category includes experiments designed primarily to determine whether or not a certain criterion variable (X) depends on, or is related to, a certain experimental variable (Y). Such an experiment may be termed an "exploratory" experiment, whose purpose is to determine if Y is or is not "a factor" of X. If a significant result is *not* obtained in an exploratory experiment, the conclusion is tentatively drawn that Y is not a factor, and the experimenter's attention is usually turned to other possible causes of, or factors of X. If a significant result is obtained in the exploratory experiment and it is concluded that Y is a factor of X, the experiment may be followed by an experiment (or series of experiments) belonging to the second category. Experiments in this category are designed to determine the nature of the functional relationship between Y and X — preferably to describe this relationship in algebraic form. Exploratory experiments, then, are those that, when significant results are obtained, lead to further experiments with the same factor or factors.

If a Type I error is made in the exploratory experiment, that is, if a "significant" result leads to a *false* conclusion that Y is a factor of X, the likely consequence is that time and effort will be wasted on further experiments designed to determine the nature of the relationship between Y and X. To minimize the danger of thus following a false lead, we usually set a high level of significance for tests made in exploratory experiments.

If we make a Type II error in the exploratory experiment, that is, if the null hypothesis is false but we fail to get a significant result and therefore falsely conclude that Y is not a factor, the likely consequence is simply that we will fail to follow up a true lead. In a sense this is not as serious as to have wasted time following up a false lead, since in the meantime we may be trying out other possible leads, all of which might eventually have to be tried out anyway. Furthermore, it will be generally understood that we have not *proved* that Y is not a factor, so that anyone else who has his own reasons to believe that Y is a factor is at liberty to plan experiments to prove his contentions.

The preceding is, of course, an oversimplification of the situation. In practice we are frequently not so much concerned with whether Y is or is not a factor, categorically, as with whether or not it is a *relatively important* factor. Having performed exploratory experiments with a number of possible factors, all of which may be real but not equally important, we would like to give priority in subsequent experimentation to the factors which are most important. If we always set a high level of significance for our tests at the exploratory level, we may be quite sure that we will not follow many completely false leads, and at the same time, we will have some assurance that the true leads which we ignore (because of Type II errors) are probably among the less promising ones.

The distinction between "exploratory" experiments and others is an arbitrary one. Any experiment may be termed an exploratory experiment if its results provide the basis for further experimentation which may be fruitless if those results are not sound. Accordingly, what has been said about the consequences of the two types of error in exploratory experiments is really applicable to all experiments.

It is perhaps on the basis of reasoning somewhat like the preceding that experimenters have usually been much more concerned about the consequences of Type I than of Type II errors, and have typically set a rather high level of significance for their tests of treatment effects. However, the analysis just presented is still considerably oversimplified. There are many situations in which the consequences of a Type II error are clearly more serious than those of a Type I error. For example, suppose that a given public school system has been employing a certain method (Method A) of teaching elementary school spelling, and that it has been suggested that another method (Method B) be substituted for it. Suppose also, that the change could be made at relatively little cost and inconvenience, and that the continuing instructional costs under Method B would be about the same as those under Method A. The superintendent of schools decides to base his decision on the outcome of an experimental comparison of the two methods. He decides that he will introduce Method B only if a statistically significant difference is found in favor of that method, but reasons that he need not set a high level of significance for the test, and decides on the 20% level. Since the consequences of a Type II error are, in this case, considerably more serious than those of a Type I error, he might easily have justified a still lower level. Suppose, on the one hand, that Method B is really superior to Method A but that, nevertheless, no significant difference is found in the experiment. A Type II error is thus made, with the consequence that the school retains Method A and continues indefinitely to secure poorer results in spelling than it might otherwise have secured. On the other hand, suppose that A and B are really equally good, but that a significant result in favor of B is nevertheless obtained in the experiment. A Type I error is thus made, with the consequence that a needless but slight expenditure is made to substitute one equally good method for the other. Clearly, the consequences of the Type II error are the more serious in this case. Had the cost of a changeover and the cost of continued operation under B been very much higher, the consequences of a Type I error would have been relatively much more undesirable, and a much higher level of significance might then have been set for the test of significance.

It should now be clear that it is dangerous to attempt any generalization about the relative seriousness of Type I and Type II errors. The experimenter should always give careful consideration to the consequences of errors of both types, and should set the level of significance of his test accordingly. In other words, the whole problem should be thought through independently in each new situation.

Effect of the Precision of the Experiment on the Risk of Type II Errors: Unfortunately, we never know in practice to what extent, if any, the null hypothesis is false; therefore, we never know what risk we are running of making a Type II error. We do know, however, that this risk is frequently very large.

How large this risk is (for any given relationship among the true treatment means) depends partly on the precision of the experiment. Suppose again that there are certain real differences among a number of treatments, and that a series of similar experiments to test the null hypothesis are performed with these treatments. Suppose, on the one hand, that very large treatment groups have been employed, so that the precision of the experiment is relatively high.

We have noted earlier that when both numerator and denominator of the F-ratio have their expected values, the numerator is ms_w plus a constant, and the denominator is ms_w, the constant being $\sum_{j=1}^{a} n_j(\mu_j - \mu)^2/(a - 1)$. The value of this constant depends not only upon the magnitude of the differences among treatment means $(\mu_j - \mu)$, but also upon the sizes (n_j) of the treatment groups. Thus we see that the effect of real treatment differences when n_j is large is to add a relatively large constant to the numerator, but the effect of the *same* treatment differences when n_j is small is to add a relatively small constant, so that the F-ratio tends to be large when n_j is large and small when n_j is small. This means, in terms of Figure 3 and the accompanying discussion on page 67, that when the null hypothesis is false, the actual sampling distribution (B) of the obtained ratios will be farther to the left when n_j is small than when it is large, and that this distribution will also be more variable when n_j is small. The result is that with a small n_j there will be a much greater overlap in the F and B distributions, or that the risk of a Type II error will be greater when n_j is small than when it is large. In other words, the lower the precision of the experiment, the greater is the risk of retaining a seriously false null hypothesis.

Statisticians sometimes refer to the "power" of a test. By this they mean the probability of rejecting a false hypothesis, that is, $(1 - p)$, p being the probability of a Type II error. The power of a test, then, is dependent, among other things, on the precision of the experiment.

Possibilities of Controlling the Risk of Type II Errors: We have seen that in testing the treatments effect in a simple-randomized experiment, the risk of a Type II error depends (1) on how false the null hypothesis is, (2) on the precision of the experiment. The precision of the experiment depends upon the variability of the experimental material (measured in this case by the *error* mean square, that is, by the within-groups mean square) and on the sizes of the treatment groups. The sizes of the treatment groups are, of course, subject to the experimenter's control. Ideally, therefore, it would seem that in planning the experiment, the experimenter's aim should be to make the experiment just precise enough (or the groups just large enough) so that the danger of retaining a "seriously false" hypothesis would not exceed a specified risk. More specifically, the ideal procedure would seem to be as follows: first, decide how large a departure from the truth we are willing to tolerate in the null hypothesis (define exactly what we mean by a "seriously false" null hypothesis); second, specify the risks we are willing to take of making Type I and Type II errors, respectively; third, secure a dependable estimate of the error variance; and fourth, calculate exactly how large our samples need be in order that the risk of a Type II error may not exceed the specified value.

There are three major reasons why, in psychological research practice, this ideal cannot often be attained. One is that we are seldom able to secure in advance any useful estimate of the error variance. In many experiments the criterion measure to be employed is one with which we have had little or no previous experience. Frequently, therefore, we are unable to estimate in advance of the experiment what variability our experimental subjects will show in relation to this criterion. Furthermore, in practice most of our designs are relatively complex designs in which the error variance depends not only on Type S errors, but on Type G and Type R errors as well, about which we know even less. In most instances, therefore, in order to obtain a useful estimate of the error variance, we would have to perform a preliminary experiment conducted simply in order to provide such an estimate, and this is often impracticable.

A second difficulty is that we are rarely able to attach any fundamental or absolute meanings to the *scale* along which, or to the units in terms of which, the criterion measures are expressed. For this reason, we often have only an inadequate basis for defining just what we mean by a "seriously false" null hypothesis. There are some situations, however, in which as the result of some advance experience with the criterion, a fairly useful empirical basis for such a decision may be available.

The third difficulty is that, for most experimental designs, we lack the theoretical basis for making the necessary calculations. This basis has been worked out for the simple case of a simple-randomized experiment involving only two treatments with treatment groups of the same size,[1] but not for the F-tests in complex designs involving several treatments. Students working on specific experimental problems who have available an estimate of the population variance, and who can meaningfully define a "serious discrepancy"

[1] William G. Cochran and Gertrude M. Cox, *Experimental Designs* (New York: John Wiley and Sons, Inc., 1950), pp. 15–26.

between fact and hypothesis, are advised to acquaint themselves with this procedure.[1]

In general, then, we cannot often design an experiment so as to be sure that a specified risk of retaining a "seriously false" null hypothesis will not be exceeded, even where we can provide a meaningful definition of a "seriously false" hypothesis. Even after the experiment has been conducted and an unbiased estimate of the error variance is available, we usually still cannot state what risk of a Type II error is involved in the test of significance, either because we cannot meaningfully describe what we mean by a "seriously false" hypothesis, or because the theoretical basis for calculating the risk has not been worked out.

However, in interpreting any F-test, we *can* always recognize the possibility of a Type II error, and we can always give some thought to the consequences of such errors. We can take these consequences into consideration in deciding what level of significance we will adopt in the test of the null hypothesis, knowing that the higher the level of significance, the greater is the risk of a Type II error. If we fail to find a significant result and accept the null hypothesis, we can always say that the error, if any, in that hypothesis is "not sufficiently large to have been revealed as such by our experiment." That is, we may *always* contend that the risk of retaining a "seriously false" null hypothesis is negligible *if* we always define a "seriously false" null hypothesis as one in which the error is so large that it will nearly always be revealed in an experiment as precise as that which we have conducted.

From this point of view, what we mean by a "seriously false" null hypothesis is determined when we decide on what numbers of cases to employ in the experiment. Frequently, in planning the experiment we make it as precise as our resources will permit, or as precise as we can justify in terms of its cost in relation to the importance of the problem under investigation. Our position may be that if the error in the null hypothesis is not sufficiently large to be revealed by an experiment with this precision, then the error is of little practical consequence anyway, and we will continue to use the null hypothesis as a working hypothesis. It is extremely important, however, to recognize that this is the nature of the decision we are making when we decide on the scope of our experiment; and we should do our best, both on the basis of our knowledge of underlying theory and of our previous experience with similar data, to make as meaningful as possible the degree of falsity we will tolerate in the null hypothesis.

The Importance of the Assumptions Underlying the F-Test

The General Effect of a Failure to Satisfy an Assumption: It is very important, in any application of the simple-randomized design, to consider very carefully

---

[1] *Ibid.*

the assumptions underlying the F-test of the null hypothesis and the effects on the validity of this test of the failure to satisfy one or more of these assumptions. The ratio of treatments to within-groups mean squares is distributed as F if all four of the following conditions are satisfied.[1]

1) All treatment groups were originally drawn at random from the same parent population.

   After administration of the treatments, each group may then be regarded as a simple random sample from a different (hypothetical) treatment population.

2) The variance (σ^2) of the criterion measures is the same for each of these treatment populations.

3) The distribution of criterion measures for each treatment population is normal.

4) The mean of the criterion measures is the same for each treatment population (the null hypothesis).

If any one of these conditions is not satisfied, the sampling distribution of mean square ratios may differ from the F-distribution. Generally, if one or more of the conditions is not satisfied, the distribution of ms_A/ms_w will be more variable than the F-distribution. This means that if a "significant" mean square ratio is obtained in an experiment, it *could* have resulted from a failure to satisfy any one of these conditions. Therefore, before concluding from a significant F that it is Condition 4 (our hypothesis) which is not satisfied, we must assure ourselves that a failure to satisfy any of the other conditions is not likely to have any consequential effect on the sampling distribution of ms_A/ms_w.

The Assumption of Random Sampling: It is very seldom that an experimenter can draw his subjects strictly at random from the real population in which he is basically interested. Usually, he must be content to work with those members of that population who are readily *accessible* to him, even though the accessible members of the population may differ systematically from those who are not accessible. A research worker in psychology, for example, might wish to work with random samples from a population consisting of "all adult American males," but may have to be content with a sample consisting of male students in a sophomore course in general psychology in a particular college or university. A research worker in education may wish to conduct an experiment from which he can fairly draw inferences about "all fourth-grade pupils in American public schools," but he may have to conduct his experiment in a single school in which the principal or superintendent is known to him and is willing to let him have the necessary facilities for his experiment.

---

[1] See footnote on page 51.

Very frequently, however, the experimenter can draw his experimental subjects strictly at random from those subjects that *are accessible* to him. If not, he can nearly always at least *randomize* his experimental subjects with reference to the treatments. That is, by use of a table of random numbers he can leave it strictly to chance which subjects are to constitute each treatment group. Having done this, he may then fairly contend that his experimental groups are all random samples from the same *hypothetical* parent population — a population which may be roughly defined as consisting of all individuals "like those involved in the experiment." In the case of the psychological experiment earlier referred to, this might be "all male students who have taken or might take a course in general psychology in College X"; or in the case of the educational experiment, it might be "all pupils who have been or might become fourth graders in School Y" — in each case assuming stable general conditions.

The device just suggested, of assigning the experimental subjects at random to the treatment groups and of defining a hypothetical parent population to fit the subjects actually used, must very frequently be employed in experimental work in order to make possible any statistical test of an exact hypothesis. Having employed this device, of course, the experimenter should thereafter restrict his *statistical* inferences to this hypothetical parent population. If he wishes to extend these inferences to any real population, he must do so on a "judgmental" rather than on a statistical basis; that is, he must do so without benefit of the safeguards provided by the logic of statistical inference. The extent to which he may thus extrapolate his inferences to a real population depends upon his own judgment of the extent to which the *relative* effects of the treatments are the same for the real as for the hypothetical parent population. (He need not assume that the *absolute* effects of each treatment are the same for both these populations, but only that the relative effects of the treatments are the same.) The average sophomore student in general psychology, for example, might make a higher criterion score than the average "adult American male" in general, but one might still plausibly contend that whatever treatment is most effective for college sophomores is also most effective for adult American males in general. However this may be, if the experimenter randomizes his experimental subjects with reference to treatments in a simple-randomized design, he may, so far as the *hypothetical* parent population is concerned, regard Condition 1 as completely satisfied.

The repeated use of "hypothetical" with different specific references in this discussion may tend to be confusing. The student should guard particularly against confusing the hypothetical parent population with the hypothetical treatment populations.

A mistake that has very frequently been made in educational research is to regard as a simple random sample of pupils a group consisting of several intact school classes, in situations in which the classes differ systematically with reference to the criterion variable. For example, in an experiment designed to compare two methods of teaching a school subject, the experimenter may arrange to have Method A used with, say, seven classes in this subject in as many different schools, and Method B used with nine classes in another set of schools. In another experiment, Method A and Method B may both be used in the same schools, Method A being given to one class and Method B to another class in the same subject in the same school, or Method A being given to a random half of a class and Method B to the other half in each school. Experiments involving more than two methods have frequently been similarly designed. To test the significance of the differences among the "treatment" groups, the t-test for independent random samples or the F-test of the simple-randomized design has been used, regarding the treatment groups of combined classes as simple random samples of pupils. This practice is legitimate only if there are no systematic differences among classes so far as the criterion variable is concerned. With the criteria usually employed in these experiments (achievement in school subjects), this is very rarely the case. Differences among teachers, among communities, among school facilities (school plant, instructional equipment, libraries, etc.) and other factors typically cause the schools to differ markedly in achievement. Sometimes the differences in mean achievement from school to school are of almost the same magnitude as the differences in achievement among individual pupils in a single school. In such experiments, the treatment groups might be regarded as random samples of schools or of school classes, but not as random samples of pupils. Appropriate methods of analyzing the results of such experiments and other designs more appropriate in such situations will be considered in later chapters, particularly Chapters 7 and 8.

To justify this practice of combining a number of intact school classes and regarding them as simple random samples in statistical tests, experimenters have sometimes applied preliminary tests to the means and variances of the classes (such as the F-test of analysis of variance and the Bartlett test of homogeneity of variance). If these tests have failed to reveal significant differences among the classes, the experimenters have contended that the combined classes might legitimately be regarded as simple random samples. The weakness of this logic is that the precision of these tests is usually low, due to the small sizes of the classes, and the danger of accepting a false null hypothesis is therefore large. (See page 70.) The fact that a statistical test has a non-significant outcome does not prove the hypothesis tested, but only demonstrates that the observed results *could* have arisen by chance *if* the hypothesis were true. In every case, there are many other hypotheses, of course, under which the same results might also arise. Sometimes (although perhaps rarely) the criterion variable employed may be such that consequential systematic differences among schools are unlikely, and the combined classes may legitimately be regarded as simple random samples, granting that no significant differences can be found among them. In general, however, school classes should thus be combined and regarded as simple random samples of pupils only if the assumptions of homogeneity of the means and variances of the classes are strongly supported by *a priori* considerations as well as by the outcomes of statistical tests.

The Assumption of Homogeneity of Variance: Before considering the effect upon the validity of the F-test of the failure to satisfy the assumption of homogeneity of variance, it will be well to consider first how it is that heterogeneity of variance arises in educational and psychological experiments.

Suppose that, just before administering the treatments in a simple-randomized experiment, observations are made of the criterion variable for all of the experimental subjects. That is, suppose that an *initial* as well as a final criterion measure is obtained for each subject. We could then define the "effect" of a given treatment on a given subject as the difference between his final and his initial measure. (Strictly, this is the effect of the *treatment* plus the effect of any extraneous factors which may be associated with the treatment in the experiment.)

It is generally likely that this effect will vary from subject to subject for the same treatment, but it is often possible that the variance of these effects is the same for all treatments, and it is also often possible that these effects are uncorrelated with the initial measures. The variance of the final criterion measures for each treatment group would then be equal to the variance of the initial measures plus the constant variance of the treatment effects. In this case, since the variance of the initial measures is, except for chance, the same for all treatments, it follows that the assumption of homogeneity of variance of the final criterion measures would be satisfied.

A more likely possibility is that the variance of the treatment effects differs from treatment to treatment, and also that the effects are correlated with the initial measures, but differently for different treatments. For example, in an experimental comparison of several methods of teaching a given school subject, certain methods might be more effective with bright than with dull students, and others may tend to be equally effective for students at all levels of intelligence. If the criterion measure is the score on an achievement test, it is likely that for some treatments these scores will be substantially correlated with intelligence, from which it follows that the treatment effects will be correlated with the initial measures. We know that the variance of the sum of two related variables is given by $\sigma_{1+2}^2 = \sigma_1^2 + \sigma_2^2 + 2r_{12}\sigma_1\sigma_2$. Other things being equal, the variance of the final criterion measures will then be larger for the treatments whose effects are correlated with the initial measures than for those for which they are not. In cases of this kind, then, the assumption of homogeneity of variance would not be exactly satisfied.

We may note, however, that the variance of the *final criterion measures* might be of very much the same magnitude for all treatments even though the variance of the *treatment effects* for individual subjects differs considerably from treatment to treatment, and/or even though the correlation of the treatment effects with the initial measures also differs considerably from treatment to treatment. This would be true if, for all treatments, the variance of the treatment effects were small in relation to the variance of the initial measures. Suppose, for example, that in an experiment involving two treatments, the initial variances were each 20 and the variances of the treatment effects were 2 and 5, respectively, and that these effects were uncorrelated with the initial measures in both cases. The variance of the final criterion measures would then be 22 for one treatment and 25 for another. This difference amounts to only about 10% of either variance, even though the variance of the treatment effects is more than twice as large for one treatment as for another. The difference would still be small if the treatment effects were moderately but not highly correlated with the initial measures. This type of situation may prevail in many educational and psychological experiments. Very frequently the criterion measure employed is one in which the parent population shows a large variance and in which the superimposed variances of the treatment effects are small in relation to this variance. In this case, even in the unlikely event that the variance of the treatment effects is several times larger for some treatments than for others, the variance of the final criterion measures may nevertheless be substantially the same for all treatments. It is quite common to find, in psychological experiments, that the treatments do not differ sufficiently to cause the observed *means* to differ by more than a relatively small percent of the general mean. In such a situation, it is hard to believe that the treatments would cause the within-groups *variances* for one treatment to differ greatly — so much, say, as to be twice as large for one treatment as for another.

The type of experimental situation in which marked heterogeneity of variance is particularly likely to occur is that in which the variance of the initial measures of the criterion variable, if available, would be found to be small in relation to the final variance for any treatment, and/or in which the final variances of the treatment groups are substantially correlated with their means. This frequently happens in trend studies, that is, in experiments designed to measure the effects upon a criterion variable of increasing amounts of a single experimental variable. Suppose, for example, that in a certain learning experiment the criterion measure is the *improvement* or gain made in a certain variable under the experimental conditions, the "treatments" representing different *durations* of the same experimental condition. By definition of the criterion measure, the population variance is 0 at the beginning of the experiment, and the variances of the treatment effects will be closely related to the means of these effects for the various treatments. In this situation, the relation of the variances and means of the criterion measures for the treatment groups may be as represented in the figure on page 78. In such an experiment, the differences among the variances would be just as marked as the differences among the treatment means, whatever the latter differences might be. In a case of this kind, the over-all *F*-test of the null hypothesis might be seriously invalidated by the failure to satisfy the assumption of homogeneity of variance.

The safest generalization that we can make is that the assumption of homogeneity of variance is practically never strictly satisfied in educational

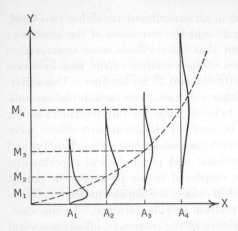

$X = duration\ of\ experimental\ condition$

$Y = criterion\ measure$

and psychological experiments, but that in most instances the heterogeneity is not marked. Fortunately, the form of the sampling distribution of the mean square ratios is not very markedly affected by moderate degrees of heterogeneity of variance, and hence, the F-test may still be satisfactorily used in many experimental situations.

A number of empirical studies [1] have been made of the effect upon the F-distribution of failure to satisfy the underlying assumptions. By far the most comprehensive and significant of these studies is that which was conducted by Dee W. Norton [2] at the State University of Iowa. A brief summary of the Norton study is presented in the following section.

The Norton Study of the Effects of Non-normality and Heterogeneity of Variance

To investigate the effects of non-normality and of heterogeneity of variance upon the F-distribution, Norton constructed "card populations" of 10,000 cases each, from which samples could be conveniently drawn by means of electric tabulating equipment (International Business Machines). The first phase of this study was concerned with the situation in which the distribution

---

[1] M. S. Bartlett, "The Effect of Non-Normality on the t-distribution," *Proceedings of the Cambridge Philosophic Society*, vol. 31 (1935), pp. 223–231; W. G. Cochran, *op. cit.*, pp. 28–32; William G. Cochran, "Some Consequences When the Assumptions for the Analysis of Variance Are Not Satisfied," *Biometrics*, vol. 3 (1947), pp. 22–38; R. A. Fisher, "On the Mathematical Foundations of Theoretical Statistics," *Philosophical Transactions of the Royal Society of London*, vol. 22 (1922), pp. 309–368; R. H. Goddard and E. F. Lindquist, "An Empirical Study of the Effect of Heterogeneous Within-Groups Variance Upon Certain F-tests of Significance in Analysis of Variance," *Psychometrika*, vol. 5 (1940), pp. 263–274; H. L. Rietz, "Topics in Sampling Theory," *Bulletin of the American Statistical Society*, vol. 43 (1937), pp. 209–230.

[2] This study was first reported in an unpublished Ph. D. dissertation, "An Empirical Investigation of Some Effects of Non-normality and Heterogeneity on the F-distribution," Ph. D. Thesis in Education, State University of Iowa, 1952. At the time of the completion of the manuscript for this book, Norton had begun an extension of his original studies and was planning to report the complete extended study in monograph form.

of criterion measures is identical for all treatment populations, but in which each differs from the normal population. Six different forms of distributions, selected as representatives of the range of forms of distributions most frequently met in educational and psychological research, were investigated. Figure 4 presents histograms representing the distributions of criterion measures for these populations. Population I, except for a finite range and lack of complete continuity, is essentially a normal distribution, and was included as a check upon the sampling procedures employed. These distributions have been plotted with approximately the same variance and the same area, so that they may be readily compared.

From each of these populations independently, Norton selected 3,000 *sets* of k random samples of n cases each (k and n taking different values for different F-distributions). Each set thus corresponded to a hypothetical simple-randomized experiment with k treatments and n cases in each treatment group. For each set (or experiment) the ratio of the mean squares for "between-treatments" and "within-treatments" was computed, and a distribution of these ratios was tabulated for the 3,000 experiments. An empirical distribution of 3,000 F's was thus obtained for either one or two combinations of k and n for each of the six populations.

The discrepancies, in the critical upper-tail region, between the empirical distributions thus obtained and the normal-theory F-distribution are described by the data in Table 4. The entry in a given row and column of this table represents the percent of mean square ratios in the empirical distribution (for sets drawn from the population identified at the left in the same row) which exceeds the percent point in the theoretical F-distribution identified at the top of the same column. For example, the entry 12.93 in the second row and fourth column of the body of the table indicates that in the empirical F-distribution for sets of 3 samples of 3 cases each ($df = 2,6$) drawn from the leptokurtic distribution, 12.93 percent of the obtained F's exceeded the value 3.46, which is the 10% point in the F-distribution for the same degrees of freedom. At this point, then, the discrepancy is $12.93 - 10.00 = 2.93\%$.

The data in the first row of Table 4 provide a check on the sampling procedures employed in this study. The method of sampling [1] used may be described as one of continuous sampling without replacement from a finite,

---

[1] The 10,000 cards (containing the criterion measures) were arranged in random order, and were then tabulated by fives to provide means and sums of squares for 2,000 samples of 5 cases each, these data being punched in a summary card for each sample of 5. The 10,000 cards were then arranged in a new random order, and again tabulated by fives to produce another 2,000 summary cards. The 4,000 summary cards were then arranged in random order and tabulated by fours to provide the necessary data for computing the F's for 1,000 sets of 4 samples of 5 cases each. The 4,000 summary cards were then arranged in a new random order and again tabulated by fours to provide another 1,000 F's, and then finally arranged in a third and independent random order to provide still another 1,000 F's.

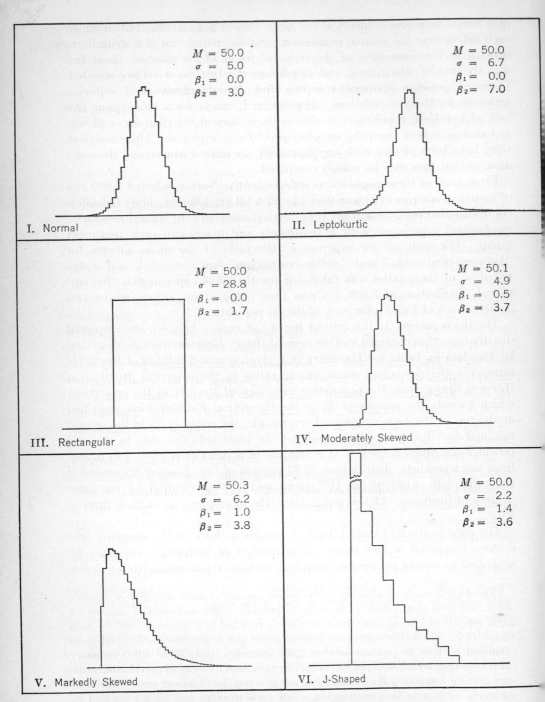

FIGURE 4. *Histograms of populations for which empirical F-distributions were obtained in Phase 1 of the Norton Study*

but very large, population ($N = 10,000$). As will be noted in the first row of Table 4, the empirical sampling distribution of F for samples drawn from Population I contained a larger proportion of large F's than the theoretical, but the discrepancies are not significant at the 10% level. They are, however, large enough to suggest that this kind of sampling may tend to produce slightly more large F's than would be found in simple random sampling from an infinite normal population. There is no apparent logical basis for this suggestion, but if the suggestion is true, the discrepancies reported in the remainder of Table 4 are due in part to the method of sampling, rather than to lack of normality or heterogeneity of variance alone, or the effects of the latter factors are somewhat smaller than those reported.

It is evident from Table 4 that the F-distribution is amazingly insensitive to the form of the distribution of criterion measures in the parent population, granting that the same form is common to all treatment populations. Discrepancies significant at the 5% level are found only for the leptokurtic and rectangular distributions, and even then the absolute discrepancies are quite small. Apparently, the F-distribution is practically unaffected by lack of symmetry, *per se*, in the distributions of criterion measures, but is slightly affected if the distribution of criterion measures is roughly symmetrical but either very flat or very peaked. In the latter cases, the probabilities read from the normal-theory F-table are too small to represent the true risk of a Type I error, and due allowances should be made for this in the interpretation of results. In such cases, judging by the results reported in Table 4, when the "apparent" risk (as read from the F-table) of a Type I error is 5%, the true risk may be as large as 8%, and when the apparent level of significance of an F-test is the 1% level, the actual level of significance may be the 2% level (approximately).

In a second phase of his study Norton investigated the effect of heterogeneity of variance alone upon the F-distribution. For this purpose he constructed three card populations, all of which were like Population I (normal), with the same mean, but with markedly different variances. Specifically, the population variances were approximately 25, 100, and 225, or the standard deviations 5, 10, and 15, respectively.

The instances would be rare, of course, in which the effect of the treatments in an experiment would be to bring about large differences among the variances without also affecting the means. Generally, both mean and variance would be affected together, so that if the mean of one treatment population were higher than that of the others, the variance of this population would tend to be larger also. In many such experiments, the purpose of the experimenter is not to test the hypothesis that the treatment population means are identical, but rather that they lie along some specified line, either straight or curved. If this hypothesis is true, the form of the distribution of the F employed in testing the hypothesis is independent of the form of the line, and the distribution would be the same if the means lie along a straight horizontal line (the usual null-hypothesis), or along any other line (see Chap-

TABLE 4

Phase 1 of the Norton Study
Percents of Mean Square Ratios in Empirical Distributions
Exceeding Given Percent Points in the Normal Theory F-Distribution

Number of Population	Type of Population	k	n	df	Percent: 0.10	0.50	1.00	2.50	5.00	10.00	20.00	25.00	50.00
				Points: $df = 2,6$	27.00	14.54	10.92	7.26	5.14	3.46	2.13	1.76	.780
				$df = 3,16$	9.00	6.30	5.29	4.08	3.24	2.46	1.74	1.51	.823
I	Normal	4	5	3,16	0.17	0.74	1.44	2.94	5.61	9.98	19.95	25.13	50.88
II	Leptokurtic	3	3	2,6	0.80	1.53	2.76	4.63	7.83	12.93	23.40	28.07	53.00
II	Leptokurtic	4	5	3,16	0.37	1.00	1.63	3.76	6.56	11.26	22.43	28.53	54.02
III	Rectangular	3	3	2,6	0.13	0.90	1.77	3.24	6.07	11.54	20.44	25.03	47.78
IV	Mod. Skew	4	5	3,16	0.13	0.69	1.32	2.75	5.15	10.28	20.21	25.30	51.08
V	Ext. Skew	3	3	2,6	0.13	0.40	0.80	2.07	4.77	9.67	19.47	24.23	49.97
V	Ext. Skew	4	5	3,16	0.10	0.70	1.00	2.33	4.76	10.16	20.39	25.63	51.19
VI	J-Shape	3	3	2,6	0.20	0.53	1.00	2.57	4.80	9.43	19.43	23.83	50.96

ter 15, pages 343–347). In the second phase of his study, then, Norton really investigated the form of the F-distribution in the general case in which a *true* hypothesis concerning the population means is being tested under the condition that the population variances differ as described.

As in the first phase of his study, Norton selected 3,000 sets of 3 samples of 3 cases each, but this time each set consisted of 3 samples drawn one from each of the three different populations (differing variances). The *F-ratio* was again computed for each set (or hypothetical experiment), and the distribution of F-ratios obtained for all sets. This procedure was repeated with 3,000 sets of 3 samples of 10 cases each, yielding a second empirical F-distribution with 2 and 27 degrees of freedom. The discrepancies between these two empirical F-distributions and the corresponding normal-theory F-distributions may be inferred from the data reported in the first two lines of Table 5, in the same manner as in Table 4.

It is apparent from these results that marked heterogeneity of variance has a small but real effect on the form of the F-distribution. If one used the probabilities read from the normal-theory F-table in interpreting the results of an experiment with this degree of heterogeneity, he might think he was making a test at the 5% level when actually he was making it at the 7% level, or might think he was testing at the 1% level, when actually he was doing so at the 2+% level of significance, etc. Accordingly, where marked (but not extreme) heterogeneity is expected, it is desirable to allow for the discrepancy by setting a slightly higher "apparent" level of significance for this test than one would otherwise employ (the "apparent" level being that indicated by the F-table). For example, if one wished the risk of a Type I error to be less than 5%, he might require that the obtained F exceed the 2.5% point in the normal-theory F-distribution. The "apparent" level of significance would then be the 2.5%, but the actual level would be the 5% level.

In a third phase of his study, Norton investigated the effect of heterogeneity in *form* of distribution (accompanied by only a slight degree of heterogeneity of variance). In each "experiment" of this phase, one sample was drawn from each of three populations. The first population was the same as Population V in Figure 4, with a σ of 5.0. The second population was approximately normal, but with a limited range (5 σ's) and a σ of 7.4. The third population was exactly like Population V, except that the skew was in the opposite direction. Experimental situations of this kind are quite frequently met in educational and psychological research, when, due to the limited range of the criterion test (that is, to the effect of a low test "ceiling" or a high "floor"), the distribution of test scores is skewed in one direction for the "low" treatment group, and in the opposite direction for the "high" treatment group.

As previously noted, variations in form and variance of the type just described would usually also be accompanied by variations in the population means. That is, such variations in form and variance would most often be found in "trend" studies where the hypothesis to be tested is that the treat-

TABLE 5

Phases 2, 3, and 4 of the Norton Study
Percents of Mean Square Ratios in Empirical Distributions Exceeding Given Percent Points in the Normal Theory F-Distribution

Points:	50.00	25.00	20.00	10.00	5.00	2.50	1.00	0.50	0.10
$df=2,6$	.780	1.76	2.13	3.46	5.14	7.26	10.92	14.54	27.00
$df=2,15$	.726	1.52	1.79	2.70	3.68	4.76	6.36	7.70	11.34
$df=2,27$	.710	1.46	1.71	2.51	3.35	4.24	5.49	6.49	9.02
$df=3,8$	.860	1.67	1.95	2.92	4.07	5.43	7.59	9.60	15.83
$df=3,36$	.803	1.43	1.62	2.24	2.87	3.51	4.38	5.07	6.77

No. Sets	Description	k	n	df	50.00	25.00	20.00	10.00	5.00	2.50	1.00	0.50	0.10
3333	Heterogeneous Variances	3	3	2,6	50.12	27.48	23.01	13.47	7.26	4.29	2.13	1.23	0.36
3000		3	10	2,27	49.46	26.83	21.56	11.73	6.56	3.83	2.00	1.20	0.37
3333	Heterogeneous Forms	3	3	2,6	49.89	26.85	22.56	13.23	6.72	3.84	1.65	1.02	0.15
3333		3	6	2,15	49.78	26.25	21.69	11.37	6.81	3.93	1.98	1.29	0.39
3333	Heterogeneous Forms and Variances	4	3	3,8	48.84	28.53	24.63	15.88	10.02	6.33	3.57	2.16	0.84
3000		4	10	3,36	47.35	26.90	23.13	13.37	8.10	5.30	2.93	1.90	0.87

ment-population means lie along some specified line, other than a straight
horizontal line. So long as the hypothesis being tested is true, however,
the form of the distribution of the F used to test the hypothesis is independent
of the nature of the line. Accordingly, in the third phase of his study, Norton
investigated the general case in which *any* true hypothesis concerning the
population means is being tested, but in which the forms and variances of
the populations differ in the manner described.

In this third phase of his study, Norton selected 3,333 sets of 3 samples
of 3 cases each ($df = 2,6$) and also 3,333 sets of 3 samples of 6 cases each
($df = 2,15$). The discrepancies between each of the empirical F-distributions
and the corresponding normal-theory F-distributions may be inferred from
the data in lines 3 and 4 of Table 5. As in the case of heterogeneous variance
only, the discrepancies in the extreme upper-tail region are significant, but
small, and due allowances should be made for these discrepancies in interpreting the results of an F-test. Again it is remarkable how slightly
this degree of heterogeneity of form and variance affects the F-distri-
bution.

In the fourth phase of the study, Norton investigated the type of situation
graphically portrayed on page 78 — a situation frequently met in learning
experiments and trend studies in psychological research. In this phase of
the study, each "experiment" involved 4 samples, drawn one from each of
four different populations. The first population was the same as Population
VI in Figure 4, with a σ of 2.2. The second was the same as Population V
in Figure 4, with a σ of 6.2. The third population was like Population IV,
except that the σ was 10.0, rather than 4.9, and the fourth population was
like Population I, except that the σ was 14.9, rather than 5.0. Thus the
variance of one of the populations was almost 45 times that of another, so
that the heterogeneity both of form and of variance was extreme.

As in previous instances, Norton investigated the specific case in which
the population means are identical, but as before, this is equivalent to inves-
tigating the general case in which any *true* hypothesis concerning the population means is being tested, the forms and variances of the populations being
as described.

In this final phase of the study, Norton drew 3,333 sets of 4 samples of
3 cases each, and 3,000 sets of 4 samples of 10 cases each. The discrepancies
between the two empirical F-distributions thus obtained and the corresponding normal-theory F-distributions may be determined from the data in the
last two rows of Table 5.

Even with the violent departure from the theoretical requirements represented in this fourth phase of the study, the F-distributions still represent
a fairly good fit to the normal-theory distribution. The discrepancy between
the distributions is highly significant at nearly all points, but the absolute
discrepancy is still not large enough to render the ordinary F-table valueless
in such situations. True, the actual risk of a Type I error may be larger than
that indicated by the ordinary F-table (about twice as large at the 1% point),

but if one knows that this is the case and makes due allowance for it, one may still use the normal-theory table to good advantage.

The results of the Norton study should be extremely gratifying to anyone who has used or who contemplates using the F-test of analysis of variance in experimental situations in which there is serious doubt about the underlying assumptions of normality and homogeneity of variance. Apparently, in the great majority of situations, one need be concerned hardly at all about lack of symmetry in the distribution of criterion measures, so long as this distribution is *homogeneous* in both form and variance for the various treatment populations, and so long as it is neither markedly peaked nor markedly flat. Most non-normal distributions met in practice are probably non-normal primarily because of lack of symmetry rather than because of lack of the "normal" degree of peakedness. In general, the F-distribution seems so insensitive to the form of the distribution of criterion measure that it hardly seems worthwhile to apply any statistical test to the data to detect non-normality, even though such tests are available. Unless the departure from normality is so extreme that it can be easily detected by mere inspection of the data, the departure from normality will probably have no appreciable effect on the validity of the F-test, and the probabilities read from the F-table may be used as close approximations to the true probabilities.

The findings of the Norton study are not quite so encouraging with reference to situations in which the treatment populations are *heterogeneous*, either in form, or in variance, or in both. However, the heterogeneity must be quite extreme to be of any serious consequence. While statistical tests of heterogeneity of variance are available (one is presented in the following section), there will be relatively few situations in which any such test is required. In general, unless the heterogeneity of either form or variance is so extreme as to be readily apparent upon inspection of the data, the effect upon the F-distribution will probably be negligible. In general, when the heterogeneity in form or variance is "marked" but not "extreme," allowance may be made for this fact by setting a higher "apparent" level of significance for the tests of treatment effects than would otherwise be employed. In cases of very marked heterogeneity, for example, if one wishes the risk of a Type I error not to exceed 5%, he might require the effect to be "significant" at the 2.5% level, or if he wants the risk of a Type I error not to exceed 1%, he might set the "apparent" level of significance of the test at 0.1%.

The preceding is not meant to imply, of course, that allowance may *always* be made for heterogeneity of form or variance by "corrections" of the type suggested. On the contrary, there undoubtedly are some situations in psychological research in which the heterogeneity in either form or variance, or both, may be considerably more extreme than in any of the hypothetical situations investigated by Norton. In these situations it is not known what "corrections" should be applied to the ordinary F-test, and special procedures to be considered in a later section (the use of transformations) must be employed in analyzing and interpreting the results.

The Test for Homogeneity of Variance: Several tests [1] of homogeneity of variance have been suggested, of which the most useful and convenient is perhaps that devised by M. S. Bartlett. Before considering this test, we may note that an estimate of the population variance (σ^2) can be derived from each of the a treatment groups by

$$\text{est'd } \sigma^2 = \sum_{}^{n_j}(X - M_j)^2/n_j - 1.$$

We have noted also that a better estimate of σ^2 is provided by the mean square for within-groups (ms_w), which is essentially an "average" of the estimates obtained from the a groups.

Bartlett's test is based upon the difference between the logarithm of this "average" estimate and the sum of the logarithms of the individual estimates. More precisely, Bartlett has shown that the expression

$$\frac{2.3026}{C}\left[(N - a)\log(ms_w) - \sum_{j=1}^{a}(n_j - 1)\log\left(\frac{\sum(X - M_j)^2}{n_j - 1}\right)\right]$$

is distributed approximately as χ^2 with $a - 1$ df, the notation being precisely that we have used earlier.

$$\text{The } C \text{ is a constant} = 1 + \frac{1}{3(a - 1)}\left[\sum_{j=1}^{a}\frac{1}{(n_j-1)} - \frac{1}{\sum_{j=1}^{a}(n_j-1)}\right]$$

but need not be computed if the χ^2 for the expression before division by C is not significant, since C is always larger than 1.00. The value of 2.3026 is the ratio between a natural and a common logarithm.

In the example on page 57, the application of this test is as follows:

Treatments

	A_1	A_2	A_3	A_4
$n_j =$	5	4	6	4
$\sum^{n_j}(X - M_j)^2 = \sum X^2 - \dfrac{T_j^2}{n_j} =$	13.20	14.75	6.00	2.00
$\sum^{n_j}(X - M_j)^2/(n_j - 1) =$	3.30	4.92	1.20	0.67
$\log\left[\sum^{n_j}(X - M_j)^2/(n_j - 1)\right] =$	0.51851	0.69197	0.07918	9.82607−10
$(n_j - 1)\log\left[\sum^{n_j}(X - M_j)^2/(n_j - 1)\right] =$	2.07404	2.07591	0.39590	9.47821−10

---

[1] A modification of the Bartlett test which is slightly more accurate when the n_j's are very small has been provided by H. O. Hartley, "Testing the Homogeneity of a Set of Variances," *Biometrika*, vol. 31 (1940), pp. 249–255.

.082607
3

.247821

$log = 9.47821 - 10$

$$\sum_j^a (n_j-1) \log\left[\sum^{n_j}(X-M_j)^2/(n_j-1)\right] = 4.02406$$

$$(N-a)\log ms_w = 15 \times .38021 = 5.70315$$

$$\chi^2 = \frac{2.3026}{C}(5.70315 - 4.02406) = \frac{3.87}{C}$$

20% value of χ^2 for 3 $df = 4.642$

Hence, $\dfrac{3.87}{C}$ is not significant.

As previously noted, the usefulness of this test is quite limited. In view of the results of the Norton study, it is apparent that the test is needed at all only when the treatment groups are quite small. When the treatment groups are large, one has only to tally the distributions of criterion measures for the various treatment groups to tell by inspection if the heterogeneity is sufficiently marked to be likely to have any appreciable effect on the F-distribution. When the treatment groups are small, the Bartlett test may be needed to determine whether or not *any* heterogeneity of variance characterizes the treatment populations, but the Bartlett test will not indicate how marked the heterogeneity really is, nor how seriously it affects the validity of the usual F-test.

The Use of Transformations: The assumptions of homogeneity of variance and of normality of distribution are often intimately related, so that a serious failure to satisfy one condition is accompanied by a failure to satisfy the other. For example, in any instance in which there is a definite relationship between the means and variances of the treatment groups, there is likely also to be a tendency for some of the distributions to be sharply skewed to the right. Sometimes it is possible to overcome such difficulties by *transforming* the criterion measures into derived measures whose variances are more homogeneous and whose distributions are also more nearly normal. For example, the standard deviations of the treatment groups may tend to be linearly related to their means, as could be true in the type of situation considered on page 78. In this case, if the logarithm of X or of $(1+X)$ is substituted for X as a criterion measure, it may be found that the variances of the transformed measures are much more homogeneous than those of the original measures and that the transformed distributions are much more nearly normal as well. In that case, the F-test of significance applied to the transformed measures will, of course, be more valid than that applied to the original measures. Other functions of X that have been frequently employed in transformations are its square and square root. Transformations of the type $Y = f(X)$ are appropriate only when there is a relationship between the means and variances of the treatment groups; or, if the means of the treatment groups do not differ markedly, only when the distribution of the criterion measures is of the same *form* for all treatments. If the treatments cause the variances of the criterion measures to differ but do not create differences among the means, or if they cause the variances to differ independently of the differences among the means, then no valid transformation is possible. Again, if the distributions are homogeneous in variance but differ in form of distribution, no valid transformation is possible. Sometimes the variances are homogeneous and all distributions are of the same form, but this form is one that cannot be normalized by a transformation of the type $Y=f(X)$. In this case, it may be possible to normalize the distribution by means of an "area transformation" based on a large independent sample from one of the treatment populations, or from a population known to be closely similar to this population. If the treatments have identical effects, the distribution will then, of course, be normalized for all treatment populations. This is done by transforming each value of the original measure into a derived measure whose percentile rank in a normal distribution of selected mean and variance is the same as the percentile rank of the original measure in the independent sample. Students of educational and psychological measurement will recognize the McCall "T-score" as a transformation of this type. Scores on educational and psychological tests are frequently normalized in this fashion, and when thus normalized may more appropriately be used in analysis of variance tests than could the original measures. There are many important types of psychological data which require transformation before the test of analysis of variance may be validly applied, and the subject of transformations is therefore of considerable importance to many psychological research workers. A thoroughgoing treatment of this subject is beyond the scope of this text but helpful discussions of this problem are readily available elsewhere.[1]

Difficulties due to the non-normality of the criterion measures may sometimes be avoided by employing a different criterion variable than that originally contemplated. Very frequently, in educational and psychological research, the choice of a criterion is quite arbitrary, and several alternate criteria may be available, all of which are about equally appropriate to the general purpose of the experiment, but some of which are more nearly normally distributed than others or some of which can more readily be transformed to normally distributed measures. Research workers in psychology have often caused themselves needless trouble by failing to give consideration to this possibility in the early stages of planning their experiments.

There are some experimental situations in which the data show extreme deviations from normality of distribution, and which are not amenable to transformation. This is particularly likely to be true when the criterion

---

[1] Students particularly interested in this subject should see C. G. Mueller, "Numerical Transformations in the Analysis of Experimental Data," *Psychological Bulletin*, vol. 46, no. 3 (May, 1949), pp. 198–223. This is perhaps the most comprehensive of available discussions of the use of transformations in psychological research and contains an excellent bibliography of forty-nine references. A useful discussion of transformations is also found in Oscar Kempthorne, *The Design and Analysis of Experiments* (New York: John Wiley and Sons, Inc., 1952), pp. 153–158.

measures represent *frequencies of occurrence* of a certain type of behavior, such as frequency of aggressive behavior, frequency of stuttering, number of trials needed to run a maze, number of trials required to learn to perform a task, etc. With such data, the distribution is sometimes J-shaped, with a large number of undistributed cases at the zero point on the scale. Such non-continuous or discrete distributions are frequently not amenable to successful transformation, and the tests of analysis of variance may therefore not be applicable to the data. Fortunately, considerable interest has been shown recently in the development of non-parametric tests, that is, tests that make no assumptions about population parameters, and some effective work has been done in the development of such tests.[1] Non-parametric tests will undoubtedly soon occupy a very important place in psychological research. However, all of these tests are less powerful than those assuming normality and homogeneity of variance. It is highly probable, therefore, that the more powerful tests of analysis of variance will continue indefinitely to be employed in the majority of experiments performed in education and psychology, or in all situations in which the necessary assumptions seem satisfied.

Testing the Significance of the Difference in Means for Individual Pairs of Treatments

In a simple-randomized experiment, our ultimate interest is usually in the differences between individual treatments. For instance, we may wish to know if A_1 differs from A_3, or if A_3 differs from A_4, or if A_2 differs from any and all of the other treatments, etc. The F-test of the over-all null hypothesis is regarded as essentially a way of applying a test of significance simultaneously to the observed differences for all possible pairs of treatments. If the F of this over-all test proves to be non-significant, we know at once

---

[1] A non-parametric test based on runs is described by A. Wald and J. Wolfowitz, "On a Test of Whether Two Samples Are from the Same Population," *Annals of Mathematical Statistics*, vol. 11 (1940), pp. 147–162; The "*U*-test" is described by H. B. Mann and D. R. Whitney, "On a Test of Whether One of Two Random Variables is Stochastically Larger than the Other," *Annals of Mathematical Statistics*, vol. 18 (1947), pp. 50–60. Both of these tests are concerned with the hypothesis that the two samples in question are drawn from populations with a common cumulative frequency distribution and both are influenced by differences in form or differences in central tendency between the two distributions. Excellent general discussions concerning non-parametric inference are those by S. S. Wilks, "Order Statistics," *Bulletin of the American Mathematical Society*, vol. 54 (1948), pp. 6–50; and Henry Scheffe, "Statistical Inference in the Non-parametric Case," *Annals of Mathematical Statistics*, vol. 14 (1943), pp. 305–332. Both of these papers are quite comprehensive and provide extensive bibliographies. See also Alexander F. Mood, *Introduction to the Theory of Statistics* (New York: McGraw Hill Book Company, Inc., 1950), Chapter 16, "Distribution Free Methods," pp. 385 ff.

that *all* observed differences among individual treatments are simultaneously attributable to chance alone.   Knowing this, there would be little point in applying the t-test successively to the differences for individual pairs of treatments.   If we did so, we would be guilty of the fallacy discussed on pages 48–49.   Accordingly, if the over-all F proves non-significant, we usually go no further with the analysis.

However, if ms_A/ms_w does prove significant, it does not necessarily follow that the population mean for *each* treatment differs from that for every other. In an experiment involving four treatments, for example, it is quite possible that three of the treatments have identical average effects on the population, that only one differs from the others, and that it is the effect of this one treatment which accounts for the significant F.   Accordingly, before concluding that any one treatment differs from any other, we must apply a test of significance to the difference in the observed means for these two treatments alone.   The preliminary over-all F-test is then regarded simply as a way of determining whether or not it is necessary and legitimate to apply the t-test to individual pairs of means.   If the over-all F proves significant, we nearly always go on to these more specific tests.

We know that the error variance of the difference between the means of two random samples $(\sigma^2_{M_1-M_2})$ drawn from populations with the same variance (σ^2) is given by

$$\sigma^2_{M_1-M_2} = \sigma^2\left(\frac{1}{n_1} + \frac{1}{n_2}\right)$$

in which n_1 and n_2 are the numbers of cases in the samples involved.   We know also that in a simple-randomized experiment, on the assumption of homogeneous variance, the mean square for within-groups (ms_w) is an unbiased estimate of the common variance (σ^2) of the treatment populations (page 60). Accordingly, an unbiased estimate of the error variance of the difference between two observed treatment means is given by

$$\text{est'd } \sigma^2_{M_1-M_2} = ms_w\left(\frac{1}{n_1} + \frac{1}{n_2}\right)$$

and on the assumption of normality, the difference may be tested for significance by means of

$$t = \frac{M_1 - M_2}{\sqrt{ms_w\left(\dfrac{1}{n_1} + \dfrac{1}{n_2}\right)}}, \tag{19}$$

for which the degrees of freedom are those for ms_w, that is, $N - a$.   For the illustrative exercise on page 57, this t for $M_1 - M_2$ is

$$t = \frac{4.60 - 7.25}{\sqrt{2.40\left(\dfrac{1}{5} + \dfrac{1}{4}\right)}} = 2.55,$$

with 15 degrees of freedom.   Suppose we had decided to make the test at the 1% level of significance.   For 15 degrees of freedom, the smallest t which is significant at the 1% level is 2.947. Hence, we would regard this particular difference of 2.55 as non-significant.

In situations of this kind, the practice has been very common of computing the t for each of the possible differences among treatment means, consulting the t-table to determine the relative frequency with which each value of t would be exceeded (in absolute amount) in the long run if the hypothesis were true, and reporting this probability for each difference separately. This is equivalent to reporting the *maximum* level at which each difference is significant. Thus, in effect, one difference might be reported as significant at the 19.13% level, another at the 0.18% level, another at the 5.22% level, etc. This means, essentially, that the experimenter selects the level of significance for each test *after* the t for that difference has been computed. This practice is logically inconsistent. Strictly one should decide what risk he is willing to take of rejecting a true hypothesis — whether it be the over-all null hypothesis or a more specific null hypothesis concerned with a particular pair of treatments — *before* he examines the experimental results. That is, he should decide in advance on the level of significance of all tests that he is to make, taking into consideration the consequences of both Type I and Type II errors. If the over-all F is then not significant at this level, he need go no further with the analysis. In this case, the over-all null hypothesis may be retained, which, of course, means that the null hypothesis concerning any particular pair of treatments may be retained also. On the other hand, if the over-all F is significant, he should report for each difference whether or not it exceeds the value required for significance *at the selected level*. That is, he should report each difference as simply either "significant" or "non-significant" in all instances with reference to the selected level only.

The practice of reporting a different (maximum) level of significance or a separate probability for each individual difference is objectionable because it ignores Type II errors, or else implies that one is willing to accept different risks of a Type II error in testing different specific hypotheses (see pages 66–70). It is undesirable also because it encourages the use of the t or of the corresponding probability as a measure of the "importance" of the difference. This may result from a tendency to attach to "significance" as a statistical concept some of the connotations of "significance" as a general term. It should be remembered that the purpose of the t-test of significance is simply to decide categorically whether or not to reject the null hypothesis, and not to estimate the magnitude of, or to describe the importance of, the corresponding difference in population means. The problem of estimation should not be confused with the problem of testing hypotheses. The best estimate of the difference in population means for any two treatments is the difference in the corresponding means observed in the experiment, regardless of the maximum level at which the associated t is significant. Quite obviously, the smaller of two differences can be significant at a higher level than the larger, if the smaller difference is based on larger numbers of cases. Even though the t's for both differences have the same degrees of freedom, the maximum levels at which they are significant are obviously not indicative of the relative magnitudes of the corresponding population differences. One should never attempt, then, to draw any inferences about the relative importance or magnitude of a difference from the maximum level at which the difference is significant nor does one need to compute the t for a difference in order to draw any inferences concerning its magnitude or importance. The t corresponding to an obtained mean or difference may be needed to describe its reliability as an estimate of the corresponding population value, or to establish a confidence interval for the population value, but the t is not needed for the single-valued estimate itself. Regardless of the value of the corresponding t, the obtained mean or difference is the best estimate of the corresponding population value.

If all treatment groups are of the same size, it is not necessary to compute the t for any difference. In this case, one may compute the "critical difference" corresponding to the selected level, and report as significant all differences exceeding this "critical difference." The formula for computing the critical difference is obtained by solving for $d = M_1 - M_2$ in (19), which yields

$$d = t\sqrt{\frac{2ms_w}{n}}, \tag{20}$$

t representing the value of t which is just significant at the selected level for the given degrees of freedom.

To illustrate the recommended procedure, suppose that an experiment has been performed with five treatments, all treatment groups being of the same size ($n = 10$). Suppose it is decided to take a 1% risk of rejecting a true hypothesis; that is, suppose it is decided to make the tests of significance at the 1% level. For 4 and 45 degrees of freedom, the 1% value of F is 3.83. Suppose the mean square ratio is then computed and found to be 8.32. Accordingly, the over-all null hypothesis is rejected. The next step is to determine from the t-table what value of t would be significant at the 1% level for the degrees of freedom for ms_w. (Note that it would not be consistent to employ a different level of significance for the t-tests than was employed for the over-all F-tests.) Suppose that $ms_w = 28.80$. The critical value of t at the 1% level for 45 degrees of freedom may be read from the normal probability integral table, and is 2.58. (Note that this is a two-tailed test.) Accordingly, by means of (20) we find the critical difference is

$$d = 2.58\sqrt{\frac{2 \times 28.80}{10}} = 6.20.$$

Suppose that the individual means and differences have been computed and found to have the values indicated in the table which follows. (The entry in each cell in the right-hand table is the difference between the means for the treatments indicated in the margins of the table.)

Means		A_2	A_3	A_4	A_5
$M_1 = 47.2$	A_1	3.8	10.5*	6.9*	1.4
$M_2 = 43.4$	A_2		6.7*	3.1	5.2
$M_3 = 36.7$	A_3			3.6	11.9*
$M_4 = 40.3$	A_4				8.3*
$M_5 = 48.6$				*Table of Differences*	

We may then indicate with an asterisk all differences that exceed 6.20, that is, all differences significant at the 1% level. The specific null hypothesis would then be rejected for each of the pairs of treatments thus identified.

Some might argue that a better procedure would be to compute the t for each difference, to report with each difference in the table of differences the probability corresponding to the t, and then to identify as "significant" all differences for which the risk of a Type I error is less than the selected risk, that is, all differences for which the reported probability is less than a pre-selected value. All specific null hypotheses would then be tested at the same level of significance, keeping constant the risk of accepting a "seriously false" null hypothesis (assuming that "seriously false" has the same meaning for all specific hypotheses). This procedure would have the apparent advantage of accomplishing all that is accomplished by the recommended procedure and, at the same time, of revealing that certain specific hypotheses may be rejected with "more confidence" than others. However, it is impossible to show in *operational* terms that any real advantage is gained by the extra labor involved in computing the t and reporting the probability for each difference individually. The rejection of the null hypothesis in each case is categorical — either the hypothesis is rejected or it is retained — there are no degrees of rejection. The subsequent operations — the administrative decisions made and the actions taken on the basis of the test of significance — will be exactly the same whether the hypothesis is rejected at the 0.1% level or at the 10% level, so long as it is rejected at all. The recommended procedure is simpler and more economical and avoids any danger that the probabilities or maximum levels of significance will be used as measures of the relative importance of the differences.

The only valid justification for the practice of reporting a separate probability for each difference is that the reader of the research report may then more conveniently employ any level of significance he prefers in interpreting the results. In this writer's opinion, this argument, while valid, is not a sufficient reason for the practice (but this is an opinion by no means shared by all statisticians). The group n's and the error mean square should of course be reported, so that the reader may make his own tests if he wishes, but the recommended procedure is less likely to result in misinterpretations by the less sophisticated readers of the report.

If the number of cases varies from group to group, the recommended procedure in the form illustrated cannot be followed. If there are several treatments, one may first compute the critical difference for the two treatment groups with the two smallest numbers of cases. All differences exceeding this value may then be immediately identified as significant, even though based on larger numbers of cases. The critical difference for the two largest groups may then be computed. All differences smaller than this may at once be identified as non-significant. Specific critical differences need then be computed only for the remaining comparisons.[1]

If we then wish to rank the treatments on the basis of their estimated relative potency, we may do so on the basis of the observed treatment means. In the illustration just used, the best estimate we can make is that A_5 is the most effective treatment, A_1 the next most effective, etc. We need not refer to any t's to make these estimates, and the estimates are the best available regardless of the sizes of the treatment groups or of the estimated standard errors of the means. Knowledge of the standard errors would help us judge the reliability of the ranking, but would not change the estimated ranks.

We noted earlier in this chapter that in a simple-randomized experiment, it is not legitimate to select the largest of the observed differences among treatment means and to apply the ordinary t-test to this difference. If this were done, the risk of rejecting a true hypothesis would be very much larger than that indicated by the t table. A similar difficulty still exists even though a significant over-all F has already been obtained. Regardless of the outcome of the over-all F-test, it is still true that if one selects the largest of the observed differences for individual pairs of means and applies a t-test to this difference, the risk of rejecting a true null hypothesis specific to these two treatments is not that indicated by the probability read from the t-table. However, if one sets the same level of significance for both the over-all F-test and the t-test for the largest difference, and then finds that both the F and the t are significant at this level, one may safely say that the risk of rejecting a true hypothesis is no larger than that indicated by the level of significance set. Exactly what is the risk under these circumstances of rejecting a true hypothesis concerning only these particular two treatments, we cannot say. The logical difficulties encountered in attempting a rigorous interpretation of the joint outcome of these F and t-tests is far too involved to be considered here. However, statisticians are agreed that if the over-all F proves significant, one may safely, for any practical purposes, interpret the t-tests applied to individual differences as if they were independent t-tests.

It should be noted that, particularly when a large number of treatments is involved, the over-all F-test is not very sensitive to the effect of a single

---

[1] Students interested in pursuing this problem farther should consult John W. Tukey, "Comparing Individual Means in the Analysis of Variance," *Biometrics*, vol. 5, no. 2 (June, 1949), pp. 99–114.

treatment which differs from all the others — all the others being practically identical in effect.   This is just another way of saying that the more nearly the over-all null hypothesis is true, the greater is the risk of a Type II error. If only one treatment really differs from the others, it could readily happen that the t corresponding to the difference between this particular treatment mean and the *average* of the remaining treatment means is "significant," even though F of the over-all test is non-significant.   If this happens in an actual experiment, however, we cannot be sure whether the significant t is due to a real difference between this one treatment and the other treatments, or is to be explained in the manner suggested on pages 48–49.   About all that could be done in a situation of this kind is to regard the observed results as a *suggestion*, rather than as evidence, that the given treatment differs from the others, and to design a new and independent experiment to determine whether or not this one treatment does really differ from the others.

The Significance of the Difference Between Two Sample
Means When the Population Variances Differ

As has been noted earlier, there are many important applications of the simple-randomized design in educational and psychological research, in which the variances of the treatment populations differ markedly.   However, unless the heterogeneity of variance is extreme, one may still employ the usual over-all F-test of the treatments effect, making due allowance for the fact that the probabilities read from the F-table will tend to underestimate the true probabilities.   However, *the fact that the usual F-test is still valid does not mean that the usual t-test is valid also* — that is, the t-test based on the mean square for within-treatments computed from the entire experiment.   Suppose, for example, that in a certain experiment involving four treatments, two of the treatment populations have very nearly equal variances, but the other two treatment populations have markedly larger and differing variances. Quite obviously, in this case, the error variance of the difference in the obtained means for the first two treatments would be seriously overestimated by $2ms_w/n$ and a t-test based on this error estimate would be seriously biased. When marked heterogeneity of variance is suspected, therefore, the t-test of the difference between the means of any two treatment groups should be based on the data for those two treatment groups alone, rather than on the mean square for within-treatments computed from all treatment groups.   If the particular treatment populations involved presumably have nearly equal variances, the usual t-test of the difference between the means of two independent random samples may be employed.   However, if the two treatment populations presumably have markedly differing variances, only an approximate t-test is possible.

Before presenting this approximate test, we may note that the standard error of the difference between the means of two independent random samples is always given, regardless of the variances of the parent populations or the forms of their distributions, by

$$\sigma_{M1-M2} = \sqrt{\sigma_{M1}^2 + \sigma_{M2}^2};$$

and an unbiased estimate of the standard error of the difference may always be obtained by

$$\text{est'd } \sigma_{M1-M2} = \sqrt{\frac{\Sigma d_1^2}{n_1(n_1 - 1)} + \frac{\Sigma d_2^2}{n_2(n_2 - 1)}}. \tag{21}$$

When n_1 and n_2 are both large, the ratio

$$\frac{M_1 - M_2}{\sqrt{\dfrac{\Sigma d_1^2}{n_1(n_1 - 1)} + \dfrac{\Sigma d_2^2}{n_2(n_2 - 1)}}}$$

is very nearly normally distributed and the normal probability table may be used to interpret this ratio in testing the significance of the difference, even though the population variances differ. This is the "significance ratio" technique traditionally employed in large sample theory. If either n_1 or n_2 is small, this ratio is not normally distributed, nor is it distributed as t if the population variances differ. However, if n_1 and n_2 are both small and different, one may employ a test suggested by Behrens and discussed in Fisher and Yates' *Statistical Tables* (Oliver and Boyd), 1948, page 3. Behrens has shown that the difference between the means $(M_1 - M_2)$ of two samples of N_1 and N_2 cases respectively, drawn from populations with different variances, is significant if

$$\frac{M_1 - M_2}{\sqrt{\text{est'd } \sigma_{M1}^2 + \text{est'd } \sigma_{M2}^2}} \geq d,$$

where d is a value tabled (see page 46 in Fisher and Yates) for the 5% and 1% levels and dependent on the three values,

$$n_1 = (N_1 - 1),$$

$$n_2 = (N_2 - 1),$$

and

$$\theta = \arctan \frac{\text{est'd } \sigma_{M1}}{\text{est'd } \sigma_{M2}}.$$

A somewhat less exact but in most cases a quite satisfactory test for practical purposes has been suggested by Cochran and Cox.[1] To apply this test, we let df_1 and df_2 be the numbers of the degrees of freedom corresponding to est'd σ_{M1}^2 and est'd σ_{M2}^2 respectively. We then determine from the t-table the

---

[1] W. G. Cochran and Gertrude M. Cox, *Experimental Designs* (New York: John Wiley and Sons, Inc., 1950), pp. 92–93.

values t_1 and t_2 of t which are significant at the selected level for df_1 and df_2 respectively. We then compute

$$t' = \frac{(\text{est'd } \sigma_{M_1}^2)t_1 + (\text{est'd } \sigma_{M_2}^2)t_2}{\text{est'd } \sigma_{M_1}^2 + \text{est'd } \sigma_{M_2}^2},$$ (22)

and use (21) to estimate $\sigma_{M_1-M_2}$.
If, then,

$$\frac{M_1 - M_2}{\text{est'd } \sigma_{M_1-M_2}} > t',$$

we may say that $M_1 - M_2$ is significant at the desired level.

For example, in the computational exercise on page 57, est'd $\sigma_{M_2}^2 = 1.23$, est'd $\sigma_{M_3}^2 = .20$, est'd $\sigma_{M_2-M_3}^2 = 1.43$, and est'd $\sigma_{M_2-M_3} = 1.196$.   Accordingly,

$$\frac{M_2 - M_3}{\text{est'd } \sigma_{M_2-M_3}} = \frac{5.25}{1.196} = 4.39.$$

At the 5% level of significance for 3 degrees of freedom, $t_1 = 3.182$ and for 5 degrees of freedom $t_2 = 2.571$. Hence,

$$t' = \frac{1.23 \times 3.182 + .20 \times 2.571}{1.23 + .20} = 3.10.$$

Thus we find, since $4.39 > 3.10$, that $M_2 - M_3$ is significant at the 5% level.

When $n_1 = n_2 = n$, it follows that $t_1 = t_2$ and $t' = t_1 = t_2$. Thus, when the two groups are the same size, the Cochran-Cox test reduces[1] to the ordinary t-test for the difference of the means of two independent random samples, but with the number of degrees of freedom equal to $n - 1$ instead of $n_1 + n_2 - 2 = 2(n-1)$. This shows clearly that the Cochran-Cox test is less sensitive than that which assumes homogeneity of variance.

Types of Applications of the Simple-Randomized Design

to Experimental Data

The treatments classification in a simple-randomized design may be of either of two general types. On the one hand, the "treatments" may represent different degrees, or amounts, or intensities, etc., of a single experimental variable or factor. For example, the treatments may represent different intensities of illumination under which the subject reads, or various durations of a certain stimulus, etc. We will call such a classification a "single-factor" classification. On the other hand, the treatments may represent complex

[1] Otherwise viewed, when $n_1 = n_2$ the Cochran-Cox test is essentially equivalent to pairing the measures from the two samples on a random basis, finding the difference between the measures in each pair, and applying the simple t-test to the mean of this random sample of n differences.

combinations of a variety of factors or variables many of which may not even be identified. For example, the treatments in an educational experiment may represent two methods of teaching fourth-grade arithmetic, one of which may be described as a "workbook" method, the other as the "traditional" method, and there may be many respects instead of only one in which these methods differ. Method A_1 may represent greater amounts of some components than Method A_2 and smaller amounts of other components, so that there may be no clear basis for ranking the treatments in any order. A treatment classification in which the treatments are thus complex and unordered will be called a "categorical" classification.

The purpose of an experiment of the single factor type may be simply to determine if the experimental factor is one on which the criterion variable depends, or if there is any relationship between the experimental and control variables. In this case, whether two or more than two "levels" (amounts, degrees, intensities, durations, etc.) of the experimental variable should be represented in the experiment depends upon *how* the experimental variable is related to the criterion variable, if it is related at all. It is possible that the relationship is such that for any given value of the experimental variable (Y), the accompanying value of the criterion variable (X) is always equal to or larger than that for any lower value of Y. In this case the sequence of Y values would be described as a "monotonic increasing sequence." A monotonic sequence may be either increasing or decreasing. For convenience in later discussions, we will say that the relationship between X and Y is "monotonic" if there is a monotonic sequence of X values for successive values of Y. Now suppose we are planning an experiment in which we are quite certain on *a priori* grounds that the relationship, if any, between X and Y is monotonic, and the purpose of the experiment is simply to determine if any relationship exists. In that case, the obvious thing to do is to compare only *two* levels of Y in the experiment; the more widely separated these two levels, the better. If we were to include a third or additional treatment at intermediate levels of Y, we would only lower the power of the test of the over-all null hypothesis. However, in many situations we may be uncertain that the relationship between X and Y is monotonic. That is, we may recognize the possibility that X may increase with increases in Y at some levels and decrease at others, and that while the value of X may be the same for two widely separated values of Y, it may differ for intermediate values. In that case, we would wish to represent in our experiment a number of levels of Y throughout the range in which we are interested.

Sometimes we may be quite sure that the relationship between X and Y is monotonic. We may wish nevertheless to represent several levels of Y in our experiment, since our purpose may be not only to demonstrate that X is a function of Y but also to describe the nature of the relationship. For example, we might wish to determine if the relationship is linear, in which case we would have to represent at least three levels of Y. In this case, on the assumption that the relationship is monotonic, we would do best to test the over-all null hypothesis by means of a *t*-test of the difference between the criterion means for the two extreme levels rather than by means of the over-all *F*-test. The *t*-test based upon the difference in the means of the extreme levels of *Y* is more likely to reveal the presence of a relationship than is the over-all *F*-test; that is, the *t*-test is a more powerful test for the presence of a relationship. The decision to make this test, however, should be made before examination of the experimental data, and should not be suggested by the data.

Experiments designed not only to detect the presence of a relationship, but also to determine the nature of the relationship between the experimental and criterion variables constitute a very important class of psychological experiments. Such experiments may employ the simple-randomized design or any of the more complex designs to be considered later. Because of its importance, separate consideration will be given to this class of experiments in Chapter 15, after all of the basic designs which might be employed in such experiments have been introduced.

Applications of the Simple-Randomized Design to Observational Data

In subsequent discussions it will be useful to distinguish between "experiments" and "investigations" — between "experimental data" and "observational data." An experiment usually involves the *administration* of treatments to groups that have been specially constituted by the experimenter for the purposes of the experiment, and the analysis of "effects" that have been *produced* or *induced* in the subjects during the course of the experiment. In contrast to this, we will, for present purposes, define an "investigation" as a study in which observations are made of effects that are *already present* in a real population; an investigation is thus usually to be described as a sampling study or as a normative study. "Observational data" are defined as data collected in an investigation or a sampling study. This arbitrary distinction in these terms is not consistent with their general meanings, but if its purpose is understood, the distinction should cause no confusion, and it will result in considerable convenience and economy in reference in later discussions.

Many of the designs to be considered in this text may be applied to "observational" data as well as to "experimental" data, and consideration will be given to applications of both types. The methods of analysis of variance appropriate with the simple-randomized design may be employed whenever one wishes to determine if the sub populations of a given population differ in the mean value of some criterion variable. Suppose, for example, that one wishes to determine if persons of different religious affiliations differ in their mean response to a test of "cynicism." [1] One might then select a random sample from each "religious affiliation" sub population, ad-

---

[1] This example was suggested by a study by Neidt and Fritz in *Educational and Psychological Measurement*, vol. 10 (Winter, 1950), p. 4.

minister the test to the samples, and apply the method of analysis of variance to test the differences among the group means just as with a simple-randomized design. In this case, it matters little, so far as the tests of significance or the interpretation of results are concerned, what sizes of samples are drawn from the subpopulations. One might select the same size sample from each subpopulation or draw the entire sample at random from the parent population and then divide the subjects into subgroups after the initial sampling has been made, or follow still other procedures.

As an additional example of the application of a simple-randomized design to observational data, suppose we wish to determine if the high schools in a certain state differ significantly in the quality of students sent to the state university. The criterion measure in this study might be the grade point averages earned by the students during their first semester at the university. The entire freshman class at the university might be subdivided into groups corresponding to individual high schools (excluding high schools not contributing more than one student) and the methods of analysis of variance applied to these groups just as to the treatment groups in a simple-randomized design. The ratio of the mean square for between-schools to that for within-schools would then provide the basis for the test of the null hypotheses that the schools are alike in mean quality of student.

The application of the simple-randomized design to observational data presents no problems not already considered with reference to experimental data. As we shall see later, however, the applications of other basic designs to observational data do present problems of their own, concerned primarily with the relations among the subgroup numbers, and with bias in sampling.[1] Furthermore, the *interpretation* of the results is usually more difficult in an observational study of effects already present than in a controlled experiment. As already implied, this is primarily due to the lack of positive control over extraneous factors. In the "religious affiliation" example, for instance, it is very difficult, if not impossible, to be sure that the observed differences in cynicism are due at all to the religious affiliations, rather than to something else which happened to be associated with them. It is also frequently more difficult to *define* an effect already present than one imposed by the experimenter.

STUDY EXERCISES[2]

1. An experiment carried out by Grice and Saltz [3] involved comparisons of amounts of stimulus generalization in the white rat. Animals were trained to

---

[1] See Eli S. Marks, "Selective Sampling in Psychological Research," *Psychological Bulletin*, vol. 44, no. 3 (May, 1947), pp. 267–275.

[2] See second paragraph on page viii.

[3] G. R. Grice and Eli Saltz, "The Generalization of an Instrumental Response to Stimuli Varying in the Size Dimension," *Journal of Experimental Psychology*, vol. 40 (December, 1950), pp. 702–708.

make a simple instrumental response to white circles of a particular size, and then separate groups were tested for extent of generalization to circles of differing sizes.

The subjects were 80 experimentally naïve albino rats randomly selected from the available colony. The ages of the animals ranged from 70 to 110 days at the beginning of the experiment.

The size stimuli employed in this experiment were white circles cut from sheet metal with a small, square, hanging door in the center. The door was flush with the surface of the disc and could be pushed open by the rat's nose. Attached to the back of the disc, just below the door, was the food dish. The rat could easily obtain the food by pushing its nose through the door.

The apparatus is shown in the diagram below:

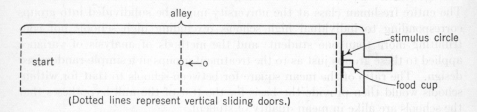

(Dotted lines represent vertical sliding doors.)

The alley is mounted on a pivot at the center (O) so that each end could become in turn the starting end and the reaction end. By rotating the alley after each trial, it was unnecessary to handle the animals except at the beginning and end of each experimental session. The circle was mounted at the front of a 2-inch continuation of the alley, which could be slid back to permit rotation of the alley.

All of the animals were given two days of *preliminary training* in learning to obtain a food pellet by opening the small door in the center of the stimulus circle. Five animals which did not learn to open the door during this preliminary training period were eliminated. The circle used in the preliminary training was the same as the one to be used in the subsequent reinforcement training. The purpose of the preliminary training period, then, was simply to select rats that could be used in the experiment.

Following the preliminary training period, the rats were given 20 reinforced (rewarded) trials per day for three days on a 79 sq. cm. stimulus circle. As soon as the food pellet was obtained, the vertical sliding door in front of the stimulus circle was lowered, and the animal was allowed to eat the food before the alley was rotated for the next trial.

After this reinforcement training, the animals were assigned at random to five groups of 15 each. Each of these groups was given a series of 25 extinction (non-rewarded) trials on a different size circle — i.e., one group was extinguished on a 79 sq. cm. circle, another on a 63 sq. cm. circle, a third on a 50 sq. cm., the fourth on a 32 sq. cm., and the fifth on a 20 sq. cm. circle. On these trials, the door in the circle under test was locked so that it would open only

$\frac{1}{8}$ inch, and there was no food in the food dish. Latencies were recorded as the time from raising the center door to contact of the rat's nose with the door in the stimulus circle. If the animal failed to respond in 60 seconds, the trial was scored as a failure of response. The measure of generalization employed was the *number of responses made during the series of 25 extinction trials*. The criterion measures, together with a part of the computations needed in the analysis, are presented below:

Numbers of Responses in 25 Extinction Trials

Area of Test Circle

79	63	50	32	20
15	16	5	9	7
18	8	10	8	7
9	12	10	8	0
11	5	7	14	8
13	9	17	5	11
20	10	17	11	7
9	12	11	9	9
13	8	7	16	9
5	11	7	7	2
10	18	6	4	6
22	12	6	9	8
18	8	5	8	3
17	11	7	8	1
10	10	4	8	0
12	12	9	10	0

n_j	15	15	15	*15*	*15*
T_j	202	162	128	*134*	*78* = *704 Σ*
$\dfrac{M_j}{n_j}$	13.5	10.8	8.5	*8.9*	*5.2*
$\sum X^2$	3036	1896	1314	*1326*	*608* = *8180 Σ*
T_j^2/n_j	2720	1750	1092	*1197*	*406*

Summary Table

Source	df	ss	ms	
Circle Size	*4*	*557*	*139.15*	*9.60*
Within-Groups (w)	*70*	*1015*	*14.50*	
Total	*74*	*1572*		

T Σy² = 8180 − $\frac{704^2}{75}$ = 8180 − 6608 = 1572

B + Σy² = 2720 + 1750 + 1092 + 1197 + 406 − 6608 =

B + Σy² = 7165 − 6608 = 557

W Σx² = 1572 − 557 =

a) Complete the computations and fill in the summary table.

b) Define carefully the treatment populations concerning which inferences may be drawn from this experiment by the logic of statistical inference. Distinguish between the "parent" population and the treatment populations.

c) Compute the ratio of the mean square for circle size (the between groups mean square) to the within-groups (error) mean square. State the hypothesis to be tested by this ratio. What F is required for significance at the 1% level? May the hypothesis be rejected?

d) Tabulate the frequency distribution of criterion measures for each of the treatment groups. Does an inspection of these distributions suggest a sufficiently marked departure from normality to affect the F-distribution appreciably? A sufficiently marked heterogeneity of variance? Explain.

e) What effect does the rotating of the alley between trials, as contrasted to the alternative of handling the rats between trials, have on the precision of the experiment? Why? Would the F-test be equally valid if this feature were lacking?

f) Establish the "critical difference" between two treatment means. Provide a table of differences, indicating those that are significant.

g) The data in the table of differences suggest the hypothesis that the treatment means tend to decrease as the area of the test circle decreases. Why may one not conclude from the F-test of significance in (c) above that this hypothesis is true?

2. In an experiment concerned with the relative effectiveness of certain incentives on schoolwork, Hurlock [1] divided the 48 pupils in a class in Grade IV of a particular school into four random groups of 12 pupils each. Five equivalent forms (A, B, C, D, and E) of a 30-item addition test were prepared. On the first day of the experiment, Form A was administered to all the pupils in the class at one sitting. On the following four days one group (Control) was separated from the rest of the class during the experimental period and took a different form of the test on each day. The administration of the tests to the control group was handled by the regular teacher. The only direction given to the control pupils was to "work as usual."

The other three groups remained together during the experimental periods and each day took a different form of the addition test, administered by the experimenter. Each day before the tests were distributed, the pupils in one group (Praised) were called to the front of the room and praised for the excel-

---

[1] E. B. Hurlock, "An Evaluation of Certain Incentives Used in Schoolwork," *Journal of Educational Psychology*, vol. 16 (March, 1925), pp. 145–149.

lence of their work on the preceding day, and for their general superiority over the rest of the class. Following this, the pupils in another group (Reproved) came forward and were reproved for their poor work on the preceding day and for their general inferiority. The third group (Ignored) heard the comments made to the Praised and Reproved groups but received no specific recognition.

The criterion measure was the *number of correct answers* on Form E of the addition test administered on the fifth (last) day of the experiment. The original criterion scores are not provided, but the sums of these scores and of their squares for each treatment group are presented in the table below.

	A_1 Praised	A_2 Reproved	A_3 Ignored	A_4 Control
n_j	12	12	12	12
T_j	195.12	135.12	105.48	109.68
M_j	_____	_____	_____	_____
$\sum^{n_j} X^2$	3503.40	1927.92	1071.60	1178.52
T_j^2/n_j	_____	_____	_____	_____

a) Analyze the results and prepare a summary table of the analysis.

b) Suggest some of the bases on which, in an actual situation like this, you would decide what risk you are willing to take of rejecting a true hypothesis. Suppose you decided on a 5% risk; what is the value of $F \ (= ms_A/ms_w)$ at the corresponding point in the F-distribution? State explicitly the hypothesis tested by this F-ratio. May the hypothesis be retained? Suppose the F had been non-significant. Could this be regarded as evidence that the treatments do *not* differ? Why?

c) Define the parent population to which any *statistical* inferences from this experiment should be restricted. Suggest some arguments (non-statistical) by which the conclusions might be extended to fourth graders in general.

d) Describe the specific operations by which you would go about dividing the pupils in an experiment like this into four *random* groups of equal size.

e) Suggest some specific Type G errors that might have affected the results of this experiment. What effect do such errors have on the interpretation of the F-test as a test of the hypothesis of no *treatment* effect? Under what experimental conditions may one safely infer from a significant F that the *treatments* differ?

f) How large must the difference between any two treatment means be in order to be significant at the 5% level? Why would it be inconsistent to ask, "What is the level of significance of the largest difference?" Do these results suggest that the over-all F may sometimes be significant because of the effect of a single treatment?

3. One purpose of an investigation carried out by Baten and Hatcher [1] was to compare the achievement in home economics classes in different high schools in a particular city. A four-week unit in consumer buying was taught to the sophomore home economics classes in four selected high schools. The classes were taught by the regular teachers who had had in common a short period of instruction regarding methods and objectives. At the close of the unit, all the classes took an objective test over the material covered. The scores on this test served as the criterion measures. The scores were as follows:

School

A			B				C	D		
39	40	31	35	49	42	39	27	38	43	40
32	46	43	40	42	34	39	44	45	45	
42	31	32	37	44	40	35	40	35	35	
32	31		38	40	42	27	29	53	41	
40	38		47	27	40	37	43	45	45	
36	32		36	39	40	47	45	39	45	
30	32		44	39	40		39	47	46	

a) Analyze the scores and prepare a summary table of the results.

b) At the 1% level, what value of F is required for rejection of the null hypothesis regarding the population means? May we reject this hypothesis at this level? Describe the populations involved as accurately as you can.

c) An assumption of random sampling underlies the F-test of question (b) preceding. What is the population from which the 17 pupils in School A were presumably a random sample?

d) Comment briefly on the assumptions of normality and homogeneity as they apply in this situation. Specify carefully the distributions to which the assumptions apply and suggest some possible a priori arguments for or against the assumptions. In view of the results of the Norton study, need one be concerned about the validity of the usual F-test in this situation? Explain.

e) Does the outcome of the test of question (b) permit one to conclude that home economics is not "equally well taught" in these four schools? Ex-

[1] William D. Baten, and Hazel M. Hatcher, "Testing for Grade and School Differences Among the Scores of Home Economics Students," *Journal of Experimental Education*, vol. 16 (March, 1948), pp. 176–180.

plain, showing how this situation differs from the usual experimental situation.

f) Following the procedure explained on page 95, indicate which of the six differences between school means are significant and which are non-significant.

g) The difference between the A and D means is significant. On what reasoning is this result nevertheless *consistent* with the hypothesis that the teaching of home economics *is* equally effective in these two schools?

③

Source	df	mean sq.	F
BT	407.52	3	135.84	4.85
W/in	1735.46	62	27.99	
Total	2142.98	65		

②

Source	df	M-sq.	F
B+	426.6393	3	142.2131	5.92
W/in	1057.6932	44	24.0385	
Total	1484.3325	47		

$$M_1 - M_2$$

$$t = \sqrt{MS_\omega \left(\frac{1}{n_1} + \frac{1}{n_2} \right)} \qquad n_1 \neq n_2$$

$$d = t \sqrt{\frac{2 MS_\omega}{n}} \qquad n_1 = n_2 = n_3 \ldots$$

4

Analysis of Variance in Double-Entry Tables

Introduction

There are a number of different basic designs in which the criterion measures can be presented in a double-entry table. The columns in the table may correspond to the different treatments in a certain treatment classification, and the rows may correspond to levels, or to subjects, or to replications, or to the categories in a second treatment classification, depending on the design involved. In all such designs, the total sum of squares may be analyzed into either three or four components, depending on whether only one or several measures are contained in each cell of the table. The analysis of the total sum of squares is exactly the same no matter what the rows or columns may represent. Accordingly, we shall first show in the most general terms (*rows* and *columns*) how the total sum of squares in a double-entry table may be analyzed into its components. The specific meanings of these

		Columns				
	1	2	j		c	
1		cell 12	– – –	cell 1j	– – –	
2		22	– – –	2j	– – –	
	¦	¦		¦		¦
Rows i	¦1	¦2	– – –	ij	– – –	ic $M_{i.}$
	¦	¦		¦		¦
r				rj		rc

$$M_{.j}$$

components with reference to various basic designs will then be considered in later chapters.

Notation: Suppose we have a total sample of N measures which is constituted of c separate groups, each divided into r subgroups — *corresponding subgroup frequencies being in the same proportion for all groups* (that is, the ratio between any two cell frequencies in one column being the same as the ratio of the corresponding cell frequencies in any other column). These measures could then be presented in a double-entry table, the columns corresponding to the groups, and the cells to the subgroups, as represented on page 108. The notation we will employ is as follows:

X = any measure

r = number of rows

c = number of columns

n_{ij} = number of measures in the ith cell of the jth column. The first sub script always represents a row, the second a column.

$n_{i.} = \sum\limits_{j=1}^{c} n_{ij}$ = number of measures in row i

$n_{.j} = \sum\limits_{i=1}^{r} n_{ij}$ = number of measures in column j

(The dots are needed to indicate whether the subscript accompanying the dot represents a row or a column. For example, $n_{.3}$ represents the number of measures in the third column, while $n_{3.}$ represents the number in the third row.)

$N = \sum\limits_{ij} n_{ij} = \sum\limits_{i=1}^{r} \sum\limits_{j=1}^{c} n_{ij}$ = total number of measures. ($\sum\limits_{ij}$ represents a double summation, and may be read "sum for all values of i and j.")

$T_{ij} = \sum\limits^{n_{ij}} X$ = sum of measures in cell ij

$T_{i.} = \sum\limits^{n_{i.}} X$ = sum of measures in row i

$T_{.j} = \sum\limits^{n_{.j}} X$ = sum of measures in column j

$T = \sum\limits_{ij} \sum\limits^{n_{ij}} X = \sum\limits_{i=1}^{r} \sum\limits_{j=1}^{c} \sum\limits^{n_{ij}} X$ = sum of all measures

$M_{ij} = \dfrac{1}{n_{ij}} T_{ij}$ = mean of cell ij

$M_{i.} = \dfrac{1}{n_{i.}} T_{i.}$ = mean of measures in row i

$M_{.j} = \dfrac{1}{n_{.j}} T_{.j}$ = mean of column j

$M = \dfrac{1}{N} \sum\limits_{j=1}^{c} \sum\limits_{i=1}^{r} \sum\limits^{n_{ij}} X$ = general mean

Analysis of Total Sum of Squares into Four Components
(Method of Arithmetic Corrections)

To help the student develop the clearest possible understanding of the analysis of the total sum of squares, two different proofs will be presented. The first involves successive applications of the method of analysis into two components, together with arithmetic corrections applied to the individual measures. The other is algebraic in character. The arithmetic proof will be presented first.

We have already seen that in any sample consisting of a number of separate groups, the total sum of squares may be analyzed into two components, a between-groups and a within-groups component. (See pages 55–56.) There are three different ways in which we can regard the data in the preceding table as divided into groups. First, we can disregard the columns and consider the measures as divided into just r groups, corresponding to rows. Thus viewed, the total sum of squares can be analyzed into its between-rows and within-rows components. Second, we can disregard rows and regard the measures as divided into just c groups, corresponding to columns, in which case the total sum of squares may be analyzed into its between-columns and within-columns components. Finally, we can regard the whole sample as consisting of rc groups corresponding to cells, in which the total sum of squares may be analyzed into its between-cells and within-cells components. Thus,

$$ss_T = ss_R + ss_{wR}$$
$$ss_T = ss_C + ss_{wC} \qquad\qquad (23)$$
$$ss_T = ss_{\text{cells}} + ss_{w\text{ cells}}.$$

Now suppose that in each row the deviation of the row mean from the general mean is subtracted from each individual measure in the row. For instance, if the mean of Row 3 is 5 units above the general mean, then 5 will be subtracted from every measure in Row 3. Similarly, if the mean of Row 4 is 2 units below the general mean, then 2 will be added to every measure in Row 4. For each row then, the mean of the corrected measures will be the same as the general mean of the uncorrected measures. That is, there will be no differences among the row means in the table of corrected measures, and hence, no between-rows sum of squares in the corrected table. If we let a prime (ss') on the symbol for a sum of squares indicate that it is based on the corrected measures, we may then write

$$ss_T' = ss_R' + ss_{wR}' = ss_{wR}'.$$

But the addition of a constant to every measure within a given row will have no effect upon the differences among the measures in that row. Accordingly,

$$ss_{wR} = ss_{wR}'$$

and the total sum of squares in the corrected table is the same as that for within-rows in the original table. That is,

$$ss_{wR} = ss_T'. \qquad\qquad (24)$$

The total sum of squares in the corrected table can now be analyzed into its between-columns and within-columns components.

$$ss'_T = ss'_C + ss'_{wC}. \tag{25}$$

From (23), (24) and (25), we may then write

$$ss_T = ss_R + ss'_C + ss'_{wC}. \tag{26}$$

We may note next that, since the cell frequencies are proportional from column to column, the corrections applied to rows do not affect the column means. This point is basic to the analysis and should be thoroughly understood. Let a_i represent the constant correction to all measures in Row i, in which case $a_i n_{i.}$ is the sum of the corrections in Row i. Now we know that $\sum_i^r a_i n_{i.} = 0$, since the total effect of all corrections in all rows is to leave the general mean unchanged. We know also that corresponding cell frequencies are in the same proportion from row to row, that is, we know $n_{ij}/n_{i.} = k_{.j}$ is a constant for all cells in Column j, and hence, $n_{ij} = n_{i.}k_{.j}$.

If $\sum_i^r a_i n_{i.} = 0$ for the table as a whole, then $\sum_i^r a_i n_{i.}k_{.j} = 0$ also. But $\sum_i^r a_i n_{i.}k_{.j} = \sum_i a_i n_{ij}$, which is the sum of the corrections for Column j. Since this sum is equal to zero, the column mean is unchanged by the corrections. From this it is apparent that

$$ss_C = ss'_C.$$

Hence, (26) may be written

$$ss_T = ss_R + ss_C + ss'_{wC}.$$

Now suppose that for each column in the once-corrected table we subtract the deviation of the column mean from the general mean from each measure in that column. This would eliminate all differences among column means in the twice-corrected table. If we let a double prime (ss'') indicate that a sum of squares is based on the twice-corrected measures, we may then write

$$ss''_C = 0$$

from which it follows that

$$ss''_T = ss''_C + ss''_{wC} = ss''_{wC}.$$

But, since a constant correction to all measures in a column does not affect the differences among those measures,

$$ss'_{wC} = ss''_{wC}.$$

Hence,

$$ss''_T = ss'_{wC}$$

and

$$ss_T = ss_R + ss_C + ss''_T.$$

The total sum of squares in the twice-corrected table may now be analyzed into its between-cells and within-cells components,

$$ss_T'' = ss_{cells}'' + ss_{w\ cells}'',$$

from which it follows that

$$ss_T = ss_R + ss_C + ss_{cells}'' + ss_{w\ cells}''. \tag{27}$$

Since any correction applied to the measures in a cell is the same for all measures in that cell, the within-cells sum of squares must be the same in all three tables. That is,

$$ss_{w\ cells} = ss_{w\ cells}' = ss_{w\ cells}''.$$

If we now let $ss_{cells}'' = ss_{RC}$ (read "sum of squares for R by C," or "... for rows by columns"), and if we let the sum of squares within-cells ($ss_{w\ cells}$) be represented more simply by ss_w, (27) may be rewritten

$$ss_T = ss_R + ss_C + ss_{RC} + ss_w. \tag{28}$$

Three of these four components of ss_T may be computed from the original table and the fourth obtained as a residual. Thus the total sum of squares in the original table may be analyzed into four components without actually having to make any arithmetic corrections.

The number of degrees of freedom for ss_T, ss_R, ss_C, and ss_w, all of which are computed from the original table, are $N-1$, $r-1$, $c-1$, and $N-rc$, respectively. The number of degrees of freedom for cells, however, is not the same for the twice-corrected as for the original table. In the original table, this number of degrees of freedom is $rc-1$, but one degree of freedom has been lost for each row but the last in the first correction (see page 52), and one for each column but the last in the second correction. Hence, the number of degrees of freedom for cells in the twice-corrected table, that is, for ss_{RC}, is

$$rc - 1 - (r - 1) - (c - 1) = rc - r - c + 1 = (r - 1)(c - 1).$$

The sum of the degrees of freedom for the various components must, of course, equal the degrees of freedom for total. The student may check for himself to see that this is true here.

Analysis of Total Sum of Squares into Four Components (Algebraic Method)

We shall now prove again, this time by an algebraic method, that the total sum of squares in any double-entry table may be analyzed into four components. Students who are adept at algebra will find it worth while to work through this proof. Others can perhaps afford to rely entirely on the arithmetic proof of the preceding section.

Using the notation on page 109, we may first write the identity

$$(X - M) = (X - M_{ij}) + (M_{i.} - M) + (M_{.j} - M) + \\ [(M_{ij} - M) - (M_{i.} - M) - (M_{.j} - M)]$$

We will now let

$$a = (X - M_{ij})$$
$$b = (M_{i.} - M)$$
$$d = (M_{.j} - M)$$
$$e = [(M_{ij} - M) - (M_{i.} - M) - (M_{.j} - M)]$$
$$= (M_{ij} - M_{i.} - M_{.j} + M).$$

With reference to the method of arithmetic corrections, e represents the deviation of a *twice-corrected* cell mean from the general mean, the two corrections $(M_{i.} - M)$ and $(M_{.j} - M)$, having both been subtracted from the deviation of the original cell mean from the general mean. In this notation, then,

$$(X - M) = a + b + d + e.$$

Squaring each member of this identity,

$$(X - M)^2 = a^2 + b^2 + d^2 + e^2 + 2ab + 2ad + 2ae + 2bd + 2be + 2de.$$

Summing over the n_{ij} measures in cell ij (and noting that $\sum^{n_{ij}} a = 0$),

$$\sum^{n_{ij}}(X - M)^2 = \sum^{n_{ij}}a^2 + n_{ij}b^2 + n_{ij}d^2 + n_{ij}e^2 + 2n_{ij}bd + 2n_{ij}be + 2n_{ij}de.$$

Summing for the c cells in Row i,

$$\sum_{j=1}^{c}\sum^{n_{ij}}(X - M)^2 = \sum_{j=1}^{c}\sum^{n_{ij}}a^2 + n_{i.}b^2 + \sum_{j=1}^{c}n_{ij}d^2 + \sum_{j=1}^{c}n_{ij}e^2 + 2\sum_{j=1}^{c}n_{ij}bd$$
$$+ 2\sum_{j=1}^{c}n_{ij}be + 2\sum_{j=1}^{c}n_{ij}de.$$

Now, letting k = the constant ratio of $n_{.j}/n_{ij}$,

$$2\sum_{j=1}^{c}n_{ij}bd = 2b\sum_{j=1}^{c}n_{ij}d = \frac{2b}{k}\sum_{j=1}^{c}n_{.j}(M_{.j} - M) = 0.$$

Hence,

$$\sum_{j=1}^{c}\sum^{n_{ij}}(X - M)^2 = \sum_{j=1}^{c}\sum^{n_{ij}}a^2 + n_{i.}b^2 + \sum_{j=1}^{c}n_{ij}d^2 + \sum_{j=1}^{c}n_{ij}e^2 + 2\sum_{j=1}^{c}n_{ij}be$$
$$+ 2\sum_{j=1}^{c}n_{ij}de.$$

Summing for the r rows,

$$\sum_{i=1}^{r}\sum_{j=1}^{c}\sum^{n_{ij}}(X - M)^2 = \sum_{i=1}^{r}\sum_{j=1}^{c}\sum^{n_{ij}}a^2 + \sum_{i=1}^{r}n_{i.}b^2 + \sum_{i=1}^{r}\sum_{j=1}^{c}n_{ij}d^2 + \sum_{i=1}^{r}\sum_{j=1}^{c}n_{ij}e^2$$
$$+ 2\sum_{i=1}^{r}\sum_{j=1}^{c}n_{ij}be + 2\sum_{i=1}^{r}\sum_{j=1}^{c}n_{ij}de.$$

Now

$$\sum_{i=1}^{r}\sum_{j=1}^{c}n_{ij}d^2 = \sum_{j=1}^{c}d^2\sum_{i=1}^{r}n_{ij} = \sum_{j=1}^{c}n_{.j}d^2,$$

and

$$\sum_{i=1}^{r}\sum_{j=1}^{c}n_{ij}be = \sum_{i=1}^{r}\sum_{j=1}^{c}n_{ij}b[(M_{ij}-M_{i.})-(M_{.j}-M)]$$

$$= \sum_{i=1}^{r}\sum_{j=1}^{c}n_{ij}b(M_{ij}-M_{i.}) - \sum_{i=1}^{r}\sum_{j=1}^{c}n_{ij}bd$$

$$= \sum_{i=1}^{r}\sum_{j=1}^{c}n_{ij}b(M_{ij}-M_{i.}) - 0$$

$$= \sum_{i=1}^{r}b\sum_{j=1}^{c}n_{ij}(M_{ij}-M_{i.})$$

$$= 0.$$

Similarly,

$$\sum_{i=1}^{r}\sum_{j=1}^{c}n_{ij}de = 0.$$

Hence,

$$\sum_{i=1}^{r}\sum_{j=1}^{c}\sum^{n_{ij}}(X-M)^2 = \sum_{i=1}^{r}\sum_{j=1}^{c}\sum^{n_{ij}}a^2 + \sum_{i=1}^{r}n_{i.}b^2 + \sum_{j=1}^{c}n_{.j}d^2 + \sum_{i=1}^{r}\sum_{j=1}^{c}n_{ij}e^2 \qquad (29)$$

$$= \sum_{i=1}^{r}\sum_{j=1}^{c}\sum^{n_{ij}}(X-M_{ij})^2 + \sum_{i=1}^{r}n_{i.}(M_{i.}-M)^2$$

$$+ \sum_{j=1}^{c}n_{.j}(M_{.j}-M)^2 + \sum_{i=1}^{r}\sum_{j=1}^{c}n_{ij}(M_{ij}-M_{i.}-M_{.j}+M)^2$$

or

$$ss_T = ss_w + ss_R + ss_C + ss_{RC}.$$

The Case of One Observation per Cell

Let us now consider briefly the special case in which only one observation has been recorded in each cell, or in which $n_{ij} = 1$. This is frequently the case in *treatments* × *subjects* designs, in which "rows" correspond to "subjects," and in which only one criterion measure is obtained for each subject under each treatment. Whenever there is only one observation per cell, there can of course be no within-cells sum of squares, and the sum of squares for cells is the total sum of squares. Hence, the total sum of squares is analyzed into three components, and the interaction sum of squares (ss_{RC}) is computed as a residual by subtracting the sums of squares for rows and for columns from that for total.

Computational Procedure

We have seen that in any double-entry table the analysis of the total sum of squares into its four components is accomplished essentially by successive applications of the method of analysis into two components. Thus the basic computational formulas already provided, Formulas (8) and (9), are all that are needed. The sum of squares for between-rows is obtained by squaring each row total and dividing by the number of cases in the row, summing these terms and subtracting the square of the grand total divided by the total number, that is

$$ss_R = \sum_{i=1}^{r} n_i.(M_i. - M)^2 = \sum_{i=1}^{r} \frac{T_i^2.}{n_i.} - \frac{T^2}{N}.$$

The sums of squares for columns and for cells are similarly obtained, and the sum of squares for interaction is obtained as a residual. These computational procedures are summarized in the table below. Ordinarily, the results actually obtained in an analysis are summarized in a similar table. (An example is given on page 117.)

Source of Variation	df	ss	ms
Columns (C)	$c - 1$	$ss_C = \sum_{j=1}^{c} T^2_{.j}/n_{.j} - T^2/N$	$ms_C = ss_C/(c-1)$
Rows (R)	$r - 1$	$ss_R = \sum_{i=1}^{r} T^2_{i.}/n_{i.} - T^2/N$	$ms_R = ss_R/(r-1)$
(Cells)	$(rc - 1)$	$(ss_{\text{cells}} = \sum_{i=1}^{r}\sum_{j=1}^{c} T^2_{ij}/n_{ij} - T^2/N)$	
Rows × Columns (RC)	$(r-1)(c-1)$	$ss_{RC} = ss_{\text{cells}} - ss_R - ss_C$	$ms_{RC} = ss_{RC}/(c-1)(r-1)$
Within-Cells (w)	$N - rc$	$ss_w = ss_T - ss_{\text{cells}}$	$ms_w = ss_w/(N - rc)$
Total	$N - 1$	$ss_T = \sum_{j=1}^{c}\sum_{i=1}^{r}\sum^{n_{ij}} X^2 - T^2/N$	

A Worked Example

The following worked example will make clear the application of the computational procedures just described.

The example is based on the data in the double-entry table presented below, with five measures in each cell. The individual measures are presented in the column along the left margin of each cell. The figure to the right in each cell represents the cell mean.

	Col 1		Col 2		Col 3		Col 4		Row Means
Row 1	34 19 24 36 25	27.60	16 35 18 16 12	19.40	30 23 39 29 24	29.00	38 32 21 36 15	28.40	26.10
Row 2	7 24 12 43 41	25.40	41 30 17 31 24	28.60	28 34 40 27 42	34.20	48 25 29 22 28	30.40	29.65
Row 3	39 25 40 57 39	40.00	19 49 30 46 28	34.40	20 36 42 12 53	32.60	30 23 24 38 37	30.40	34.35
Col Means		31.00		27.47		31.93		29.73	30.03
									General Mean

The basic computations are presented on the following page. For instance, for the first cell in the first row, $34 + 19 + 24 + 36 + 25 = 138$. Likewise, $34^2 + 19^2 + 24^2 + 36^2 + 25^2 = 4014$, and finally, $138^2/5 = 3808.80$. The entries for the other cells are similarly computed.

The rest of the example should be self-explanatory.

It would not have been necessary in this case to compute T_{ij}^2/n_{ij} for each cell individually. In general, when n_{ij} is constant for all cells in a row (or column), it is simpler to compute T_{ij}^2 for each cell in the row (or column), add these squared sums for all cells in the row (or column) and then divide by the constant n_{ij} for that row (or column). When n_{ij} is constant throughout the entire table, as in this example, it would have been simpler to add the squared cell totals for all cells in the table and then divide this sum by the constant n_{ij}, in this case 5. This could be done on an automatic computing machine by cumulating the squared cell totals as they are squared and without having to record any individual T_{ij}^2.

	Col 1	Col 2	Col 3	Col 4	$T_{i.}$	$T_{i.}^2/n_i$
Row 1 T_{ij}	138	97	145	142	522	13,624.20
ΣX^2	4014.00	2205.00	4367.00	4430.00		
T_{ij}^2/n_{ij}	3808.80	1881.80	4205.00	4032.80		
Row 2 T_{ij}	127	143	171	152	593	17,582.45
ΣX^2	4299.00	4407.00	6033.00	5038.00		
T_{ij}^2/n_{ij}	3225.80	4089.80	5848.20	4620.80		
Row 3 T_{ij}	200	172	163	152	687	23,598.45
ΣX^2	8516.00	6562.00	6413.00	4818.00		
T_{ij}^2/n_{ij}	8000.00	5916.80	5313.80	4620.80		
$T_{.j}$	465	412	479	446	$T = 1802$	
$T_{.j}^2/n_{.j}$	14,415.00	11,316.26	15,296.07	13,261.07		

$$\sum_{i=1}^{r}\sum_{j=1}^{c}\sum X^2 = 4014.00 + \ldots + 4430.00 + 4299.00 + \ldots + 5038.00$$
$$+ 8516.00 + \ldots + 4818.00 = 61,102.00$$

$$\sum_{i=1}^{r}\sum_{j=1}^{c}T_{ij}^2/n_{ij} = 3808.80 + \ldots + 4032.80 + 3225.80 + \ldots + 4620.80$$
$$+ 8000.00 + \ldots + 4620.80 = 55,564.40$$

$$\sum_{i=1}^{r}T_{i.}^2/n_{i.} = 13,624.20 + 17,582.45 + 23,598.45 = 54,805.10$$

$$\sum_{j=1}^{c}T_{.j}^2/n_{.j} = 14,415.00 + 11,316.26 + 15,296.07 + 13,261.07 = 54,288.40$$

$$T^2/N = (1802)^2/60 = 54,120.07$$

$$ss_T = 61,102.00 - 54,120.07 = 6981.93$$
$$ss_R = 54,805.10 - 54,120.07 = 685.03$$
$$ss_C = 54,288.40 - 54,120.07 = 168.33$$
$$ss_{\text{cells}} = 55,564.40 - 54,120.07 = 1444.33$$
$$ss_{RC} = 1444.33 - 685.03 - 168.33 = 590.97$$
$$ss_w = 6981.93 - 1444.33 = 5537.60$$

Summary Table

Source of Variation	df	ss	ms
Columns (C)	3	168.33	56.11
Rows (R)	2	685.03	342.51
(Cells)	(11)	(1444.33)	
Rows × Columns (RC)	6	590.97	98.49
Within-Cells (w)	48	5537.60	115.36
Total	59	6981.93	

The Generalized Meaning of Interaction

The mean square for *interaction* (ms_{RC}) plays an extremely important part in the interpretation of results for many basic experimental designs. It will be well, therefore, before going further, to ascertain as exactly as possible just what this "interaction" represents in any double-entry table, or what may be said about it in the most highly generalized terms of rows, columns, and cells.

We have seen (28) that the interaction sum of squares is the sum of the weighted squared deviations of the cell means from the general mean in the twice-corrected table, in which all differences among row means and column means have been eliminated.

The twice-corrected mean of cell *ij* is $[M_{ij} - (M_{i.} - M) - (M_{.j} - M)] = [(M_{ij} - M_{i.} - M_{.j} + 2M)]$ and the deviation of this twice-corrected mean from the general mean is $(M_{ij} - M_{i.} - M_{.j} + M)$. The quantity $(M_{ij} - M_{i.} - M_{.j} + M)$ may be termed the "interaction effect" for cell *ij*. In the illustrative exercise (page 116), for example, the interaction effect for the second cell in the second row is $(M_{22} - M_{2.} - M_{.2} + M) = (28.60 - 29.65 - 27.47 + 30.03) = +1.51$. The interaction effects for the entire table are given below. The weighted sum of the squares of these interaction effects is $5(+0.53)^2 + 5(-4.14)^2 + \ldots + 5(-3.65)^2 = 590.97$ which is the same as the sum of squares for interaction computed on page 117.

+0.53	−4.14	+1.00	+2.60
−5.22	+1.51	+2.65	+1.05
+4.68	+2.61	−3.65	−3.65

If the interaction effect for every cell in the table is equal to zero, that is, if all the twice-corrected cell means are equal to the general mean, the observed interaction for the table as a whole will of course be zero. The more variable the interaction effects for the individual cells, the greater is the interaction mean square, or the greater is the observed interaction for the table as a whole.

If the measures in all cells of the table were simple random samples from the same population, that is, if there were no *real* differences among rows or among columns or among cells, we would still expect the twice-corrected cell means to differ from one another for no other reason than that of chance fluctuations in the means of simple random samples. That is, we would never expect the *observed* interaction effect (the interaction mean square) to be zero. In any practical application of this analysis, then, one would want to know whether or not the observed interaction effect can be entirely accounted for in terms of sampling fluctuations alone. In other words, one would want to test the significance of the observed interaction. Ways of doing this will be considered later.

While the interaction effect is defined basically in terms of the twice-corrected cell means, it may be described also in terms of the relationships among the original or uncorrected means. Suppose that any two columns are selected from the complete $r \times c$ table and that a new table is formed from these two columns alone. The total sum of squares for this two-column table may then be analyzed into its *rows, columns, rows $\times$ columns,* and *within-cells* components. The interaction sum of squares for this table is given (29) by

$$ss_{RC} = \sum_{i=1}^{r} \sum_{j=1}^{c} n_{ij}[(M_{ij} - M_{i.}) - (M_{.j} - M)]^2$$

which, in a two-column table with constant $n_{ij} = n$, reduces to

$$ss_{RC} = \sum_{i=1}^{r} n \left\{ \left[(M_{i1} - M_{i.}) - (M_{.1} - M) \right]^2 + \left[(M_{i2} - M_{i.}) - (M_{.2} - M) \right]^2 \right\}$$

$$= \sum_{i=1}^{r} n \left[\left(\frac{M_{i1} - M_{i2}}{2} - \frac{M_{.1} - M_{.2}}{2} \right)^2 + \left(\frac{M_{i1} - M_{i2}}{2} - \frac{M_{.1} - M_{.2}}{2} \right)^2 \right]$$

$$= \frac{n}{2} \sum_{i=1}^{r} [(M_{i1} - M_{i2}) - (M_{.1} - M_{.2})]^2$$

$$= \frac{n}{2} \sum_{i=1}^{r} (D_{i.} - \bar{D})^2$$

in which $M_{.1}$ and $M_{.2}$ are the means of the two columns, $D_{i.} = (M_{i1} - M_{i2})$, and $\bar{D} = M_{.1} - M_{.2}$.

Thus it is apparent that the mean square for interaction in the two-column table depends upon the *variability* of the *differences* between cell means for the various rows of the table. If all these differences are the same, the interaction mean square will be zero. Even if only one of these differences differs from the others there will be an interaction sum of squares.

In the table on page 116, for example, the difference in the first two cell means in Row 1 is $27.60 - 19.40 = 8.20$ and the difference in the corresponding cell means in Row 2 is $25.40 - 28.60 = -3.20$. We need not go further to say that there is an observed interaction in the table as a whole, since if the difference between any two cell means in any row differs from the corresponding difference in any other row, the mean square for interaction will have a value other than zero. The difference for Row 3 is $40.00 - 34.40 = 5.60$, and the mean of the three differences is $31.00 - 27.47 = 3.53$.

The interaction sum of squares for Columns 1 and 2 of the table is

$$\frac{n}{2} \sum (D_{i.} - \bar{D})^2 = 5/2 \, [(8.20 - 3.53)^2 + (-3.20 - 3.53)^2 + (5.60 - 3.53)^2]$$

$$= 5/2 \, (71.39) = 178.48$$

and the mean square for interaction for these two columns is 89.24. Similarly the mean square for interaction for Columns 2 and 3 is 83.65, for Columns 1 and 3 is 164.45, for 1 and 4 is 141.25, for 2 and 4 is 106.05, and for 3 and 4 is 6.40. The mean of these six mean squares is 98.51, which agrees with the value of the interaction mean square for the table as a whole. It is further apparent that the mean square for interaction computed for a certain pair of columns selected from the total table may differ markedly from that computed for some other pair of columns.

We have just seen that in a table in which n_{ij} is a constant, the mean square for interaction in the entire table is the simple average of the mean squares for interaction computed for all possible individual pairs of columns in that table. The same would be true if n_{ij} were a constant within each row, even though it differed from row to row.

5

Treatments X Levels Designs

Generalized Case of the Treatments × Levels Designs

The basic features of the *treatments × levels* design have already been considered (pages 13–16) and the design illustrated in a simple restricted case. (The student should review these features carefully before proceeding with this chapter.) The major purpose of the design is to increase the precision of the treatment comparisons by "matching" the treatment groups with reference to a "control" variable related to the criterion variable. In the generalized case of this design, involving a number (a) of treatments, all available subjects (presumably either a random or a representative sample from some specified population) are divided into l different groups or "levels," the numbers in these groups being in the same proportion as the numbers in the corresponding levels in the entire population. This division may be based either on a continuous control variable (Y) or on the categories (ordered or non-ordered) in any classification applicable to the members of the population. In either case, in accordance with the purposes of the design, it is assumed that the levels differ appreciably in the mean value of the criterion variable (X), or that there is a substantial correlation between the control and criterion variables. Within each level, the subjects are assigned at random to the a subgroups corresponding to the treatments. Ordinarily, the same number of subjects would be assigned to each treatment subgroup within each level. However, we will consider here the more highly generalized case in which the subgroup numbers vary within each level and from level to level, but in which the numbers for corresponding subgroups are in the *same proportion* for all levels. The criterion measures for the subjects may then be tabulated in a double-entry table of l rows and a columns, the rows corresponding to levels, the columns to treatments, and the cells to subgroups within the various levels. In the manner described on pages 110 to 114 the *total* sum of squares (ss_T) for this table may then be analyzed into four components: treatments (ss_A), levels (ss_L), treatments × levels (ss_{AL}), and within-subgroups (ss_w), unless there is only one observation per cell, in which case ss_w does not appear.

The major purpose of an experiment of this type is usually to determine if the treatments would have different *average* effects on the members of the specified population. For this purpose, we would wish to test the null hypothesis that the population mean is the same for all treatments. Each such mean, of course, represents the average effect of the treatment for individuals in all "levels" in the control classification. This hypothesis does not imply that the relative effects of different treatments are the same for all levels; one treatment might be much more effective than another at one level but less effective or even inferior to the same treatment at another level.

A second purpose of the experiment may be to determine whether or not the treatments do have the same relative effects at all levels, that is, to determine whether or not there is any "interaction" of treatments and levels. The corresponding hypothesis to be tested is that the *differences* among corresponding treatment population means are the same for all levels. If either or both of these general hypotheses must be rejected, we may become interested in various subordinate or more specific hypotheses concerned with individual pairs of treatments or with individual levels.

For the purposes of subsequent discussions, it will be convenient to define the "effect" of a treatment somewhat differently from the way it was defined in Chapter 3. In Chapter 3 we were concerned with the effect of a given treatment on a single subject. We shall now be concerned with the effect of a treatment on a group of subjects or, on the corresponding "treatment group." In the simple-randomized design, we will now regard the "effect" of a single treatment as corresponding to the deviation of the treatment group mean from the general mean $(M_{.j} - M)$. If all treatment group means are the same, the observed "effect" of each treatment will be zero. We will also need to refer to the collective effects of all treatments. We will call this the "treatments" effect (note the plural) and will regard it as corresponding to the mean square for treatments. Again, if all observed treatment means are the same, the observed treatments effect will be zero.

The treatment effects in a treatment × levels design are similarly defined, except that we must distinguish between the effects of a treatment at a given level and its average effect for all levels. We will call the effect of a given treatment at a given level the "simple" effect of the treatment. The average effect of the treatment at all levels will be called the "main" effect of the treatment. A simple effect of a given treatment is associated with the deviation of the corresponding treatment subgroup mean from the mean for its level. For example, the simple effect of Treatment A_2 at the third level is associated with $(M_{32} - M_{3.})$. In the double-entry table, a simple effect is associated with the deviation of the corresponding cell mean from its row mean. The main effect of a treatment is associated with the deviation of the treatment mean from the general mean, that is, by the deviation of the column mean from the general mean $(M_{.j} - M)$. The main effect of a treatment is thus the weighted average of all its simple effects. In accordance with the preceding definitions, the main effect of treatments is associated with the mean square for treatments for the table as a whole, while a simple effect of treatments is associated with the mean square for treatments computed only for the data from the given level.

The Analysis of the Total Sum of Squares

The analysis of the total sum of squares in the treatments × levels design is exactly like that already described in general terms for all double-entry tables (pages 110–114), except that in our notation we will let A, L, a, and l take the place of C, R, c, and r respectively. The analysis may be summarized in a table like the following:

Source of Variation	df	ss	ms
Treatments (A)	$a - 1$	$ss_A = \sum\limits_j^a \dfrac{T_{.j}^2}{n_{.j}} - \dfrac{T^2}{N}$	$ss_A/(a - 1)$
Levels (L)	$l - 1$	$ss_L = \sum\limits_i^l \dfrac{T_{i.}^2}{n_{i.}} - \dfrac{T^2}{N}$	$ss_L/(l - 1)$
(Cells)	$(al - 1)$	$\left(ss_{\text{cells}} = \sum\limits_i^l \sum\limits_j^a \dfrac{T_{ij}^2}{n_{ij}} - \dfrac{T^2}{N} \right)$	
Treatments × Levels (AL)	$(a - 1)\times$ $(l - 1)$	$ss_{AL} = ss_{\text{cells}} - ss_A - ss_L$	$ss_{AL}/(a - 1)(l - 1)$
Within-Subgroups (w)	$N - al$	$ss_w = ss_T - ss_{\text{cells}}$	$ss_w/(N - al)$
Total	$N - 1$	$ss_T = \sum\limits_i^l \sum\limits_j^a \sum\limits^{n_{ij}} X^2 - \dfrac{T^2}{N}$	

The Meaning of Interaction

Before considering the other features of this design, it will be well to explore more thoroughly the meaning of "interaction." Let us first consider its meaning when there are just two treatments and two levels, as in the design diagrammed below.

	A_1	A_2
L_1	M_{11}	M_{12}
L_2	M_{21}	M_{22}

In this case, the *observed* interaction for the experimental sample is measured by the difference between the differences between treatment means for the two levels. That is, it is measured by $d = (M_{11} - M_{12}) - (M_{21} - M_{22})$. We know that each of the subgroup means is subject to random sampling fluctuations; hence the observed interaction might be due entirely to such fluctuations. Before drawing any inferences about the population, therefore, we would wish to test the significance of the observed interaction. This could be done by the *t*-test (see page 15)

$$t = d/\text{est'd } \sigma_d.$$

(The more highly generalized *F*-test of the significance of the interaction in the multiple-treatment, multiple-level case which we shall consider later is essentially the equivalent of this *t*-test in the two-treatment, two-level case.)

If, according to this *t*-test, the observed interaction is too large to be due entirely to chance, that is, if it is "significant," we may conclude that there *is* an interaction in the population — *granting that the population is subject to exactly the same influences as those affecting the experimental sample.* That is, we may conclude that $(\mu_{11} - \mu_{12}) \neq (\mu_{21} - \mu_{22})$, where the μ's represent population means.

Intrinsic Versus Extrinsic Interaction: We may not conclude from a significant *t*, however, that the larger-than-chance interaction is necessarily due to differences in the relative effects of the *treatments* at the two levels. Part or all of the observed difference in subgroup means at the upper level $(M_{11} - M_{12})$ may be due, not to a difference in treatments, but to some extraneous factors associated with the treatments at that level in the experiment, and similarly for the lower level. That is, the observed *d* may be due in whole or in part to Type G errors. A significant *t* only tells us that the observed *d* is too large to be reasonably accounted for entirely in terms of random Type S fluctuations. Only on the assumption that Type G errors have been completely eliminated in the experiment (or equalized for the two levels), may we conclude from a significant *t* that the difference in *treatment* effects is not the same at both levels in the population.

In any experiment of this type, there are three possible components of the *observed* treatments × levels interaction, measured in this case by *d* (and in the general case by the interaction mean square). One component is due to Type S errors, one to Type G errors, and one to the treatments alone. That part due to treatments alone we will give the name "intrinsic" interaction; that due to Type G errors we will call "extrinsic" interaction. If the observed interaction is significant, we may conclude that something more than Type S errors is present, or that there *is* an interaction in the population. The fact of significance, however, does not enable us to say whether the interaction is intrinsic or extrinsic, or a mixture of both. In nearly all experiments of this type, a significant interaction is a mixture of intrinsic and extrinsic interaction, but there is no way of determining from the experiment alone what proportion is intrinsic and what extrinsic.

Two Treatments — Several Levels: Let us now consider the case in which there are several levels but still only two treatments, as diagrammed below.

	A_1	A_2	
L_1	M_{11}	M_{12}	$D_{1.} = M_{11} - M_{12}$
L_2	M_{21}	M_{22}	
	⋮	⋮	
L_i	M_{i1}	M_{i2}	$D_{i.} = M_{i1} - M_{i2}$
	⋮	⋮	
L_l	M_{l1}	M_{l2}	$D_{l.} = M_{l1} - M_{l2}$
	$M_{.1}$	$M_{.2}$	$\overline{D} = M_{.1} - M_{.2}$

The observed interaction now depends on the differences among the differences between the treatment means for all levels; it is measured by the variability of these differences. If $D_{i.} = M_{i1} - M_{i2}$ represents the difference at level i, then the observed interaction depends on the variability of these $D_{i.}$'s or, more strictly, on a variance estimate derived from these differences. If the number of cases in all of the treatment subgroups is the same (n), the observed interaction is measured by $\frac{n}{2}\sum_i^l (D_{i.} - \overline{D})^2/(l - 1)$, which is the mean square for interaction, $\overline{D}$ representing the mean of the $D_{i.}$'s (see page 119). Again it is possible that the observed interaction is due entirely to chance fluctuations in the subgroup means. As in the simpler case, therefore, we will wish to test the significance of the observed interaction before drawing any inference about the population. We shall see later how this may be done.

The Multiple-Treatment, Multiple-Level Case: If there are more than two treatments as well as more than two levels, the observed interaction for the table as a whole may be regarded as a weighted average of the observed interactions for all possible *pairs* of treatments (columns) in the entire table. For example, if there are three treatments, we could compute the mean square for interaction from the data for Treatments A_1 and A_2 alone, and likewise for Treatments A_2 and A_3 alone, and A_1 and A_3 alone. If all subgroups are of the same size, the mean square for interaction for the entire table would be the simple mean of these three mean squares. The observed interaction for the entire table may also be regarded as depending on the variability of the interaction effects for the individual treatment subgroups (cells), that is, on the deviations of the twice-corrected cell means from the general mean. For many purposes, however, it is more meaningful to think of interaction as depending upon the variability of the differences between treatment means at the various levels for individual pairs of treatments.

It may be helpful to regard the case of *no* interaction as that in which the effects of the treatments (and any associated extraneous factors) are "additive." Suppose that *before* a certain treatment is administered, the population mean of the criterion variable for each level is ascertained. This initial mean will of course differ from level to level, but within each level all subpopulation means will be the same. If the average effect of the treatment at each of these levels is the same, that is, if the effect is equivalent to having *added a constant* to all initial level means, we may say that the treatment effect is "additive." If all treatments are additive in their effects, there will be no interaction in the table. That is, the effect of one treatment will be to add one constant to all initial level means for that treatment, and the effect of each other treatment will be to add another constant to all initial level means for that treatment. This will create differences in the final criterion means for any level, but the corresponding differences will be the same for all levels; hence there will be no interaction.

It may also be helpful to define an "interaction effect" as the difference between a simple effect and the corresponding main effect. The interaction effect for Treatment A_2 at the third level is thus the difference between the simple effect of A_2 at this level and the main effect of A_2, that is, $(M_{32} - M_{3.}) - (M_{.2} - M) = (M_{32} - M_{3.} - M_{.2} + M)$. If the simple effect of each treatment is the same at all levels, all interaction effects will be zero and there will be no observed interaction in the table. To say that there is an interaction, then, is to say that the simple effects of all treatments are not the same at all levels.

It may be well to note here that in all our discussions of interaction we should distinguish carefully between the "observed" interaction (which characterizes the experimental data) and the interaction which characterizes the population. We should also distinguish carefully between intrinsic and extrinsic interaction. Generally, when on the basis of the experimental results we say without qualification that there "is an interaction," we imply that the observed interaction has been found to be significant, and our statement is an inference about the population. If we say without qualification that there is "no interaction," we imply that the observed interaction has been shown to be nonsignificant, and our statement is an *assumption* or hypothesis about the population. Whenever we mean *observed* interaction, we shall say so.

Heterogeneity of Interaction: When we say that there "is an interaction" in the table as a whole, we usually mean that *somewhere* in the entire table the difference between corresponding (observed) treatment means differs from level to level by more than is reasonably attributable to chance. This statement does not imply, however, that there are "larger-than-chance" differences everywhere in the table.

If there are three treatments, it is possible that Treatments A_1 and A_2 are both additive in their effects, but that the effect of Treatment A_3 is not additive. In that case, there would be no interaction with levels so far as A_1 and A_2 are concerned, but there would be an interaction so far as A_1 and A_3, or A_2 and A_3, are concerned. Again, all three treatments may be non-additive in their effects, but Treatments A_1 and A_2 may be much alike in their effects at all levels, while the relative effectiveness of A_3 may differ markedly from level to level. In that case, we would say that there is a "weak" or "slight" interaction so far as A_1 and A_2 are concerned, but a strong interaction so far as A_1 and A_3, or A_2 and A_3, are concerned. That is, the variance of the differences between treatment means for the various levels may be small for A_1 and A_2 but large for A_1 and A_3 and for A_2 and A_3. In that case, we would say that the interaction for the table as a whole is "heterogeneous," or that the interaction is stronger for some pairs of treatments than for others. On the other hand, if the variance of the differences between treatment means for the various levels is the same for all possible pairs of treatments, we would say that the interaction for all treatments and levels considered together is *homogeneous*. Another way of describing heterogeneity of interaction is to say that the simple effects of some treatments are more variable than those for other treatments, or that the variance of the interaction effects is greater for some columns (treatments) than for others. This concept of heterogeneity or homogeneity of interaction, as we shall see, is a very important concept in the interpretation of results obtained in many experimental designs.

The Uniformity Trial: It might be helpful, in distinguishing between intrinsic and extrinsic interaction, to consider what might happen if a particular experiment were repeated with a fresh but equivalent sample of subjects under exactly the same experimental conditions, with the exception that in the repetition of the experiment, the *same* treatment (any one of the experimental treatments) was administered to all treatment groups. This is sometimes described as a "uniformity trial." In the uniformity trial, of course, there could not possibly be any intrinsic interaction, and whatever interaction is observed would have to be due entirely to sampling fluctuations and experimental errors. If a much larger observed interaction were obtained in the actual experiment than in the uniformity trial, this would suggest the presence of an intrinsic interaction in the experiment. A test of the significance of the difference between the two observed interactions would then be a test of the hypothesis that there is no intrinsic interaction in the original experiment. This test could be made by $F = ms_{AL}/ms'_{AL}$, in which ms'_{AL} is the mean square for interaction obtained in the uniformity trial. This would be a one-tailed test like the test of ms_A/ms_w.

In a single experiment of the treatments $\times$ levels type, it is not possible to separate the intrinsic and extrinsic interactions, but it is possible to estimate what part of the observed interaction is due to sampling fluctuations (Type S error) only, and it is possible to determine whether or not the observed interaction can reasonably be attributed to sampling fluctuations alone. The test of significance appropriate to the purpose will be considered later (pages 138–139).

Constituting the "Levels" in an Experiment

In any application of the treatments $\times$ levels design, what inferences may legitimately be drawn from the experiment will depend in part on the manner of constituting the levels in the experimental sample. This division of subjects into levels may be accomplished in at least two different ways.

Representative Sampling from a Real Population: In some situations, the distribution of the control variable for the entire population may be known. In that case, it may be possible to draw a strictly representative sample from this population. A *representative* sample is here defined as one in which the numbers of subjects in the various levels or categories in the sample are exactly proportional to the numbers in the corresponding levels in the entire population, and in which the sampling is strictly random within each level independently. If the levels are based on a continuous control variable, the distribution of that variable may be broken up into as many intervals or levels as the experimenter desires. If the reason for introducing the control variable is solely to increase the precision of the experiment, the larger the number of levels the better. However, the number of levels will be limited by the requirement that there be at least two subjects in each cell of the double-entry table, and by the total number of subjects to be employed. The intervals need not be of the same size.

Suppose, for example, that in a learning experiment involving three treatments, the control variable is the score on a general intelligence test. The distribution of scores on this test for a very large sample taken from the entire population (the sample on which the test was standardized) is known to be that given in Column 2 in Table 6. Since the sample is so large, the distribution in Column 2 may, for practical purposes, be regarded as the distribution for the entire population. Suppose the distribution of intelligence test scores for the *available* subjects is that given in Column 3 of the table, and it has been decided to employ approximately 100 subjects in the experiment. We might then divide the scale of intelligence test scores into a number of relatively coarse intervals, as indicated by the lines across the columns. These intervals are determined on a "cut and try" basis, in an effort to have the percent of individuals in the whole population that is contained in each interval as close as possible to a multiple of 3 (not less than 6). The population distribution for these intervals is given in Column 4. The number in parentheses following each frequency expresses this frequency as a percent of the total population. It will be noted that most of these percents are quite close to a multiple of 3. The distribution in these intervals for the *available* subjects is given in Column 5. For the purpose of the experiment, 6 subjects are selected *at random* from the 25 subjects available in the first interval, 9 are selected at random from those in the second interval, 18 at random from those in the third, etc. Accordingly, by comparing Columns 4 and 6, we note that the frequencies in the various intervals in the experimental sample are very nearly proportional to the corresponding percents in the entire population. The experimental sample may, in other words, be regarded as a representative sample so far as the distribution of intelligence test scores is concerned.

This method of sampling is the only one *strictly* satisfying the require-

TABLE 6

Distribution of Intelligence Test Scores for an Experimental Sample
and for the Population Represented by the Sample

(1) Intelligence Test Scores	(2) Frequency Distribution for the Population	(3) Distribution for Available Subjects	(4) Distribution for Population	(5) Distribution for Available Subjects	(6) Distribution for Selected Samples
45	1				
44	0				
43	2				
42	8	1			
41	11	4			
40	15	3			
39	28	1			
38	35	2	495 (4.8%)	25	6
37	43	4			
36	75	2			
35	109	3			
34	168	5			
33	227	6			
32	317	6	928 (9.1%)	20	9
31	384	8			
30	483	10			
29	586	9	1731 (16.9%)	31	18
28	662	12			
27	740	11			
26	785	15	1525 (14.9%)	26	15
25	861	18			
24	789	21	2393 (23.4%)	56	24
23	743	17			
22	667	16			
21	582	12			
20	480	22	2115 (20.7%)	60	21
19	386	10			
18	307	14			
17	224	9			
16	162	6			
15	105	8			
14	76	4			
13	44	2	1029 (10.1%)	52	9
12	31	6			
11	29	2			
10	18	0			
9	13	1			
8	9				
7	5				
6	4				
5	2				
	10216	270	10216	270	102

ments of the hypothesis to be tested, but for obvious practical reasons it can rarely be used. We will refer to this method of sampling as the method of representative sampling from a specified *real* population.

The "Counting Off" Method: A more common situation is that subjects from some real population are available for experimental purposes, but it is not known that the available subjects are a strictly random sample from that population. In this situation, also, the distribution of the control variable for the population may be unknown. In this case, we can regard the available subjects as a representative sample from a *hypothetical* population — one defined to fit the sample (see pages 73–74). The available subjects are first arranged in order of the control variable (arranging in random order all individuals having the same value of the control variable). The levels are then constituted by counting off na subjects at a time from the top of the distribution, n being larger than 1 but otherwise selected at the experimenter's convenience. Thus, if there are 3 treatments, the first 6 subjects (those with the 6 highest scores) might be those in the first level, the next 6 those in the second level, the third 6 those in the third, etc. All subjects can thus be used except the number less than 3 that may be left over after the last complete set of 6 or 9 has been selected. Suppose, for example, that 47 subjects are available for the experiment and that their control measures are as indicated in the list below:

25	21	36	27	16	47
34	35	33	51	24	18
15	44	26	20	33	23
46	15	55	10	~~21~~	16
33	27	22	17	38	29
29	19	41	40	34	32
42	37	46	29	39	14
27	~~36~~	19	25	28	

Two subjects are eliminated at random in order to leave a multiple of 3. The control measures of those eliminated are crossed out in the list above. The remaining subjects are then arranged in order of their control scores and divided into groups of 6, as indicated below. Note that there are 9 subjects in the last level.

55	36	27	19
51	35	27	18
47	34	27	17
46	34	26	16
46	33	25	16
44	33	25	15
			15
42	33	24	14
41	32	23	10
40	29	22	
39	29	21	
38	29	20	
37	28	19	

The experimental sample may now fairly be regarded as a representative sample from a hypothetical population showing the same relative distribution of the control variable as the sample itself. For the experimental subjects in the illustration used, the distribution of control scores is as given in Column 2 of the table below, the intervals having been defined in terms of the sample drawn. The hypothetical population from which this sample may be regarded as a representative sample is one in which the proportions of individuals in these intervals are as indicated in Column 3 of the table below.

(1)	(2)	(3)	(4)
Score Interval		Proportions in Hypothetical Pop.	Proportions in Real Pop.
1) 43.0 and above	6	.1333	.1210
2) 36.5 – 43.0	6	.1333	.1433
3) 32.87 – 36.5	6	.1333	.1064
4) 27.5 – 32.87	6	.1333	.1810
5) 24.5 – 27.5	6	.1333	.0963
6) 19.0 – 24.5	6	.1333	.1487
7) 19.0 and below	9	.2000	.2033

When the levels are constituted in this manner, the distribution of the control variable for the hypothetical population will, of course, differ from that for the real population in which the experimenter is interested. Certain levels will be more heavily represented in the hypothetical population than in the real one, and others less heavily. For instance, with reference to the illustration, the distribution of criterion measures for the population in which the experimenter is really interested may be as indicated in Column 4 of the preceding table. Thus we see that the hypothetical population contains a larger proportion of individuals than the real population in intervals 3 and 5 but a smaller proportion than the real population in interval 4. If there is an interaction of treatments and levels, and if a given treatment happens to be relatively effective in intervals 3 and 5, but relatively ineffective in interval 4, that treatment may, on the average, be more effective in the hypothetical population than in the real population. Thus the treatment (column) means obtained in the experiment may be biased estimates of the means of the real population to which the experimenter wishes to generalize, but unbiased with reference to the hypothetical population.

So far as the hypothetical population is concerned, the F-test of the treatment effect (to be considered later) will be valid (if other necessary conditions are met); in the strictest sense, any statistical inferences drawn from this test should be restricted to the hypothetical population. Before extending any of these inferences to a real population, the experimenter should give very careful consideration to possible differences between the real and hypothetical populations. In general, the populations will differ with respect to many specific factors (such as intelligence, age, environmental background, heredity, etc.). If a particular factor in which they do differ does not "interact" with the experimental factor, then that difference, in itself, will offer no obstacle to generalization. For example, if the members of the hypothetical population are on the average much taller than those of the real population, and if height does not "interact" with "treatments" — that is, if the differences among the treatment effects are the same for tall as for short individuals — then the fact that the populations differ in height is of no consequence so far as generalization is concerned. The real question, then, is not "Do the populations differ?", but "Do they differ with respect to anything which *interacts* with the experimental factor?" Frequently, the best that the experimenter can do is to offer a reasoned opinion concerning the answer to this question, but at least it should be a carefully reasoned opinion, making use of all that is known about the problem.

If the experiment is to be controlled on the basis of non-ordered categories in a discrete classification, those categories must of course be accepted by the experimenter as they are found. If the maximum number of subjects is to be employed from among those available, the number selected at random from each category will be the largest possible multiple of the number of treatments. If the number of subjects available in a certain category is less than the number of treatments, this category may be combined with another, and the largest possible multiple of a subjects may be drawn at random from the combined categories.

Selection of the Control Variable

In most instances the principal reason, and often the sole reason, for using the treatments × levels design in preference to the simple-randomized design is to increase the precision of the experiment. The total sum of squares for the entire sample used in the experiment will of course be the same whether or not that sample is divided into levels. If the simple-randomized design is employed, the "error" sum of squares will be the within-treatments sum of squares, obtained by subtracting the sum of squares for treatments from that for total $(ss_{\text{error}} = ss_{wA} = ss_T - ss_A)$. If the treatments × levels design is used, the "error" sum of squares will be the within-cells sum of squares, obtained by subtracting the sums of squares for treatments, levels, and treatments × levels from the sum of squares for total $(ss_{\text{error}} = ss_T - ss_A - ss_L - ss_{AL})$. The within-cells sum of squares may also be computed by subtracting the levels and treatments × levels sums of squares from the sum of squares for within-treatments $(ss_{\text{error}} = ss_{wA} - ss_L - ss_{AL})$. It is obvious, then, that the error term will often be very much smaller in the treatments × levels design than in the simple-randomized design — how much smaller will depend on the magnitude of the differences among levels (ss_L) and on the degree of interaction (ss_{AL}). The magnitude of the differences among the levels means depends on the correlation between the control and the criterion variable. The higher this correlation, the larger will be the

levels sum of squares, and the smaller will be the error term. Clearly, therefore, if a number of possible control variables are available for an experiment,
that one should be used which shows the highest correlation with the criterion.
So far as precision alone is concerned, the choice should always be based
strictly on empirical considerations, or only on the known correlation with
the criterion, and on the convenience or economy with which the control
may be employed, even though the apparent "logic" of the situation may
suggest another control variable. Sometimes more than one control variable
may be used, and the best linear composite of these variables (determined by
methods of multiple regression) may be employed as a basis for constituting
the levels. Sometimes, also, an "initial" measure of the criterion variable
itself may show a higher correlation with the "final" measures (the criterion
measures) than any other available control variable, and may therefore be
used as the control variable.

Testing the Significance of the Main Effect of Treatments

We are now ready to consider the test of significance of the main effect
of treatments. This is a test of the hypothesis that the various treatments
would have the same effect on the mean of the criterion scores for the population from which the experimental sample was drawn. This test is based on
the ratio (ms_A/ms_w) of the mean squares for treatments and within-cells.
Under certain conditions, which are listed below, this ratio is distributed as F.
The last of the conditions listed constitutes the hypothesis to be tested; the
first three constitute the *assumptions* on which the test of this hypothesis is
valid. The conditions [1] for an F-distribution of ms_A/ms_w are as follows:

1) Each treatment group was originally a *representative* sample from a
   specified population. (That is, each treatment subgroup was originally drawn at random from the corresponding level of the given population, the number being drawn at each level being proportional to
   the number of individuals at that level in the whole population. It
   follows from this, of course, that the cell frequencies in the double-
   entry table are proportional from column to column or from row to
   row.) *After* the administration of the treatments, the treatment groups
   must be regarded as representative samples from different (hypothetical) populations. The distribution of criterion measures for each of
   these hypothetical populations is that which *would* have been obtained
   from the original population had each member received a given treatment.

2) The distribution of criterion measures for the subpopulation corresponding to each treatment subgroup is a normal distribution.

---

[1] See footnote on page 51.

3) Each of these distributions has the same variance (σ^2).

4) The means of the hypothetical populations corresponding to the various treatments are identical (the null hypothesis).

To prove that ms_A/ms_w is distributed as F, we will first write the ratio between the mean square for treatments (columns) and the mean square for within-subgroups, and divide both numerator and denominator by σ^2. We then get

$$\frac{\dfrac{\sum\limits_{j=1}^{a} n_{.j}(M_{.j} - M)^2}{a - 1}}{\dfrac{\sum\limits_{i=1}^{l}\sum\limits_{j=1}^{a}\sum(X - M_{ij})^2}{N - al}} = \frac{\dfrac{\sum\limits_{j=1}^{a} n_{.j}(M_{.j} - M)^2}{\sigma^2}}{\dfrac{\sum\limits_{i=1}^{l}\sum\limits_{j=1}^{a}\sum(X - M_{ij})^2}{\sigma^2}} \Bigg/ \frac{(a-1)}{(N-al)}. \tag{30}$$

Now the mean of any treatment (column) is equal to the weighted average of the means of the subgroups (cells) in that column. That is,

$$M_{.j} = \frac{n_{1j}M_{1j} + n_{2j}M_{2j} + \ldots + n_{ij}M_{ij} + \ldots + n_{lj}M_{lj}}{n_{.j}}$$

$$= \frac{n_{1j}}{n_{.j}}M_{1j} + \frac{n_{2j}}{n_{.j}}M_{2j} + \ldots + \frac{n_{lj}}{n_{.j}}M_{lj}.$$

Hence, under Conditions 1 and 3, since the variance of the sum of a number of independent variables is equal to the sum of their variances,

$$\sigma_{M.j}^2 = \frac{n_{1j}^2}{n_{.j}^2}\cdot\frac{\sigma^2}{n_{1j}} + \frac{n_{2j}^2}{n_{.j}^2}\cdot\frac{\sigma^2}{n_{2j}} + \ldots + \frac{n_{lj}^2}{n_{.j}^2}\cdot\frac{\sigma^2}{n_{lj}}$$

$$= \frac{\sigma^2}{n_{.j}^2}\sum_{i=1}^{l} n_{ij} = \sigma^2/n_{.j}.$$

Accordingly, under Condition 2,

$$\frac{n_{.j}(M_{.j} - \mu)^2}{\sigma^2} = \frac{(M_{.j} - \mu)^2}{\sigma^2/n_{.j}} = \frac{(M_{.j} - \mu)^2}{\sigma_{M.j}^2}$$

is distributed as χ^2 with one degree of freedom. From this it follows that $\sum\limits_{j=1}^{a} n_{.j}(M_{.j} - \mu)^2/\sigma^2$ is distributed as χ^2 with a degrees of freedom. If we now take deviations of the $M_{.j}$'s from the sample mean (M) rather than from the population mean (μ), the result is still distributed as χ^2 (see page 30) but with one less degree of freedom. That is,

$$\frac{\sum\limits_{j=1}^{a} n_{.j}(M_{.j} - M)^2}{\sigma^2}$$

is distributed as χ^2 with $(a - 1)$ degrees of freedom.

Also, under Conditions 1, 2, and 3, for a single subgroup,

$$\frac{\sum\limits^{n_{ij}}(X - M_{ij})^2}{\sigma^2}$$

is distributed as χ^2 with $(n_{ij} - 1)df$; hence

$$\sum_{i=1}^{l}\sum_{j=1}^{a}\frac{\sum\limits^{n_{ij}}(X - M_{ij})^2}{\sigma^2}$$

is distributed as χ^2 with $\sum\limits_{i=1}^{l}\sum\limits_{j=1}^{n}(n_{ij} - 1) = (N - al)\ df$.

Remembering Conditions 1 and 2, we may next note that for any one cell, $\frac{n_{ij}}{n_{.j}}M_{ij}$ is independent of $\sum\limits^{n_{ij}}(X - M_{ij})^2$ computed for that cell only, since for a random sample from a normal population the mean is independent of the variance. Accordingly, the sums of these terms for all cells in any one column must also be independent of one another. That is, $\sum\limits_{i=1}^{l}\frac{n_{ij}}{n_{.j}}M_{ij} = M_{.j}$, is independent of $\sum\limits_{i=1}^{l}\sum\limits^{n_{ij}}(X - M_{ij})^2$. Therefore, $n_{.j}(M_{.j} - M)^2$ must also be independent of $\sum\limits_{i=1}^{l}\sum\limits^{n_{ij}}(X - M_{ij})^2$, and the sums of these terms for all columns, $\sum\limits_{j=1}^{a}n_{.j}(M_{.j} - M)^2$ and $\sum\limits_{i=1}^{l}\sum\limits_{j=1}^{a}(X - M_{ij})^2$ must also be independent.

Thus we see that the right-hand term in (30) is the ratio between two *independent* χ^2's, each divided by its own degrees of freedom. Accordingly, under Condition 4, we may write

$$F = \frac{\dfrac{\sum\limits_{j=1}^{a}n_{.j}(M_{.j} - M)^2}{a - 1}}{\dfrac{\sum\limits_{i=1}^{l}\sum\limits_{j=1}^{a}(X - M_{ij})^2}{N - al}} = \frac{ms_A}{ms_w},\ df = (a - 1)/(N - al), \qquad (31)$$

and may employ this ratio between the mean squares for treatments and for within-cells to test the given hypothesis.

Interpretation of a Significant $F = ms_A/ms_w$: If, in a particular treatments $\times$ levels experiment, we find that $F = ms_A/ms_w$ is significant, we may be quite certain that at least one of the conditions listed on pages 133–134 was not met. In most applications, we may safely conclude that the condition not satisfied is the last, that is, we may reject the hypothesis that the treatments have the same average effects on the members of the specified population. However, it is important to understand the conditions under which a significant F may be due to a failure to satisfy one or more of the assumptions basic to this test (Conditions 1 − 3). We will therefore give careful consideration here to each of the three assumptions (or conditions) separately.

The extent to which Condition 1 (representative sampling) is satisfied lies wholly within the control of the experimenter. There is usually no good reason why this condition should not be completely satisfied, if not with reference to a real population, at least with reference to a hypothetical one defined to fit the sample. If the "counting off" method of constituting the levels has been employed, and the sample is regarded as representative of a hypothetical population, Condition 1 may be regarded as fully satisfied if the subjects have been *randomized* with reference to treatments in each level independently. To avoid any question of unintentional bias, it is usually best to insure randomization by using a table of random numbers in assigning subjects to treatments within each level.

When the sample is thus regarded as representative of a hypothetical population, any statistical inferences drawn from the sample should be restricted to this hypothetical population. However, if the counting off method has been employed, and if the total experimental sample may be regarded as a simple random sample (or the equivalent) from a real population, it is usually reasonable to suppose that this hypothetical population will not differ appreciably from the real population.

Proportionality of the frequencies of the corresponding treatment subgroups from level to level is important not only for the reasons just given, but also because the validity of the analysis of the total sum of squares into its components depends on this condition. There is a possibility that the experiment may originally have been properly designed in this regard, but that some subjects were "lost" during the course of the experiment, so that at its conclusion, the frequencies are no longer proportional. What to do in this event will be considered later (page 148).

The use in educational research of samples consisting of intact school classes raises the same problems with the treatments × levels design as with the simple-randomized design (see pages 74–75).

It should be noted that the requirement of normality is in general considerably more likely to be satisfied in applications of the treatments × levels design than of the simple-randomized design. In the treatments × levels design, it is no longer necessary to assume that the criterion variable (X) is normally distributed for the population sampled, but only that X is normally distributed for those members of that population who are alike or nearly alike with reference to Y, the control variable. What we assume, in effect, is that the errors of estimating X from Y are normally distributed for the population, rather than that X is normally distributed for the population. It is readily conceivable, particularly if the correlation between X and Y is high, that the errors of estimate are normally distributed even though the distribution of X itself is markedly skewed, or otherwise not normal.

A similar observation may be made with reference to the assumption of homogeneity of variance. There is always a possibility of a strong interaction between treatments and levels, in which case the differences among the subgroup (level) means for one treatment may be very much smaller than those for another; nevertheless, the variance within subgroups may remain essentially the same from treatment to treatment. If this were the case, the assumption of homogeneous variance would be invalid if the simple-randomized design were employed, but valid if the treatments × levels design were employed.

In any event, a considerable departure, either from normality in the criterion distribution, or from homogeneity of variance among various cells of the table, is permissible; yet the sampling distribution of the ratio of mean squares for treatments and within-cells will remain essentially the same (see page 78 ff.).

It is very important to observe that the test of the main effect of treatments takes no cognizance of Type G or Type R errors. If any uncontrolled extraneous factors have been associated with the experimental treatments, these factors, so far as this test is concerned, are regarded as a part of the treatments themselves. Furthermore, the inferences drawn from the sample must be restricted to the population (real or hypothetical) from which the entire experimental sample may be regarded as a representative sample. For instance, if a learning experiment is conducted in a certain school, the available subjects may be regarded as a representative sample from a "population" corresponding to that particular school only. The effectiveness of the treatments for this particular school may not be the same as for other schools. Hence, if the observed treatment effect is to be regarded as an estimate of the treatment effect for a population consisting of a large number of such schools, a Type R error is present which is not taken into consideration in this test.

In most applications of the treatments × levels design, then, if we find a significant $F = ms_A/ms_w$, we may safely conclude that a failure to satisfy Conditions 1 to 3 could hardly be responsible, and that the hypothesis contained in Condition 4 (equal treatment means) must be false. Nevertheless, Conditions 1 to 3 should never be taken for granted. In every actual experiment, each should be carefully reviewed.

It should be emphasized that the test of the hypothesis of equal treatment means does not involve any assumption about the presence or absence of an interaction between treatments and levels. Whether or not there is any such interaction, the F-test of the main effect of treatments is valid so far as Type S errors are concerned. If there is no interaction, the fact that the total experimental sample is neither a strictly random nor a strictly representative sample from the real population is of much less serious consequence than otherwise. If there is no interaction, each observed treatment mean may be a biased estimate of the corresponding real population mean, but all observed treatment means will be biased alike. Accordingly, one can draw valid inferences about the *relative* effectiveness of the treatments in the real population, even though the total experimental sample is biased so far as the distribution of criterion measures is concerned.

Test of the Significance of the Interaction

The statistical test of the hypothesis of no interaction is based on the ratio of the mean square for treatments × levels to that for within-cells (ms_{AL}/ms_w). The conditions under which this ratio is distributed as F are listed below. The last of these conditions constitutes the hypothesis to be tested. The first three are the assumptions basic to the test.

1) Each treatment subgroup has been randomly selected from the corresponding subpopulation in the parent population.

2) The distribution of criterion measures for each of these subpopulations is normal.

3) All of these distributions have the same variance (σ^2).

4) The corresponding subgroup frequencies are in the same proportion from level to level.

5) The *difference* between subpopulation means for corresponding treatments is the *same* for all levels.

We have seen that in the table in which all differences among row and column means have been eliminated by arithmetic corrections (the twice-corrected table, page 111), the interaction sum of squares is identical with the sum of squares for between-cells $(ss_{AL} = ss''_{\text{cells}})$. In this twice-corrected table, the ratio between the mean squares for cells and within-cells may be written

$$\frac{ms''_{\text{cells}}}{ms_w} = \frac{\dfrac{\sum\limits_{i=1}^{l}\sum\limits_{j=1}^{a}n_{ij}(M''_{ij} - M)^2}{(l-1)(a-1)}}{\dfrac{\sum\limits_{i=1}^{l}\sum\limits_{j=1}^{a}\sum(X - M_{ij})^2}{N - al}} = \frac{\sum\limits_{i=1}^{l}\sum\limits_{j=1}^{a}\dfrac{(M''_{ij} - M)^2}{\sigma^2/n_{ij}}\Big/ (l-1)(a-1)}{\sum\limits_{i=1}^{l}\sum\limits_{j=1}^{a}\dfrac{\sum(X - M_{ij})^2}{\sigma^2}\Big/ (N - al)} \cdot (32)$$

The third form of the ratio above is obtained by dividing both numerator and denominator of the middle ratio by σ^2. From the third form in which this ratio is written, it is apparent that under Conditions 1, 2, and 3 the ratio is that between two χ^2's, each divided by its degrees of freedom. (The student should be able to show why each of these three conditions is necessary.)

The proof that the mean square in the numerator is *independent* of that in the denominator is similar to that given on page 135. For any given subgroup, M_{ij} is independent of $\Sigma(X - M_{ij})^2$, on the assumption (Conditions

1 and 2) that each subgroup is a random sample from a normal population. Hence, $(M''_{ij} - M)^2$ must also be independent of $\Sigma(X - M_{ij})^2$. Accordingly $\sum_{i=1}^{l}\sum_{j=1}^{a}(M''_{ij} - M)^2$ must be independent of $\sum_{i=1}^{l}\sum_{j=1}^{a}\sum(X - M_{ij})^2$, and hence the numerator of (32) is independent of the denominator.

We have thus shown that (32) is the ratio between two independent χ^2's, each divided by its degrees of freedom. Accordingly, we may write

$$F = ms_{AL}/ms_w, \text{ for } (l - 1)(a - 1) \text{ and } (N - al)df,$$

and may use this ratio to test the stated hypothesis.

It may be shown that if there is no interaction in the population, the expected value of ms_{AL} is σ^2, or that ms_{AL} is an unbiased estimate of σ^2.

Interpretation of a Significant $F = ms_{AL}/ms_w$: Suppose that in an actual experiment the ratio of the mean squares for treatments $\times$ levels and within-cells is too large to be reasonably attributed to chance, and therefore, that the hypothesis of no interaction is rejected.

We may note first that the test of this hypothesis is *not* based on any assumption that the total experimental sample is a *representative* sample (with reference to levels) from any specified population (real or hypothetical). This is why Conditions 1 and 4 on page 138 have been substituted for Condition 1 on page 133. This hypothesis is concerned only with whether or not any interaction exists, and not with the effect of any possible interaction on the over-all treatment comparisons. All that is necessary, therefore, is that the numbers drawn from the various levels are in the same proportion for all treatments, and that the subjects are randomized with reference to treatments in each level. Conditions 1 and 4 (page 138) are almost wholly within the control of the experimenter and, if proper care is exercised in setting up the experiment, these conditions should be known to be satisfied so far as the hypothetical population is concerned. For reasons given earlier, this test of significance is not very sensitive to moderate departures from Conditions 2 and 3; all we need do is assure ourselves that there is no very marked departure from normality nor from homogeneity of the within-cells variances. Hence, in general, a significant F means that the hypothesis of no interaction (Condition 5) is false, or that the differences between corresponding treatment means from level to level are too large to be due entirely to sampling fluctuations (Type S errors).

It does not necessarily follow from this, however, that there is any intrinsic interaction between treatments and levels. To what extent a significant F may be taken as an indication of an intrinsic interaction depends in part on whether the treatments have been administered independently at each level or on a group basis for all levels simultaneously, and in part on the extent to which extraneous factors have been controlled or equalized throughout the entire experiment. If the treatments have been administered at each level separately, so that each level constitutes an independent replication of the whole experiment, then the observed variability in the differences between treatment means from level to level could be due primarily to the effect of Type G errors which vary from level to level. If a significant F is obtained in an experiment thus administered, it is quite possible that Type G errors alone account for its significance. The observed interaction, then, may be "significant," and yet not "intrinsic." In this design, as we have already noted, there is no possibility of differentiating the intrinsic from the extrinsic interaction.

If the treatments are administered on a group basis to the subjects from all levels simultaneously, then many (but not necessarily all) of the extraneous factors associated with treatments will tend to have the same effect at all levels. Any extraneous factors which are thus additive in their effect will of course make no contribution to the interaction mean square, even though they do affect the treatments mean square (that is, even though they do affect the column means). It is quite possible, however, that some extraneous factors associated with treatments may themselves "interact" with levels. In that case, a part of the observed interaction will again be due to error, or will be extrinsic. Accordingly, if each treatment has been administered on a group basis to subjects from all levels simultaneously, a significant F is much more likely to indicate the presence of an intrinsic interaction than if the treatments have been administered independently (and Type G errors randomized) at each level separately. In neither case does the significant F necessarily mean that an intrinsic interaction is present. In either case, the more carefully controlled the experiment, the more surely does a significant F imply an intrinsic interaction.

The fact that the obtained $F = ms_{AL}/ms_w$ is significant implies nothing whatever about the homogeneity or heterogeneity of the interaction. The significant F could be due entirely to the nonadditive effects of only one treatment; there may be no interaction at all among the remaining treatments. Indeed, a significant F could be due to what has happened to a *single* treatment subgroup, as, for example, to a large experimental error that is unique to that subgroup. However, it should be noted that the F-test of interaction for the table as a whole is not very sensitive to an interaction affecting only a small part of the entire table. It is quite possible, therefore, that an interaction characteristic of only a small part of the table, and possibly of considerable consequence so far as that part of the table alone is concerned, may not be detected by the over-all test for interaction.

If the observed interaction is significant and if an inspection of the data within the table suggests that this interaction is heterogeneous, one can apply tests of interaction independently to selected segments of the table, or to the treatments taken two at a time. If it appeared that only one of the treatments was responsible for the observed interaction, the data for this one treatment could be excluded from the table, and a test of interaction applied to the remaining table alone. Tests of interaction applied to only part of the table, however, are of dubious value if the interaction for the table as a whole had proved nonsignificant. To apply a test of interaction to selected segments of the table would in this case be to introduce a fallacy very similar to that discussed on pages 48–49 — that of applying to the largest of a number of observations the probability appropriate only for a single observation selected at random. If the interaction for the table as a whole is not significant, but the data suggest that there is an interaction for a part of the table alone, the safest procedure is to design an independent experiment only for the particular treatments and levels involved, and then apply an *independent* test of significance in this experiment.

The Meaning of ms_A/ms_{AL}

If there is an intrinsic interaction between treatments and levels for a population, ms_A/ms_{AL} will have an F-distribution with $(a - 1)/(a - 1)(l - 1)$ degrees of freedom only if the AL interaction effects are normally distributed, if the levels of L represented in the experiment may be regarded as a random sample from a population of such levels, and if the null hypothesis concerning treatment means is true. This interpretation is ruled out by the manner in which we have defined "levels" of the control variable in the treatments × levels design. However, if the number of subjects per treatment is large, the ratio ms_A/ms_{AL} still has a useful meaning (although not as an F-ratio to test the hypothesis that the means of the specified treatment populations are identical).

We have noted earlier that, so far as any *two* treatments are concerned, an intrinsic interaction may mean either of two things. It may mean that one treatment is superior to the other at *all* levels, but that its superiority is more marked at some levels than at others; or it may mean that one treatment is superior at some levels and that the other is superior at other levels. It would be worthwhile, obviously, to know which of these situations exists in any given instance. Neither of the tests of significance already considered, however, contains any implications with reference to these two possibilities.

To reveal the meaning of ms_A/ms_{AL}, let us consider a table in which $n_{ij} = n$ is constant, and in which the level (row) means have been equalized by constant arithmetic corrections within levels. These corrections, of course, will have no effect upon the column means, so that a given corrected column mean, such as $M'_{.2}$, will be the same as the corresponding original mean, in this case $M_{.2}$. In this once-corrected table, if there is a real interaction, there will probably still be significant differences in subgroup (cell) means within each treatment. These means, when plotted on a linear scale, might be distributed, for example, in either of the following ways, among many:

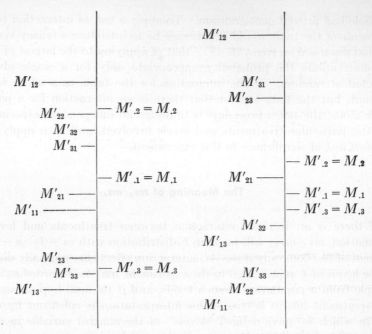

FIGURE 5. *Possible distributions of treatment and corrected subgroup means*

Let $s^2_{M_A}$ represent the variance of the observed treatment means, and $s^2_{M'_A L}$ represent the average variance of the corrected subgroup means for the various treatments. That is,

$$s^2_{M_A} = \frac{\sum\limits_{i=1}^{a}(M_{\cdot j} - M)^2}{a},$$

and

$$s^2_{M'_A L} = \frac{1}{a}\sum\limits_{j=1}^{a}\frac{\sum\limits_{i=1}^{l}(M'_{ij} - M'_{\cdot j})^2}{l}.$$

The corresponding standard deviations are then s_{M_A} and $s_{M'_A L}$. Along the left-hand scale in Figure 5, we note that the corrected subgroup means for Treatment A_2 are closely concentrated around the A_2 mean $(M_{\cdot 2})$, that the three corrected subgroups means for A_1 are closely concentrated around $M_{\cdot 1}$, and similarly for A_3. Along this left-hand scale, the differences among the three corrected subgroup means for any treatment are small compared to the differences among the three treatment means. That is, s_{M_A} is considerably larger than $s_{M'_A L}$.

In the right-hand figure, on the other hand, the three corrected subgroup means for Treatment A_1 are widely scattered around $M_{\cdot 1}$ in comparison with the spread of the treatment means. In other words, s_{M_A} is small in relation to $s_{M'_A L}$.

We can see from this illustrative figure that if s_{M_A} is very much larger than $s_{M'_{AL}}$, then the treatments will have the same rank for each level, or approximately the same rank, even though the superiority of one treatment over another at one level may be very much greater than at another level. In the left-hand figure, for instance, A_2 ranks above A_1 and A_3 at each of the three levels, and A_3 ranks third at each of the three levels, even though the superiority of A_2 over A_1 for Level 1 is very much greater than the superiority of A_2 over A_1 for Level 3. In the right-hand figure, however, A_2 ranks highest at Level 1, but A_3 ranks highest at Level 2, and A_1 ranks highest at Level 3.

The higher the ratio $s_{M_A}/s_{M'_{AL}}$ the more surely will the rank order of the treatments be the same at each of the levels. If s_{M_A} is at least twice as large as $s_{M'_{AL}}$, then, in general, the rank order of the treatments is *approximately* the same at all levels, even though there may be minor variations from level to level. The ratio between these two standard deviations is somewhat analogous to the ratio between the standard deviation of obtained scores and the standard error of measurement on a standardized test. To require that the standard deviation of obtained scores be twice the standard error of measurement is to require that the reliability coefficient of the test be at least .75. We know from experience that for a test of this reliability, examinees ranked in order of their obtained scores are also ranked approximately in the order of their true scores.

In order that s_{M_A} be at least twice as large as $s_{M'_{AL}}$, it is necessary that ms_A/ms_{AL} be at least $4(l-1)$. The proof of this follows.

In either situation, the standard deviation of the over-all treatment means (assuming $n_{ij} = n$ is constant) is given by

$$s_{M_A} = \sqrt{\frac{\sum_{j=1}^{a}(M_{\cdot j} - M)^2}{a}} = \sqrt{\frac{a-1}{a} \cdot \frac{1}{n_{\cdot j}} \cdot \frac{n_{\cdot j}\sum_{j=1}^{a}(M_{\cdot j} - M)^2}{a-1}}$$

$$= \sqrt{\frac{a-1}{aln} \cdot ms_A}$$

and the "average" standard deviation of the subgroup (cell) means within treatments is given by

$$s_{M'_{AL}} = \sqrt{\frac{1}{a}\sum_{j=1}^{a}\frac{\sum_{l=1}^{l}(M'_{ij} - M'_{\cdot j})^2}{l}} = \sqrt{\frac{(l-1)(a-1)}{al} \cdot \frac{1}{n} \cdot \frac{n\sum_{j=1}^{a}\sum_{i=1}^{l}(M'_{ij} - M'_{\cdot j})^2}{(l-1)(a-1)}}$$

$$= \sqrt{\frac{(a-1)(l-1)}{aln} \cdot ms_{AL}},$$

This follows since $M'_{i\cdot} = M$, from which $(M'_{ij} - M'_{\cdot j} - M'_{i\cdot} + M) = (M'_{ij} - M'_{\cdot j})$. Hence, the ratio between these s's is given by

$$\frac{s_{M_A}}{s_{M'_{AL}}} = \sqrt{\frac{\frac{(a-1)}{aln}}{\frac{(a-1)(l-1)}{aln}} \cdot \frac{ms_A}{ms_{AL}}} = \sqrt{\frac{1}{l-1} \cdot \frac{ms_A}{ms_{AL}}}.$$

Accordingly, if $s_{M_A}/s_{M'_{AL}}$ is to be greater than 2, ms_A/ms_{AL} must be greater than $4(l-1)$. For simplicity, we may as well require that $ms_A/ms_{AL} > 4l$.

The preceding may be taken as a basis for the following "rule-of-thumb": If the ratio between the mean squares for treatments and treatments × levels is several times as large as the number of levels, and if the number of cases in each treatment group is fairly large, one may quite safely conclude that the *rank order* of effectiveness of the treatments is approximately the same within each level, even though their relative effectiveness, precisely determined, may differ from level to level.

This is a very rough rule-of-thumb and is offered with considerable hesitation, since rules-of-thumb in general tend to be rather uncritically applied. If the total number of cases is quite large and Type G errors are negligible, the rule should be quite useful, but it is not possible to suggest exact critical values concerning the size of the sample or the magnitude of the ratio beyond which it is safe to generalize about treatment effects to all levels.

The preceding interpretation of ms_A/ms_{AL} assumes an intrinsic interaction. On the assumption that there is *no* interaction (either intrinsic or extrinsic), the ratio has another meaning. In that case, the interaction mean square is an unbiased estimate of the common within-cells variance (see page 139), and may be used in place of the within-cells mean square as the error term for testing the significance of the treatment differences. That is, on the assumption that there is no interaction, we may write

$$F = ms_A/ms_{AL}, \text{ for } (a-1) \text{ and } (a-1)(l-1)df,$$

or

$$F = ms_A \Big/ \frac{ss_{AL} + ss_w}{N - a - l + 1} \text{ for } (a-1) \text{ and } (N - a - l + 1)df,$$

and use either of these ratios to test the treatments effect.[1] However, this assumption is nearly always a dangerous one, particularly due to the ever-present possibility of extrinsic interaction; hence, even though the assumption seemed reasonable, we would use this ratio to test the treatment effects only if the more valid test earlier considered could not be applied.

---

[1] The proof that the second of these ratios is distributed as F is as follows: Suppose that in the double-entry table arithmetic corrections are applied (see page 110) so as to make all level (row) means equal to the general mean. In this once-corrected table, since there is no interaction, the differences among the subgroup (cell) means within each treatment (column) are due only to random sampling fluctuations. In other words, in this once-corrected table, the measures in each treatment group (column) may be collectively regarded as a simple random sample; the design therefore is a simple-randomized design, in which the ratio of the mean square for treatments to the mean square for within-treatments is known to be distributed as F. However, in the once-corrected table $ss'_{wA} = ss_{AL} + ss_w$, $ss'_A = ss_A$, and the degrees of freedom for $ss'_{wA} = (a-1)(l-1) + (N - al) = (N - a - l + 1)$. Thus, $ms'_{wA} = \dfrac{ss_{AL} + ss_w}{(N - a - l + 1)}$; hence, $ms'_A/ms'_{wA} = ms_A \Big/ \dfrac{ss_{AL} + ss_w}{N - a - l + 1}$ is distributed as F.

The situation is quite different if there is an extrinsic interaction but no intrinsic interaction, and if the extrinsic interaction is due only to experimental errors which have been randomized independently for each level of the experiment. If this may be assumed to be the case, the interaction mean square becomes the appropriate error term, and one which takes both Type S and Type G errors into consideration. The logic of the test of significance to be applied in this case will be discussed later (Chapter 8, pages 201–202).

Treatments × Levels Designs with One Observation per Cell

The practice has sometimes been followed in treatments × levels experiments of arranging the subjects in order of the control variable, and then counting off just a (the number of treatments) subjects at a time, letting each group of a subjects correspond to a separate level. In this case there is only one observation in each cell of the table; there is consequently no possibility of computing a within-cells mean square. The total sum of squares can nevertheless be analyzed into its treatments, levels, and treatments × levels components. In this case, *on the assumption that there is no interaction* (either intrinsic or extrinsic), the significance of the treatment differences may be tested by means of

$$F = ms_A/ms_{AL}, df = (a-1)/(a-1)(l-1). \qquad (33)$$

In this case, ms_{AL} is presumably due to random Type S errors only, and ms_{AL} would be interchangeable with ms_w if the latter were available.

This test of significance is also valid on the assumption that there is no intrinsic interaction, and that the extrinsic interaction is due only to experimental errors that have been randomized independently at each level. (See pages 201–202.)

If the treatments have been administered on a group basis to all levels simultaneously, and if there *is* an interaction (either intrinsic or extrinsic, or both), the observed interaction mean square will be larger than the mean square for within-cells had there been two observations per cell. That is, the "error" term will then contain an effect (interaction) which has been controlled in the experiment and therefore does not belong in the error term. It may be argued that this will only tend to make the ratio smaller than it would otherwise be, and that, therefore, this F-test, while strictly invalid, will err on the conservative side. In other words, It is argued that if the treatments effect is "significant" by this test it would prove even more significant if a within-cells error term could be employed. It is true that when an inflated error term is used, the risk of a Type I error is less than the level of significance of the test indicates, but it is also true that the risk of a Type II error is considerably greater than when a strictly valid error term is employed. In general, there is no good excuse for using an invalid error term when a valid one is readily available.

The use of ms_{AL} as an error term when $n = 1$ has been wrongly encouraged in some texts, and the student should be on guard against this practice.

Tests of Significance Applied to Individual Differences

If $F = ms_A/ms_w$ proves to be significant at the selected level of significance, the experimenter will usually wish to identify the differences for individual pairs of treatments that are significant at the same level of significance. If $F = ms_{AL}/ms_w$ proves to be significant, he may also wish to identify the significant differences among the treatments at each level of the control variable separately. This is done in exactly the same manner as with a simple-randomized design (see pages 90–96), the estimated standard errors of all means being again based on ms_w. Specifically,

$$\text{est'd } \sigma_{M._j} = \sqrt{\frac{ms_w}{n_{.j}}}; \quad \text{est'd } \sigma_{M_i.} = \sqrt{\frac{ms_w}{n_{i.}}}; \quad \text{est'd } \sigma_{M_{ij}} = \sqrt{\frac{ms_w}{n_{ij}}}.$$

$$\text{est'd } \sigma_{M_{13} - M_{14}} = \sqrt{ms_w\left(\frac{1}{n_{13}} + \frac{1}{n_{14}}\right)}, \text{ etc.}$$

The number of degrees of freedom for any of these tests is that for the error mean square (ms_w), namely $(N - al)$.

When ms_w computed from the entire table is used as the error term in testing the significance of the difference between two particular means, it is of course assumed that the within-subgroups variance is homogeneous for the entire table. If this assumption is questionable for the whole table, but one can safely assume that the within-subgroups variance is homogeneous for the two groups or subgroups being compared, then it would be better in these F and t-tests to use an error term computed only for the groups or subgroups involved in the comparison.

Possibilities of Confounding Extraneous Factors with Levels

In some experimental situations, certain Type G errors may be unavoidable, but some of these unavoidable errors may, nevertheless, be *assignable* to treatment subgroups by the experimenter. For example, the task of "running" the subjects in an animal experiment may have to be divided among a number of laboratory assistants, with the possibility that systematic differences in extraneous factors may be associated with these administrators of the experiment. Again, it may be necessary to run the animals on different days, and systematic day-to-day differences in extraneous factors may increase the variability of the results. In such instances the experimenter may sometimes be able to "confound" the extraneous factor with the levels factor. For example, he might assign the treatment subgroups at one level (or combination of levels) to one administrator, those at another level to another administrator, etc., or he might run the animals at one level on one day, those at another level on another day, etc. The extraneous factor would then tend to create differences among levels, but not among treatments within the same level. The effect of the extraneous factor would then be "taken out" of the error mean square and, to some extent, out of the treatments and interaction mean squares as well.

Whether or not it is desirable to confound extraneous factors with levels in this manner depends upon the purposes of the experiment, and also upon whether or not the extraneous factor interacts with the experimental factor (treatments). If the treatments × levels design is used only for the purpose of increasing the precision of the experiment, and the experimenter has no interest in the treatments × levels interaction for its own sake, then confounding unavoidable variations in extraneous factors with levels is highly desirable, and the possibility should be exploited to the maximum. Sometimes, however, one of the purposes of the experiment is to study the interaction of treatments × levels, and the ratio ms_{AL}/ms_w is used to test the hypothesis that there is no *intrinsic* interaction. In this case, the interaction term should, of course, be kept as free as possible of extraneous interaction effects. Accordingly the experimenter's objective must be to eliminate Type G errors entirely. Certainly in this case one would not wish to confound an extraneous factor with levels unless he was very confident that the extraneous factor does not interact with treatments.

Limitations and Advantages of the Treatments × Levels Design

The basic limitations and advantages of the treatments × levels design have already been considered in Chapter 1 (pages 13–16), but it may be well to review them here in relation to the generalized form of the design.

The treatments × levels design is primarily intended to serve the same purposes as the simple-randomized design, that is, to determine whether or not a number of treatments are, *on the average*, equally effective for the members of the specified population. The major advantage of the treatments × levels design over the simple-randomized design is that for the same number of subjects the treatments × levels design is more precise and thus usually more efficient. How much more precise the treatments × levels design is depends on the correlation between the control and the criterion variable. How much more efficient the treatments × levels design is depends on how the cost of organizing the subjects into levels (including the cost of securing the control measures by which the levels are constituted) compares with the cost of securing the same increase in precision with the simple-randomized design simply by adding more cases.

A second advantage of the treatments × levels design is that it may yield valuable information concerning a possible interaction between treatments and levels that could not be derived from a simple-randomized design. In most treatments × levels experiments, this information is of theoretical interest only, since whatever treatment is to be employed in practice will ordinarily be used with heterogeneous groups containing individuals from all levels. However, a demonstration of a marked and intrinsic interaction may sometimes lead to the use in practice of different treatments at different levels.

Another important advantage of the treatments × levels design has already been pointed out on pages 136–137, where it was shown that the assumptions underlying the test of the significance of the treatments effect are in general much more likely to be valid with the treatments × levels than with the simple-randomized design.

The principal limitation of the treatments × levels design is the same as that of the simple-randomized design. Neither design takes cognizance of Type G or Type R errors (with the single exception explained later on pages 201–202.)

It is worth noting that the treatments × levels design is particularly satisfactory for the purpose of testing for the presence of an *intrinsic* treatments × levels interaction when each treatment may be simultaneously administered on a group basis to subjects at all levels of the control variable. The illustration given on page 14 is of this character. In this case the possibility of systematic differences from one treatment subgroup to another within the same treatment due to extraneous factors is minimized, and hence the likelihood of an extraneous interaction is minimized also.

What to Do About Missing Cases

Sometimes, in a treatments × levels experiment, one or more cases may be "lost" during the course of the experiment; a subject may be unable to continue to participate in the experiment, a rat may die, the data for a particular subject may be rendered unusable by an accidental failure to administer the treatment to him properly, etc. In this case, the requirement of proportionality of cell frequencies from row to row or column to column of the double-entry table will not be satisfied with the incomplete data, and one may not proceed with the analysis of the total sum of squares until the missing data have been "replaced." The simplest and most practicable procedure in general is to replace each missing datum by a value equal to the mean of the remaining observations in the same treatment subgroup (cell) and then to proceed in the usual manner, having first subtracted one degree of freedom for each of the missing observations from the degrees of freedom for total, and thus also from the degrees of freedom for error. When this is done, the test of significance will no longer be exact, but if only one or two cases are missing and the number of degrees of freedom for error is reasonably large, the test will nevertheless be sufficiently exact for most practical purposes.

The Use of Transformations

The use of transformations with the treatments × levels design presents certain problems which are briefly considered here for the student with advanced interests in the subject of transformations, but which are hardly appropriate for inclusion in a first course in experimental design. The following discussion, therefore, may be skipped by most students using this text. (See footnote on page 89.)

The null hypothesis concerning the treatment population means of the original measures ($H_1 : \mu_{.1} = \mu_{.2} = \ldots = \mu_{.a}$) is equivalent to the null hypothesis concerning the treatment population means for the transformed data ($H_2 : \mu'_{.1} = \mu'_{.2} = \ldots = \mu'_{.a}$) only if the transformed measures show exactly the same distribution for each treatment population. (In the subsequent discussion, all primed terms are based on the transformed measures, the unprimed terms on the original measures.) The form of the distribution of criterion measures for a treatment population depends both on the form of the distribution within subpopulations (within-cells) and on the distribution of subpopulation (cell) means. Accordingly, if the subpopulation distributions are all normal and of the same variance, then H_1 is equivalent to H_2 only if the distribution of subpopulation means is the same for all treatments. This could be true, of course, if there were no AL' interaction. Theoretically, it could also be true even if there is an AL' interaction, as is demonstrated in the following figure. This figure presents the graphs of treatment subpopulation means for the various levels in an experiment involving three treatments and three levels. A situation such as that diagrammed, however, is so inconsistent with the usual behavior of physical and psychological laws that it need hardly be considered as a practical possibility. For practical purposes, therefore, we

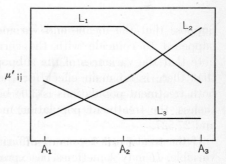

may say that the distribution of subpopulation means will be the same for all treatment populations only when there is no AL' interaction. The ratio $F = ms'_A/ms'_w$ provides a valid test of H_2 only if the subpopulation (cell) distributions are normal. Accordingly, this ratio provides a valid test of both H_2 and H_1 only if the conditions listed on pages 133–134 are satisfied with the transformed data, and if, in addition, there is no AL' interaction. If the other conditions are satisfied, however, the ratio will provide a valid test of H_2 whether or not there is an AL' interaction. In specific instances, it is quite possible that a transformation may be found which normalizes the subpopulation distributions and makes them equally variable, and also renders the AL' interaction equal to zero.   In that case, of course, both H_1 and H_2 can be readily tested with the transformed data by means of $F = ms'_A / ms'_w$.

If there is an AL' interaction, then to test H_1 with the transformed data, we must transpose H_1 into the *equivalent* hypothesis on the transformed scale. The hypothesis equivalent to H_1 will then take the form $H_3 : k_1\mu_{.1} = k_2\mu_{.2} \ldots = k_a\mu_{.a}$ with k possibly differing for each value of j.   For example, suppose that in an experiment involving just two treatments and two levels, with two observations in each subgroup, the transformation is $Y = \log X$ and the transformed measures are as given below.

	Transformed Measures				Original Measures	
	A_1	A_2			A_1	A_2
	4	5			10,000	100,000
L_1				L_1		
	3	4			1,000	10,000
	3	2			1,000	100
L_2				L_2		
	2	1			100	10
Means	3.0	3.0		Means	3,025	27,527.25

Suppose that the means and variance estimates for the various subgroups happened to coincide with the corresponding subpopulation values.   We note that the variances of the subpopulation are all the same.   We see also that there is no main effect for the transformed measures (the mean for both treatment populations is 3.0) but that there is an interaction.   Nevertheless, the treatment population means of the original measures are 3025 and 27,527.

If the treatments represent differing amounts of a common experimental variable, H may sometimes be expressed as $H_3 : \mu_{.j} = F(z_j)$, z being the experimental variable.   If one can express H_3 in either of the forms just suggested, one can then test this hypothesis with the transformed data in the manner to be explained later in Chapter 15.

The hypothesis that there is no AL interaction can never be equivalent to the hypothesis that there is no AL' interaction.   Furthermore, the interaction cannot be homogeneous on both scales.   If we let c_{ij} represent the true interaction effect in cell ij, then the hypothesis of no AL interaction may be expressed $H_4 : c_{ij} = 0$ (for all values of i and j).   The equivalent hypothesis on the transformed scale would then take the form $H_5 : k_{ij} = b$ (for all values of i and j), b representing a constant of unspecified value, and k possibly differing for each combination of i and j.   That is, if there is no AL interaction, there will be an AL' interaction and the AL' interaction will be heterogeneous. The writer has not investigated the difficulties involved in expressing H_5 in a form in which it could be tested with the transformed data, but presumably these difficulties would be considerable.

The hypothesis that there is no AL' interaction (H_6) can, of course, be tested with the transformed data, granting that the conditions listed on page 138 are met. In any psychological experiment, the hypothesis (H_4) that there is no AL interaction represents a different psychological law than the hypothesis (H_6) that there is no AL' interaction. Sometimes, once the transformation has been selected, the experimenter may conclude that the law in which he is really interested after all is that represented by H_6 rather than by H_4. In that case, of course, the difficulties considered at the close of the preceding paragraph will be obviated.

An exact hypothesis that can be expressed in terms of the original scale can always be expressed in *equivalent form* in terms of the transformed scale. This represents a specific instance of a more fundamental truth of considerable significance. It is that any psychological or natural *law* is independent of the scales on which it is expressed; the law exists apart from the scale, but may take a different *form* for different scales. One scale may lead to a much simpler form of the law than others, and is to be preferred for this reason. The scale which leads to the simplest expression of the law, however, is not necessarily that which permits the simplest statistical test of the law (or hypothesis) in an experimental situation. Quite obviously these observations have very significant implications for the whole problem of scaling in psychological and educational measurement.

STUDY EXERCISES [1]

1. A simple methods experiment, designed to compare two methods of teaching a week-long unit on community water supplies, was carried out in Grade VI of a particular school. Before the experiment began the thirty pupils were ranked on the basis of IQ scores and divided into three levels of ability with ten pupils in each level. Within each level, the pupils were randomly assigned, five to each of the two method groups, A and B. All of the pupils spent the first two days of the experimental week in general class discussion of the topic. The pupils in Group A spent the remaining three days in individual study on the unit in the school library. The pupils in Group B spent the last three days in the classroom where they prepared for a film which was shown on Thursday — and spent Friday in reviewing the film and the unit in general. A standardized test over the unit was administered to the entire class on the following Monday and the scores on this test served as criterion measures. The results were as follows:

---

[1] See second paragraph on page viii.

Criterion Test Score

	Method A	Method B
Superior (1)	82	95
	71	89
	73	92
	63	77
	60	69
Average (2)	58	72
	76	80
	69	65
	65	84
	62	66
Inferior (3)	46	53
	57	63
	42	61
	54	57
	56	58

Handwritten notes beside data:
$\bar{X}_{1A}$ $\bar{X}_{1B}$ $70 - 84 = 14$
$\bar{X}_{2A} - \bar{X}_{2B}$ $66 - 73 = 7$
$\bar{X}_{3A}$ $\bar{X}_{3B}$ $51 - 58 = 7$

Partial Computational Results

	A1	B1	A2	B2	A3	B3
$T_{ij} = \sum_{}^{5} X$	349	422	330	367	255	292
$\sum X^2$	24663	36100	21970	27221	13181	17112
$T_{ij}^2/5$	24360	35617	21780	26938	13005	17053

a) Complete the analysis of the data and prepare a summary table.

b) Define the two treatment populations in terms specific to this experiment. *individual study vs group discussion*

c) State the hypothesis tested by the ratio ms_A/ms_w. Can this hypothesis be rejected at the 5% level? *null hypothesis bt treatments*

d) Why is the variance of the criterion measures for the subpopulation corresponding to the middle level probably smaller than for either extreme level? In view of the results of the Norton study, is the heterogeneity of variance likely to affect seriously the validity of the usual F-tests of interaction and of treatment effects? Explain. *no. If random placement as to treatments variance cancel*

(margin note: greater range at extremes)

e) Granting the assumptions underlying the test in (c) to be adequately satisfied, suggest some possible explanations for the observed result other than a real difference between the *methods*. *Difference in instructors. Difference bt texts books - films. Difference in amt of study, i.e. those in library don't have to work, those in class do.*

Left margin handwritten calculations:
11.61
21.01
17

mean sq
720
1303
44
62

df
2
2
24

sum sq
720
2605
87
1494
4906

source
B+C
B+C
R×C
w/n

f) Apply a test of significance of the treatment differences in the manner that would have been appropriate had the two treatment groups been simple random samples rather than matched samples. Why is ms_A/ms_w smaller in this case? If the groups had been simple random samples, would you expect the absolute differences in means to be larger or smaller than in this experiment? Why?

g) Compute the ratio ms_{AL}/ms_w. How do the conditions which make this ratio an F differ from those related to the ratio ms_A/ms_w? May the hypothesis of no interaction be rejected at the 5% level?

h) How does the outcome of the test of no interaction affect the interpretation of the test of no methods difference?

i) What feature of this experiment makes an extrinsic interaction unlikely? What factors, operating in what manner, could conceivably give rise to an extrinsic interaction?

2. A rat-feeding experiment involved three diets and five replications at different levels of initial weight of the rats used. The 30 heaviest rats in a stock of 150 were randomly assigned, 10 to Diet 1, 10 to Diet 2, and 10 to Diet 3, and a simple controlled experiment was conducted at this level. Similar experiments were independently performed at each of four other weight levels (the second 30 heaviest rats, etc. — down to the 30 lightest rats). In each experiment, the rats under each diet were kept in a separate cage, and all possible factors affecting cages systematically were randomized with reference to cages. For example, the cages were randomly assigned to their permanent positions in the rat room. At the close of the experiment the *total gains* for individual cages were as follows:

Total Gain in Weight per Cage ($n = 10$ per cell)

	Diet 1	Diet 2	Diet 3	Total	$T^2_{Lev}/30$
Level 1	5	21	40	66	145.2
Level 2	22	11	46	79	208.0
Level 3	37	30	41	108	388.8
Level 4	18	31	54	103	353.6
Level 5	43	47	77	167	929.6
Total (T_D)	125	140	258	523	
$T^2_D/50$	312.5	392.0	1331.3	$T^2/150 = 1823.5$	

Data not available from above table:

$\Sigma\Sigma\Sigma X^2 = 2563$ Sum of squared gains for individual rats

$\Sigma\Sigma T^2_{ij} = 22925$ Sum of squared cage totals

a) Prepare a complete summary table of the analysis, giving the various degrees of freedom, sums of squares, and mean squares.

b) Compute ms_D/ms_w. Under what conditions (specific to this experiment) is this ratio distributed as F?

c) Is this F significant at the 5% level? Define precisely the parent population concerning which inferences may be drawn on the basis of this F-test.

d) Suggest several specific sources of error which are taken into account in this test of significance. Some which are not. For example, are *cage* differences taken into account?

e) Does the F-test of (b) involve the assumption of no interaction between diets and levels? Explain. Can the results of the test be more satisfactorily interpreted if one may assume no interaction? Explain.

f) What evidence from the data in the summary table shows that the use of the treatments × levels design improved the precision of this experiment (as opposed to the use of the simple-randomized design)?

g) Compute ms_{DL}/ms_w. Under what conditions (specific to this experiment) is this ratio distributed as F? Exactly what hypothesis is tested by this ratio?

h) Which type of interaction probably predominates in this experimental situation — extrinsic or intrinsic? Why? (Suppose another experiment were conducted in *exactly* the same manner in all respects except that the *same* diet was given all rats. This would constitute a uniformity trial. Why might one find a significant "interaction" in this uniformity trial?)

i) Do the conditions of this experiment suggest that one may infer from a significant $F = ms_{DL}/ms_w$ that an *intrinsic* interaction exists?

j) Do the diet means differ significantly (at the 5% level) at level 3?

k) Suppose the possibility of an intrinsic DL interaction may not be ignored. What useful conclusions may then be drawn from the magnitude of $F = ms_D/ms_{DL}$?

l) What is gained by randomizing cage conditions for the entire experiment? Are the treatment means better estimates of the treatment effects than if this had not been done? (Than, for example, if the cages had been assigned to locations in the rat room on a haphazard or casual basis, rather than strictly according to chance?) Is the *apparent* precision of the experiment (as indicated by the within-cells mean-square) dependent on how the cages are assigned to external conditions?

m) Rather than randomize cage conditions for the entire experiment, might it have been better to have made cage conditions as homogeneous as possible within each level, and thus have maximized cage differences from level to level, or "confounded" cage conditions with levels? (For example, one might have assigned the cages in one level to the three "most favorable" locations in the rat room, those in another level to the three "next best" locations, and finally those in the remaining level to the three "least favorable" conditions — and then have assigned cages to treatments at random within each level.) Would the experiment then have been better controlled or more precise? Would the *apparent* precision have been improved? Explain.

n) It would obviously be inconvenient to feed different diets to rats in the same cage. Suppose, however, that this could have been done in this experiment. Might it then have been desirable to have assigned rats at random to *cages* as well as to *treatments* within each level, rather than in the manner earlier described? Would *cage* differences then be taken into consideration in the error term and in the tests of significance?

o) Suppose that the rats at each level were randomly assigned to six cages rather than to three, and that the cages were randomly assigned both to treatments and to cage conditions within each level. There would thus be two cage totals for each cell of the two-way table. Suppose that the analysis were then based on the *cage totals*, rather than on the gains for individual rats. The total mean square would then have 29 degrees of freedom, and that for within-cells would have 15 degrees of freedom, but the degrees of freedom for the other mean squares would be the same as before. One could then test the treatment effects by $F = ms^*_D/ms^*_w$ (the asterisks indicating that the mean squares are based on cage totals, and are not to be confused with those based on individual gains). In what respects would this be a better test than that based on $F = ms_D/ms_w$ in the original experiment? Would *cage differences* within levels then be taken into consideration in the test of significance? Would any advantage of the original experiment be sacrificed?

Source		df	MSq	F
Bt Diets	·2 1 2·1 3	2	106.1	53.05
Bt. Levels	201.7	4	50.04	25.20
Diets × L	55.0	8	6.9	3.45
Within	270.5	135	2.0	—
Total:	739.5	149		

The Treatments X Subjects Design

The Generalized Case of the Treatments X Subjects Design

The treatments X subjects design is that in which the treatments are all administered in succession to the same subjects, instead of to different groups of subjects as in the simple-randomized and treatments X levels designs. The results for a treatments X subjects experiment can always be recorded in a double-entry table, in which the columns correspond to treatments and the rows to individual subjects.

The reason for using the treatments X subjects design is usually simply to increase the precision of the experiment by eliminating inter-subject differences as a source of error. In that case, only one criterion measure is usually recorded for each subject for each treatment, although this criterion measure may be the mean of a number of independent observations. Another possible reason for using this design is to permit a study of the interaction of treatments and subjects, that is, to determine if the relative effectiveness of the treatments differs from subject to subject. In this case, at least two independent criterion measures must be obtained for each subject under each treatment, in order to make available a within-cells mean square to test the significance of the interaction. Furthermore, the numbers of observations for the various treatments must be in the same proportion from subject to subject.

Analysis of the Total Sum of Squares

When the reason for using the design is simply to increase the precision of the experiment, and when only one criterion measure is recorded in each cell of the double-entry table, the analysis of the total sum of squares is as indicated in the summary table below. The analysis is exactly like that described on page 114 except that A, S, a, and s have been substituted for C, R, c, and r respectively. The total number of criterion measures (N) in this case is equal to as. $T_{.j}$ represents the sum of the criterion measures for the

jth treatment, and $T_{i.}$ that for the ith subject, and T that for the entire table, while X represents a criterion measure.

Source	df	ss	ms
Treatments (A)	$a - 1$	$ss_A = \dfrac{\sum\limits_{j=1}^{a} T_{.j}^2}{s} - \dfrac{T^2}{as}$	$ss_A/(a-1)$
Subjects (S)	$s - 1$	$ss_S = \dfrac{\sum\limits_{i=1}^{s} T_{i.}^2}{a} - \dfrac{T^2}{as}$	$ss_S/(s-1)$
Treatments $\times$ Subjects (AS)	$(a-1) \times$ $(s-1)$	$ss_{AS} = ss_T - ss_A - ss_S$	$ss_{AS}/(a-1)(s-1)$
Total	$as - 1$	$ss_T = \sum\limits_{i=1}^{s}\sum\limits_{j=1}^{a} X^2 - \dfrac{T^2}{as}$	

When one of the purposes of the experiment is to test the interaction, in which case there are at least two observations per cell, the analysis is exactly like that described on pages 114–115.

Instances in which the treatments $\times$ subjects design is used for the second of these two purposes are relatively rare. In general, the experimenter is willing to take for granted the presence of a treatments $\times$ subjects interaction and employs the design only in order to increase the precision and efficiency of the experiment. The subsequent discussion will, therefore, unless otherwise specified, be concerned only with the case in which the analysis is like that indicated in the preceding table.

Testing the Significance of the Treatments Effects

In the treatments $\times$ subjects design, the test of the significance of the treatments effects is based on the ratio of the mean squares of treatments and treatments $\times$ subjects (ms_A/ms_{AS}). The conditions [1] under which this ratio is distributed as F are listed below. The last of these conditions constitutes the hypothesis to be tested. The first three conditions constitute the assumptions basic to the test.

1) The experimental subjects were originally a simple random sample from a specified population. (*After* the treatments have been administered, the criterion measures for each treatment group may be regarded as a random sample from a hypothetical "treatment" population.)

---

[1] See footnote on page 51.

2) The treatments × subjects interaction effects are normally and independently distributed in each treatment population. (This is necessary
when $a > 2$. When $a = 2$ one must assume that the differences in the
two criterion measures are normally distributed for all subjects in the
population.)

3) The distribution of interaction effects has the same variance in each
treatment population. (This condition is not necessary with $a = 2$.)

4) The means for the various treatment populations are identical.

To show that ms_A/ms_{AS} is distributed as F, we shall employ the technique
of arithmetic corrections explained in Chapter 4, pages 110–112. Suppose
that, for a particular experiment involving a treatments and s subjects, the
criterion measures are entered in an $a × s$ table, and constant arithmetic
corrections are applied to all measures in each row, making all row (subject)
means equal to the general mean. This, as was explained on page 110, would
eliminate the mean square for S in the corrected table, but would leave the
mean squares for A and AS the same as in the original table ($ms'_A = ms_A$,
$ms'_{AS} = ms_{AS}$).

Under the specified conditions, the corrected measures in the various
columns of the once-corrected table may be regarded as constituting independent random samples, all drawn from the same population of similarly
corrected measures. That is, so far as the corrected measures are concerned,
the design is a simple-randomized design. Hence, the differences among
column means in this table may (in consideration of Conditions 1, 2, and 3)
be tested by means of the F ratio of the mean square for treatments to that
for within-treatments, that is, by $F = ms'_A/ms'_{wA}$.

The sum of squares for within-treatments (ss'_{wA}) in the once-corrected
table is the same as that for between-cells (ss''_{cells}) in the twice-corrected table
(pages 111–112). This follows because, with only one observation per cell, the
sum of squares for within-cells is equal to zero. The number of degrees
of freedom for within-treatments in the once-corrected table and for between-
cells in the twice-corrected table is the same $[(a − 1)(n − 1)]$. Hence,
$ms'_{wA} = ms''_{cells} = ms_{AS}$. We have previously noted that $ms'_A = ms_A$. Accordingly, we may write

$$F = \frac{ms'_A}{ms'_{wA}} = \frac{ms_A}{ms_{AS}}, \; df = (a − 1) \text{ and } (a − 1)(s − 1). \tag{34}$$

We may note that when there are only two treatments ($a = 2$), it is necessary only that the differences (D_i) between the two criterion measures for
the various subjects be normally distributed in the population (see page
119). In this case, the F-test is equivalent to the t-test of the example on
page 17. That is, when there are only two treatments, there is no problem
of independence of interaction effects, or of homogeneity of interaction.

Interpretation of a Significant $F = ms_A/ms_{AS}$: If in an actual experiment we secure a significant $F = ms_A/ms_{AS}$, we must, before rejecting the hypothesis of equal treatment means, assure ourselves that the assumptions underlying this test are valid.

If the experimental subjects have actually been drawn from a catalogued population by use of a table of random numbers, Condition 1 may be regarded as completely satisfied. Frequently, however, the subjects available for experimental purposes cannot be regarded as a strictly random sample from any real population. In that case, we may define a hypothetical population to fit the sample, and then restrict our statistical inferences to this hypothetical population (see page 74).

The requirement of normality (Condition 2) seems very likely to be approximately satisfied in most psychological and educational experiments. Note that we do not assume that the criterion measures are normally distributed in the specified population, but only that the deviations of these measures, each from the subject's own mean for all treatments, are normally distributed for each treatment. This, as we shall see shortly, comes very close to assuming that the errors of measurement are normally distributed — an assumption that we have little reason to question.

The requirement of homogeneous variance of interaction effects (Condition 3) in the treatments $\times$ subjects design is equivalent to the requirement of homogeneous within-treatments variance in the simple-randomized design. The variance of the interaction effects is what is left of the within-treatment variance after the effects of subject differences have been eliminated ($ss_{AS} = ss_{wA} - ss_S$). The effect of subject differences is the same for all treatments; hence, if the variance of the interaction effects is the same for all treatments, the within-treatments variance must also be the same for all treatments.

In most experimental situations, the degree to which the requirements of independence of interaction effects and of homogeneous interaction are met is within the limited control of the experimenter. The observed interaction in this design, as in the treatments $\times$ levels design, is generally in part intrinsic and in part extrinsic. The extrinsic error interaction in this case is due to what might be described as errors of measurement or observation. These in turn are due in part to the characteristics of the test or of the observational technique employed to secure the criterion measures, and in part to extraneous factors or to variations in the environmental conditions under which the test is administered. It is over these extraneous factors that the experimenter has some control. By employing forms of the criterion test that are as nearly as possible *equivalent*, by keeping the conditions of test administration as uniform as possible for all treatments, and by attempting to reduce practice or "carry-over" effects, the experimenter may minimize interdependence of interaction effects or heterogeneity of interaction. Failure to do these things, on the other hand, is likely to result in heterogeneous interaction. Suppose, for example, that in an experiment involving four treatments, the A_1 and A_2

treatments are successively administered to the subjects on one day while A_3 and A_4 are successively administered on the next day, the criterion measures being taken immediately following each treatment. Certain extraneous factors (such as temperature or humidity) having variable effects on the subjects may differ systematically from day to day. This might cause the AS interaction for A_1 and A_2 alone to differ from that for A_3 and A_4 alone, or from that for A_1 and A_3 alone or A_1 and A_4 alone. Thus the failure to hold constant the conditions of test administration might result in a heterogeneous interaction, which would tend to render invalid the F-test of significance of the treatments effect.

In general, then, the deviations from exact conformity to Conditions 1 to 3 that are likely to occur in typical educational and psychological experiments will frequently have no very serious effect on the validity of the F-test of the treatments effects. The general effect of minor deviations from Conditions 1 to 3 will be primarily that of making the probabilities from the F-table approximate rather than exact. Generally, the true probability will perhaps be somewhat larger than the apparent one, with the effect that the results may be pronounced "significant" more often than they should be. To the extent that these conditions are in doubt, therefore, the experimenter might set higher standards of significance than if they were known to be exactly satisfied.

It is extremely important to note, in all applications of this F-test, that it does not take into consideration any systematic effects of extraneous factors (Type G errors) associated with the treatments. If a significant F is obtained, we are nearly always justified in concluding that the differences in the treatment means are too large to be due to sampling fluctuations; but it does not necessarily follow from this that they are due to the effects of the treatments themselves. It is always possible that the observed differences in treatment means are due primarily to extraneous factors which have been systematically associated with the treatments in the experiment.

Limitations and Advantages of the Treatments × Subjects Design

The major limitation of the treatments × subjects design is that suggested in the last sentence of the preceding paragraph, with special reference to an extraneous factor that is unique to this particular design. When a number of treatments are administered in succession to the same subject, the response of the subject to any one treatment is often conditioned by the fact that other treatments have previously been administered to him. The treatments × subjects design may therefore be very satisfactorily employed only if the treatment effects are temporary, and if the effect of each treatment may be assumed to have been entirely dissipated before the next treatment is administered. For instance, the design might be employed in an experiment to determine the relative effects of various drugs upon a certain "reaction time" only if one could assume that before each drug is administered the cumulative effects of drugs previously administered have entirely "worn off." Furthermore, when this design is employed, the criterion measure for any subject following a given treatment may be in part determined by his experience in having been *measured* previously, quite apart from the effect of the previous treatments themselves. For instance, an experiment may be designed to determine the effect of styles of type on reading rate. The criterion measure for the first style of type may be the time required to read, at a given minimum level of comprehension, a certain reading passage printed in a given style of type. Obviously, in order to measure the effects of another style of type on reading rate, the same subjects cannot be asked to read for a second time this same passage printed in the second style of type. Rather, an entirely different and independent reading passage must be employed to secure the second series of criterion measures. Even then, the subjects may be able to perform better on the second passage simply because they have had some practice in taking this kind of "test" under the experimental conditions. More important, the two reading-rate tests may not be *equivalent* in difficulty. If they are not equivalent, the criterion measures for the two styles of type might differ, not because of the effect of style of type as such, but because of the differences in the criterion tests. The use of the treatments × subjects design in such situations, therefore, frequently requires considerable preliminary work in the construction of "equivalent forms" of the criterion test. The cost of this must of course be reckoned in determining the efficiency of the design.

It is obvious that this design can rarely be employed in *learning* experiments unless the interest is in the cumulative effects of the treatments, rather than in any comparisons of the effects of individual treatments. For instance, the "treatments" may really represent increasing amounts of practice in the same task, or increasing durations of the same experimental condition, and the hypothesis to be tested may be not that the "treatments" means are equal, but that the *trend* in treatment means is linear, or parabolic, etc. This special case of the use of the treatments × subjects design in analyses of trends will be considered later in Chapter 15.

When the treatments × subjects design can be employed, it is generally far more precise and efficient than the simple-randomized and treatments × levels designs, since it provides complete control of one of the most important sources of variation in educational and psychological experiments — namely, differences among individual subjects (inter-subject variations). Furthermore, the underlying assumption of normality of distribution is more likely to be satisfied in the treatments × subjects than in either the simple-randomized or treatments × levels design. In any situation, however, the treatments × subjects design shares with the simple-randomized and treatments × levels designs an exclusive concern with Type S errors, or a failure to take cognizance of Type G and Type R errors. Also, it introduces certain Type G errors unique to this design — the effects of rank order and of sequence of treatments, which are often of major importance.

Randomizing or Counter-Balancing Sequence and Order Effects

In many experiments, each treatment is administered on a *group* basis to all subjects simultaneously, in which case, of course, the treatments are administered in the same rank order and in the same sequence to all subjects. The treatment taken last may have a decided advantage over the others, or may be at a disadvantage, depending on the nature of the cumulative effects of the preceding treatments. It should be noted that the results obtained under any given treatment may depend not only on how *many* other treatments preceded it, but on what particular treatments preceded it, and especially on what particular treatment immediately preceded it. The results obtained under Treatment A_3 preceded by Treatments A_1 and A_2, in that order, may not be the same as those obtained under Treatment A_3 when it is preceded by Treatment A_2 followed by Treatment A_1, nor may they be the same as those obtained when Treatment A_3 is preceded by Treatments A_4 and A_5. In these discussions, the term "order" is merely an abbreviation of "rank order." That is, we will define the "order" in which a treatment is administered as depending only upon the number of preceding treatments, but not upon the many different *sequences* in which the same treatment is administered in the same order. For instance, A_2-A_1-A_3 and A_3-A_1-A_2 represent the same *order* so far as A_1 is concerned, but not the same *sequence*.

An effort may be made to eliminate any *systematic* effects due either to order or sequence by administering the treatments in different orders and different sequences to different subjects. One possibility is to administer the treatments to each subject independently in a purely random order and sequence (determined by the use of a table of random numbers). One treatment may then be slightly favored over another because by chance it drew a larger number of "favorable" orders or sequences than the other, but at any rate there will be no systematic bias due to order or sequence in the mean criterion score for any treatment. If order and sequence effects have thus been randomized for each subject independently, the ratio of mean squares for treatments and treatments × subjects is still a valid test; however, the experiment appears to be less *precise* than if the treatments are administered in the same order and sequence for all subjects. This is true since, in the former case, the order and sequence effects contribute to the error interaction, whereas in the latter case they contribute only to the treatments mean square. In the former case they are included in the error term (where they belong) and do not bias the treatment comparisons. Whenever it is practicable to do so, this randomizing procedure should be followed in a treatments × subjects experiment.

Another way of avoiding bias due to sequence and order effects is to *counterbalance* these effects. This is done by administering the treatments in all possible orders and/or sequences, using an equal number of subjects with each order or sequence. Suppose, for instance, that there are three treatments, A_1, A_2, and A_3. There are two ways of administering A_1 first in order

(A_1-A_2-A_3 and A_1-A_3-A_2), two of administering A_1 second in order (A_2-A_1-A_3 and A_3-A_1-A_2) and two of administering A_1 third in order (A_2-A_3-A_1 and A_3-A_2-A_1). That is, there are six possible combinations of order and sequence. In an experiment involving 30 subjects, 5 may be selected at random for the first combination, 5 at random for the second combination, etc.

It would be possible also to counterbalance order only, administering A_1-A_2-A_3 to one-third of the subjects, A_3-A_1-A_2 to another third, and A_2-A_3-A_1 to the remaining third, using the same *basic* sequence (A_1-A_2-A_3) in each case. When the order and/or sequence effects are thus counterbalanced, the F-test of (34) is no longer valid. In this case, the effect of order and/or sequence is not left to chance, but is made exactly the same for all treatments. Nevertheless, the resulting interaction (due to order and/or sequence) is still retained in the error term, just as it was when these effects were randomized. To use this F-test in this situation would be to make the basic mistake of eliminating a source of error from the treatment comparisons without at the same time eliminating it from the error term. The result, in general, would be to make the results of the experiment seem less significant than they really are, and to increase the risk of a Type II error. Appropriate procedures for analyzing the results in counterbalanced designs will be considered later in Chapter 13.

It should be noted that while the methods of randomizing or counterbalancing sequence and order effects eliminate bias of one kind, the results would still not tell us what to expect from any treatment if it were the *only* treatment employed with a sample of subjects. We might refer to the effects of a treatment when it is administered *first* in order as the "direct" effects of the treatment. It should be obvious that the "direct" effect of a treatment need not be the same as the average of the effects obtained with that treatment in all possible orders and sequences. In comparing many types of treatments, therefore, the only satisfactory procedure is to use a design such as the simple-randomized or treatments × levels design, in which each subject takes only a single treatment and all effects are "direct."

Confounding Extraneous Factors with "Subjects"

We noted earlier (pages 146–147) that with the treatments × levels design it is often desirable to confound assignable Type G errors with levels. A similar situation exists with the treatments × subjects design. Sometimes variations in a certain extraneous factor cannot be eliminated, but these unavoidable Type G errors may, nevertheless, be assignable to particular subjects by the experimenter. For example, certain subjects may be "run" on one day, other subjects on a second day, etc., so that "day" effects are confounded with "subjects." Such confounding is clearly desirable if one can be sure that the extraneous factor does not 'interact with treatments. If the extraneous factor does interact with treatments, such confounding may, nevertheless, be desirable, but in this case, only if the extraneous effect is also a *random* effect. "Days," for example, may be a random effect in that the particular days represented in the experiment may be a random sample from a hypothetical population of days. However, if "days" is confounded with "subjects" in the sense that n subjects are run on one day and another n subjects on another day, etc., then the design must be regarded as a random replications design with each *day* constituting a different replication (see Chapter 8).

A design in which "days" has been confounded with "subjects" is diagrammatically represented below. The analysis appropriate for this design is explained in Chapter 13, pages 267–273. This analysis permits a test of the assumption that there is no AD interaction. If AD is significant and if days is a random effect, then the appropriate test of the A-effect is $F = MS_A/MS_{AD}$. If AD is non-significant and if other considerations permit one to assume that AD is non-existent, then an appropriate test for the A-effect is $F = MS_A/MS_{\text{error}(w)}$, whether or not days is a random effect. If AD is significant and D is not a random effect, one would ordinarily have relatively little interest in the "main" effect of A, but would be concerned rather with the simple effects. That is, this is a situation in which the confounding of days with subjects is not desirable. The logic of this design and of the analysis appropriate to it will be more fully explained in later chapters.

Testing Differences in Individual Pairs of Treatment Means

We have seen (page 119) that the interaction sum of squares (ss_{RC}) in a two-column table is

$$ss_{RC} = \frac{n}{2}\sum_{i=1}^{r}(D_i - \bar{D})^2,$$

in which D_i is the difference in cell means for Row i. From this it follows that if $n = 1$,

$$\sum_{i=1}^{r}(D_i - \bar{D})^2 = 2ss_{RC}.$$

If these D_i's are a random sample from a population of D_i's, and if $n = 1$, as would be the case in the treatments $\times$ subjects design, an unbiased estimate of the variance $(\sigma_{D_i}^2)$ of the population of D_i's is given by

$$\text{est'd } \sigma_{D_i}^2 = \frac{\sum_{i=1}^{r}(D_i - \bar{D})^2}{r - 1} = \frac{2ss_{RC}}{r - 1} = 2ms_{RC}.$$

This is equivalent to writing

$$E(ms_{RC}) = \frac{1}{2}\sigma_{D_i}^2. \tag{35}$$

We know that the error variance of the mean $(\bar{D})$ of a random sample of D_i's is given by

$$\sigma_{\bar{D}}^2 = \frac{\sigma_{D_i}^2}{r},$$

and, from (35), that

$$\text{est'd } \sigma_{\bar{D}}^2 = \frac{\text{est'd } \sigma_{D_i}^2}{r} = \frac{2ms_{RC}}{r}.$$

In the notation of this chapter, $\bar{D} = M_{.1} - M_{.2}$, $ms_{RC} = ms_{AS}$ and $r = s$, hence, the preceding expression for (35) may be rewritten

$$\text{est'd } \sigma_{(M_{.1}-M_{.2})}^2 = \frac{2ms_{AS}}{s}. \tag{36}$$

The mean square for interaction $(ms_{RC} = ms_{AS})$ in the preceding expressions, as derived on page 119, is that computed for Columns 1 and 2 only. However, in a multiple-column table, if the interaction is homogeneous the mean square for interaction for different pairs of columns can differ only by chance, hence a more stable estimate of $\sigma_{(M_{.1}-M_{.2})}^2$ is obtained by using in (36) the mean square for interaction computed for the entire table, rather than from Columns 1 and 2 alone. In this case, the degrees of freedom for the estimated $\sigma_{(M_{.1}-M_{.2})}^2$ are $(s - 1)(a - 1)$.

On the assumption that the D_i's are normally distributed — which would follow if the interaction effects are normally distributed — the significance of $M_{.1} - M_{.2}$ may be tested by

$$t = \frac{M_{.1} - M_{.2}}{\sqrt{\dfrac{2ms_{AS}}{s}}}, \quad df = (a - 1)(s - 1).$$

Accordingly, the "critical difference" for a selected level of significance may be computed by

$$d = t\sqrt{\frac{2ms_{AS}}{s}}.$$

Since, in the treatments × subjects design all treatments are based on the same number of measures, only a single "critical difference" need be computed and all individual differences may be classed as either significant or non-significant by comparison with this critical difference, in the manner described on pages 93–94.

Establishing a Confidence Interval for the True Mean for Any Treatment

The obtained mean for any treatment in a treatment × subjects experiment is an unbiased estimate of the mean that would be obtained for the entire population if all members of that population had been administered the given treatment. For the purpose of establishing a confidence interval for this population mean, the obtained treatment mean must be regarded as the mean of a simple random sample. The standard error of the mean can then be estimated as for any random sample and the usual procedures followed to establish the confidence interval for the true mean.

The estimated error variance for a single treatment mean is thus $\frac{1}{s}$ times the mean square for within-treatments computed for that particular treatment alone.

It should be noted that the estimated error variance (est'd $\sigma_M^2{}_i$) appropriate for establishing the confidence interval for the true mean of a single treatment population may not be employed in a simple t-test of the significance of a difference between two treatment means for the same experiment, since these means are based on related measures.

STUDY EXERCISES [1]

1. The following data are *adapted* from a study reported by Chapanis, Rouse, and Schachter [2] concerning inter-sensory stimulation. One purpose of the investigation was to compare the effects of tactile and auditory stimuli on the performance of a visual discrimination task. The visual task was the reading of the letters of a black-on-gray eye chart under a very faint constant illumination. The same chart was used with each treatment. The chart contained over 50 letters. The tactile stimulation was effected by placing a weight on the back of the subject's hand. The auditory stimulus was simply a *tone*. The criterion measure was the *number of letters correctly identified*.

The subjects were five volunteers from an introductory course in psychology. They were given a different experimental condition each day for five consecutive days. The order and sequence of administration of the conditions was the same for all subjects. Since the experiment was carried out in a darkened room, each subject was given five minutes of dark-adaptation prior to each experimental session. The room in which the experiment was performed was sound-treated and great care was taken to eliminate extraneous stimuli.

The data are presented in the following table:

Experimental Conditions (C)

(Number of letters on eye chart correctly identified)

	I Loud	II Weak	III Heavy	IV Light	V		
Subject	Sound	Sound	Pressure	Pressure	Control	Total	$T_s^2/5$
A	21	22	20	22	22	107	2290
B	22	16	23	19	23	103	2122
C	14	14	23	24	20	95	1805
D	29	24	24	24	28	129	3328
E	16	15	14	15	13	73	1066
Total	102	91	104	104	106	507	
M	20.4	18.2	20.8	20.8	21.2		
ΣX^2	2218	1737	2230	2222	2366		
$T_c^2/5$	2081	1656	2163	2163	2247		

[1] See second paragraph on page viii.

[2] A. Chapanis, R. O. Rouse, and S. Schachter "The Effect of Inter-Sensory Stimulation on Dark Adaptation and Night Vision," *Journal of Experimental Psychology*, vol. 39 (August, 1949), pp. 425–437.

a) Complete the necessary calculations and prepare the usual summary table of the analysis of variance.

b) Define carefully the hypothetical parent population to which the results of this experiment may be generalized by the logic of statistical inference. Define also a real population to which one might wish to generalize from this experiment on a judgmental basis. Note that in defining the hypothetical population it is most important to specify those characteristics in which the real and hypothetical populations *differ* and in which the differences are most likely to "interact" with the experimental treatments.

c) At the 5% level of significance, test the hypothesis that the true "conditions" (column) means are the same. Is there any reason to believe that the column means would tend to differ systematically even though the *same* experimental condition had been employed each day (that is, are any extraneous factors confounded with the conditions effect in this design?) What assumption would have to be made to infer from a *significant* $F = ms_C/ms_{CS}$ that the *conditions* have different effects?

d) The F obtained in (c) above was not significant. Explain why this outcome does not necessarily mean that the observed differences are due entirely to chance. Is it conceivable that real and important treatment effects might have been *cancelled* by day or order and sequence effects? Aside from this possibility, why is there a large risk of a fairly serious Type II error in this situation?

e) Must the variance of criterion measures *within* each "condition population" be the same in order to satisfy the requirements of the F-test used in (c) above? Suppose these variances differed considerably; what would this indicate regarding the interaction of conditions and subjects?

f) What possible *a priori* reasons can you suggest for expecting heterogeneous interaction in this experiment?

g) Distinguish, in terms specific to this experiment, between an extrinsic and intrinsic interaction. What major source of error would result in an extrinsic interaction? Suppose an intrinsic interaction does exist. Does this invalidate the use of the treatments × subjects mean square as an error term? Explain.

h) What, in terms specific to this experiment, is the assumption of normality underlying this F-test? The assumption of independent random sampling? Why is the first of these assumptions more likely to be satisfied than the assumption that the criterion measures are normally distributed for the population of subjects?

i) Establish the 99% confidence interval for the true mean of the control condition. For what purpose might one wish to establish this confidence interval?

j) What advantage would have been gained by randomizing the order and sequence effects for each subject independently? Had this been done, how would the error terms (ms_{CS}) probably have compared with that here obtained? Why?

k) Suggest a better criterion measure for use with this experimental design, explaining why it is better.

2. A study by Black[1] was concerned with the effect of intensity of spoken stimuli on the intensity of the listener's oral response. This matter is of some consequence in aircraft intercommunication since it is known that voice intensity contributes to intelligibility.

Five 12-word lists, equated for intelligibility, were recorded, one at an intensity of -85 db (minimal for understanding), one at -65 db, one at -45 db, one at -25 db and one at 0 db (approaching pain level). The words in each list were recorded at the same constant rate and separated by five second intervals.

During the experimental session, the subject, seated in an isolated room, listened to the recordings through headphones. Immediately upon hearing each stimulus word, the subject repeated it into a microphone and the intensity (in db) of this response was automatically recorded. The order and sequence of administration of the lists was randomized for each subject independently. The lists were separated by 20 second intervals. The criterion measure for each subject for each list was the *average intensity of the 12 words repeated by him.*

The subjects were 25 male college students. Five randomly selected subjects were used on each of five successive days. The mean (M_j) of the criterion measures for each treatment group and the estimated variance of the corresponding treatment population are given below.

Intensity of Stimulus (I)

	I (-85 db)	II (-65 db)	III (-45 db)	IV (-25 db)	V (0 db)
Mean (M_j)	74.02	73.14	75.06	78.38	83.98
Estimated Population Variance (σ_j^2)	21.53	13.91	11.63	19.36	24.50

[1] J. W. Black, "Loudness of Speaking: The Effect of Heard Stimuli on Spoken Responses," *Journal of Experimental Psychology*, vol. 39 (June, 1949), pp. 311–315.

Summary of Analysis of Variance

Source	df	ss	ms
Intensity of Stimulus (*I*)	4	1953	488
Subjects (*S*)	24	1835	76.5
Intensity × Subjects (*IS*)	96	446	4.65
Total	124	4233	

a) Add the sums of squares for *S* and *IS*, and divide by the sum of their degrees of freedom. Compare the result with the mean of the estimated σ_j^2's given in the first of the preceding tables. Explain why this outcome is to be expected.

b) From the data compared in (a), what would you estimate to be the error variance of a single treatment mean in a simple-randomized experiment concerned with the same treatments and the same parent population? What is the ratio of this estimate to the corresponding error variance in this treatments × subjects experiment? According to this ratio, how many times as many subjects would have to be used in a simple-randomized experiment to make it as precise as this treatments × subjects experiment?

c) In a simple-randomized experiment, would you expect ms_I to be larger than, equal to, or smaller than that in this treatments × subjects experiment? Explain.

d) From (a) preceding it is apparent that the variances (σ_j^2) of the treatment populations contain a constant component which is due to differences among subjects, and a possibly variable component which is due to interaction of treatments and subjects. We may assume, in this instance, that the between-subjects component is the larger one in each treatment-population. This being the case, why do the data in the first of the preceding tables suggest that there is a heterogeneous interaction in this experiment?

e) What *a priori* reason can you give for expecting a heterogeneous interaction in this experiment? (Is it reasonable to suppose that some subjects are less "suggestible" than others, and that the replies of some subjects will be of nearly constant intensity for all stimulus intensities, while the replies of others will vary in intensity with the intensity of the stimulus?)

f) Why, in spite of the likelihood of a heterogeneous interaction, can you be practically certain that the "treatments" (or whatever extraneous factors may be associated with them) have a real effect in this experiment?

g) Can you suggest any types of extraneous factors that might be confounded with treatments (stimulus intensity) in this experiment, and that alone might account for the significance of $F = ms_I/ms_{IS}$?

h) Describe the operations by which the randomization of order and sequence for each subject independently might be accomplished in an experiment of this kind.

i) What systematic variations in extraneous conditions from day-to-day could conceivably affect ms_S without affecting the other mean squares, and thus not disturb the validity of the F-test of (g)? What other kinds of day-to-day variations might affect the other mean squares (ms_I and ms_{IS})? Accordingly, what assumptions must be made about day effects in applying the F-test of (g)?

j) Why is there usually little point in testing the hypothesis of no subject differences in an experiment of this kind? What extraneous factor is confounded with subject differences in this design? Is this desirable? Why?

k) How could the observations be analyzed so as to yield an error term for testing the significance of the IS interaction? Why is there usually little interest in this test?

l) May one conclude from the significant F of (g) that the response level is monotonically related to the stimulus level?

m) Determine the critical difference between any two treatment means. What conclusions may one draw from the conditions means regarding the relationship between the criterion and the stimulus level? (Note: Better ways of analyzing the data for trend will be considered in Chapter 15.)

n) Is there any reason to believe that *if* the purpose of this experiment had been only to test the hypothesis of no treatment effects, this purpose could have been served with considerably fewer subjects than were used? (Actually, the major purpose of the experiment was to investigate the *trend* in treatment means — and this experiment will be reconsidered with reference to this purpose in Exercise 2 of Chapter 15.)

(handwritten margin notes) Group as unit

(handwritten table, top left)

	A1	A2	A3
	G1	G2	G3
	G4	G5	G6
	G7	G8	G9

(handwritten table and notes, top right: "subjects are units")

A1	A2	A3
X1	X1	X1
X2	X2	X2
X3	X3	X3
X1	X1	X1
X2	X2	X2
X3	X3	X3
X1	X1	X1
X2	X2	X2
X3	X3	X3

The Groups-Within-Treatments Design

The Generalized Case of the Groups-Within-Treatments Design

Sometimes the population in which the experimenter is interested consists of a large number of groups or subpopulations, only a relatively small number of which may be represented in any single experiment. Sometimes, too, each group is such that if it is to be used at all in an experiment it must be used intact — that is, it may not be practicable to use only a part of the group. The most important instance of this kind in educational and psychological research is that in which the groups represent *classes* of school pupils, or in which the subpopulations correspond to *schools*. If a research worker wishes to experiment with school pupils, he frequently must work with classes already organized in the cooperating schools. To reorganize the classes for experimental purposes may not be administratively feasible. Furthermore, to use only a part of the class would raise the administrative problem of what to do with the rest of the class in the meantime. Usually, for this and other reasons, it is easier to use the entire class than only a part of it.

Experiments performed with selected groups or subpopulations fall into two general types. One is the type in which it is impracticable to administer different treatments simultaneously to different members of the same group, and in which each treatment is therefore administered in an independent *set* of groups. The other type is that in which it is possible to replicate the complete experiment — that is, to make all the treatment comparisons — for each of the selected groups or subpopulations independently. This chapter will be concerned with the first of these types. The latter type will be considered in the succeeding chapter.

Two illustrations of the first of these types of experiments should suffice at this point. Suppose that the purpose of an experiment is to determine which of several methods of teaching spelling in the fifth grade is most effective. Suppose also the methods are such that if all were used simultaneously or successively with different classes of pupils in the same school, there would be serious danger that some methods would be "contaminated" by the others through a possible exchange of information concerning the methods

172

among the teachers and pupils in the same school. It may therefore be necessary to use Method A_1 in one set of schools, Method A_2 in another and independent set of schools, etc.

As another illustration, suppose an experiment is to be performed with rats, and for practical reasons it is necessary to keep the rats in cages throughout the experiment. Suppose, furthermore, the treatments are such that it is impracticable simultaneously to administer one treatment to some rats and other treatments to other rats in the same cage. All rats in the same cage must be given the same treatment, and each treatment is therefore administered to the rats in independent *sets* of cages. In such an experiment, systematic differences may arise between cages due to differences in the location of the cages in the rat room, to possible non-detected, infectious illnesses affecting all rats in certain cages, to the presence of "neurotic" rats in certain cages, etc. Hence, the *cage* rather than the individual rat must be regarded as the unit of sampling in the experiment, or as a primary source of error variations, and the test of significance of the treatment differences clearly should, if possible, take such errors into consideration.

In this chapter we shall be concerned only with the case in which each of the groups is of the same size, or in which it is desirable to give all the groups the same weight in the treatment comparisons even though they differ in size. In the experiment with various methods of teaching fifth-grade spelling, for example, the experimenter might very well wish to determine the relative effectiveness of the methods for the "average *school*" rather than for the "average *pupil*." Even though the number of pupils involved in his experiment may differ from school to school, he may wish to give all schools the same weight in computing the treatment means. That is, he may wish to use *unweighted* means of the school means as measures of effectiveness of the treatments, rather than the weighted means. This is especially desirable if there are large differences in the effectiveness of the same method for different schools, or if the results for any school are markedly influenced by extraneous factors (such as the teacher used with the method) which are inextricably associated with the treatments, and which may be unrelated to size of school. In this case, it would seem clearly undesirable to give these factors, or the characteristics unique to individual schools, more weight in some schools than in others, simply because the number of pupils happened to be larger in some schools than in others.

A simple analogy may be helpful at this point. Suppose one wished to describe the distribution of intelligence for a group of pupils. Suppose that for some pupils several independent measurements of intelligence had been made with different equivalent forms of the same test, or with different tests, and that the number of scores differed markedly from pupil to pupil. For example, suppose that in a group of five pupils, one pupil had taken 8 different intelligence tests, another 4 tests, and each of the others 2 tests each, making a total of 18 *scores*. In this case, it is hard to conceive of any practical purpose for which one would be interested in the simple mean of the 18 scores. Rather, one would compute the mean of the available scores for each pupil individually, and then describe the average *pupil* in terms of the simple (unweighted) mean of the five averages.

The situation is much the same in experiments designed to determine which of several methods of instruction should be recommended for *schools* in general. The *school* is the unit of sampling. The interest is in what is true of the treatments in the average *school*, or in the average *class*. In the case in which the various groups are organized by the experimenter rather than used by him as they are found, it is usually desirable in any event to make all groups of the same size; hence in such situations the problem of varying groups is of minor importance.

When all groups are the same size, it matters little whether the group or the subject is regarded as the unit of analysis, since in this case the weighted and unweighted means of the group means are the same. There are some advantages, however, in regarding the subject as the unit of analysis. Accordingly, both possible analytical procedures will be presented.

The Analysis of Variance in Groups-Within-Treatments Designs

(The Subject as the Unit of Analysis)

We shall first see how the total sum of squares may be analyzed into its components. Since it is almost as easy to do this in the general case of variable groups as in the case of constant n's, we shall not at this point impose the restriction of uniform size of groups.

In any experiment of the groups-within-treatments type, the total experimental sample may be regarded as consisting of a number (a) of *sets* of groups (corresponding to treatments), or of a total of k groups. Using the methods of simple analysis of variance into two components, we may, by disregarding the groups, analyze the total sum of squares (ss_T) into its between-treatments (ss_A) and within-treatments (ss_{wA}) components:

$$ss_T = ss_A + ss_{wA}. \tag{37}$$

Similarly, by disregarding the sets (treatments) and considering only the groups, the total sum of squares may also be analyzed into its between-groups and within-groups components, as follows:

$$ss_T = ss_G + ss_{wG}. \tag{38}$$

Also, within any given treatment set, say Treatment j, the total sum of squares (ss_{T_j}) for that set alone may be analyzed into its between-groups (ss_{G_j}) and within-groups (ss_{wG_j}) components:

$$ss_{T_j} = ss_{G_j} + ss_{wG_j}.$$

Summing such expressions for all a sets or treatments

$$\sum_{j=1}^{a} ss_{T_j} = \sum_{j=1}^{a} ss_{G_j} + \sum_{j=1}^{a} ss_{wG_j}$$

which, if we let $\sum_{j=1}^{a} ss_{G_j} = ss_{GwA}$ and $\sum_{j=1}^{a} ss_{wG_j} = ss_{wG}$, may be written

$$ss_{wA} = ss_{GwA} + ss_{wG}. \tag{39}$$

Hence, from (37) and (39),

$$ss_T = ss_A + ss_{GwA} + ss_{wG}. \tag{40}$$

To compute the sum of squares for groups-within-treatments (ss_{GwA}), we note from (38) and (40) that

$$ss_G = ss_A + ss_{GwA}$$

from which

$$ss_{GwA} = ss_G - ss_A. \tag{41}$$

The same result as in (40) may be obtained by algebraic methods. For this purpose, we will let

X = any measure
a = number of treatments
k = total number of groups (within treatments)
M = general mean
M_j = mean of the jth set or treatment
M_{ij} = mean of the ith group in set j
n_{ij} = number of cases in the ith group in set j
n_j = number of *cases* in set j
u_j = number of *groups* in set j
N = total number of cases

$c = (X - M_{ij})$
$d = (M_{ij} - M_j)$
$e = (M_j - M).$

We may then write as an identity,

$$(X - M) = c + d + e.$$

Squaring both sides, we get

$$(X - M)^2 = c^2 + d^2 + e^2 + 2cd + 2ce + 2de.$$

Summing for the ith group for treatment j (letting Σ indicate $\overset{n_{ij}}{\Sigma}$)

$$\Sigma(X - M)^2 = \Sigma c^2 + n_{ij}d^2 + n_{ij}e^2 + 2d\Sigma c + 2e\Sigma c + 2n_{ij}de.$$

Summing for all u_j groups in set j and noting that $\Sigma c = 0$

$$\sum_{i=1}^{u_j}\Sigma(X - M)^2 = \sum_{i=1}^{u_j}\Sigma c^2 + \sum_{i=1}^{u_j}n_{ij}d^2 + n_je^2 + 2e\sum_{i=1}^{u_j}n_{ij}d.$$

Summing for all a sets and noting that $\sum\limits_{j}^{u_j} n_{ij} d = 0$

$$\sum_{j=1}^{a}\sum_{i=1}^{u_j}\sum(X-M)^2 = \sum_{j=1}^{a}\sum_{i=1}^{u_j}\sum c^2 + \sum_{j=1}^{a}\sum_{i=1}^{u_j} n_{ij} d^2 + \sum_{j=1}^{a} n_j e^2,$$

or

$$\sum_{j=1}^{a}\sum_{i=1}^{u_j}\sum(X-M)^2 = \sum_{j=1}^{a}\sum_{i=1}^{u_j}\sum(X-M_{ij})^2 + \sum_{j=1}^{a}\sum_{i=1}^{u_j} n_{ij}(M_{ij}-M_j)^2 + \sum_{j=1}^{a} n_j(M_j-M)^2,$$

or

$$ss_T = ss_{wG} + ss_{GwA} + ss_A.$$

The number of degrees of freedom for ss_T is, of course, $N-1$. The number of degrees of freedom for ss_{wG} is $\sum\limits_{j}^{a}\sum\limits_{i}^{u_j}(n_{ij}-1) = (N-k)$. The number of degrees of freedom for ss_{GwA} is $\sum\limits_{j}^{a}(u_j-1) = (k-a)$. The number of degrees of freedom for ss_A is, of course, $(a-1)$. The analysis of the total degrees of freedom is therefore

$$df_T = df_{wG} + df_{GwA} + df_A$$

or

$$(N-1) = (N-k) + (k-a) + (a-1).$$

Computational Procedures (Subject the Unit of Analysis)

The procedures for computing the various components of the total sum of squares are the same as those employed in simple analysis of variance.

$$ss_T = \sum_{j=1}^{a}\sum_{i=1}^{u_j}\sum X^2 - T^2/N$$

$$ss_A = \sum_{j=1}^{a} T_j^2/n_j - T^2/N$$

$$(ss_G = \sum_{j=1}^{a}\sum_{i=1}^{u_j} T_{ij}^2/n_{ij} - T^2/N)$$

$$ss_{wG} = ss_T - ss_G = \sum_{j=1}^{a}\sum_{i=1}^{u_j}\sum X^2 - \sum_{j=1}^{a}\sum_{i=1}^{u_j} T_{ij}^2/n_{ij}$$

$$ss_{GwA} = ss_G - ss_A = \sum_{j=1}^{a}\sum_{i=1}^{u_j} T_{ij}^2/n_{ij} - \sum_{j=1}^{a} T_j^2/n_j.$$

Thus, the computational results may be summarized in a table as follows:

Source of Variation	df	Sum of Squares	Mean Square
Treatments	$a-1$	$ss_A = \sum_{j=1}^{a} T_j^2/n_j - T^2/N$	$ms_A = ss_A/(a-1)$
Groups-within-Treatments	$k-a$	$ss_{GwA} = \sum_{j=1}^{a}\sum_{i=1}^{u_j} T_{ij}^2/n_{ij} - \sum_{j=1}^{a} T_j^2/n_j$	$ms_{GwA} = ss_{GwA}/(k-a)$
Subjects (within-groups)	$N-k$	$ss_{wG} = \sum_{j=1}^{a}\sum_{i=1}^{u_j}\sum X^2 - \sum_{j=1}^{a}\sum_{i=1}^{u_j} T_{ij}^2/n_{ij}$	$ms_{wG} = ss_{wG}/(N-k)$
Total	$N-1$	$ss_T = \sum_{j=1}^{a}\sum_{i=1}^{u_j}\sum X^2 - T^2/N$	

Analysis of Unweighted Group Means (The Group as the Unit of Analysis)

When the number of cases varies from group to group, but when it is never-theless desirable to give each group the same weight in the treatment com-parisons, the analysis is based only on the means of the various groups, all the means being treated alike regardless of differences in the numbers on which they are based. Each treatment mean is then the unweighted mean of a simple random sample of group means. In this case, therefore, the groups-within-treatments design reduces to a simple-randomized design. We will identify with an asterisk (*) any sum of squares based on unweighted group means. Accordingly, the total sum of squares (ss_T^*), i.e., the sum of squared deviations of the group means from the general mean (for which the $df = k - 1$), is analyzed into two components, the (between) treatments (ss_A^*) and groups-within-treatments (ss_{GwA}^*) components. The computational results may be summarized in a table as follows:

Source of Variation	df	Sum of Squares	Mean Square
Treatments	$a-1$	$ss_A^* = \sum_{j=1}^{a} u_j M_j^2 - T^2/k$	$ms_A^* = ss_A^*/(a-1)$
Groups-within-Treatments	$k-a$	$ss_{GwA}^* = \sum_{j=1}^{a}\sum_{i=1}^{u_j} M_{ij}^2 - \sum_{j}^{a} u_j M_j^2$	$ms_{GwA}^* = ss_{GwA}^*/(k-a)$
Total	$k-1$	$ss_T^* = \sum_{j=1}^{a}\sum_{i=1}^{u_j} M_{ij}^2 - T^2/k$	

in which $T = \sum_{j=1}^{a}\sum_{i=1}^{u_j} M_{ij}$.

It should be noted that a given sum of squares based on the unweighted group means is not the same as the corresponding sum of squares based on the individual measures. If the groups are of the same size (n), then ss_A and ss_{GwA} derived from the individual measures are each n times the corresponding sum of squares based on the unweighted means. That is, $ss_A = n(ss_A^*)$ and $ss_{GwA} = n(ss_{GwA}^*)$. The proof of this is left as an exercise for the student. If the groups vary in size, the conversion factor is the harmonic mean of the group n's, i.e., $ss_A = \tilde{n}(ss_A^*)$, etc., $\tilde{n}$ being estimated by formula (49) on page 184 when the number of groups is large.

Test of the Hypothesis of Equal Treatment Means (Unweighted)

We have already seen that when the analysis is based on the group means, that is, when the treatment comparisons are based on the unweighted means of the group means, the groups-within-treatments design reduces to a simple-randomized design. Accordingly (see page 55), the hypothesis of equal treatment means is tested by

$$F = ms_A^*/ms_{GwA}^*, \; df = (a-1) \text{ and } (k-a).$$

We have also seen that when the groups are of uniform size, $ss_A = n(ss_A^*)$ and $ss_{GwA} = n(ss_{GwA}^*)$. Accordingly,

$$F = \frac{ms_A^*}{ms_{GwA}^*} = \frac{ms_A}{ms_{GwA}}. \tag{42}$$

That is, the test of the hypothesis of equal treatment means may be based on the ratio of mean squares for treatments and groups-within-treatments, whether these mean squares are derived from the analysis of unweighted means or from the analysis of individual measures.

If the number of cases differs from group to group, ms_A/ms_{GwA} is not distributed as F. In this case, if one wishes to test the hypothesis that the *weighted* mean of the group means for the entire population is the same for all treatments, one must use other procedures that cannot be considered here.

Interpretation of a Significant $F = ms_A^*/ms_{GwA}^*$: The conditions under which ms_A^*/ms_{GwA}^* is distributed as F have been given on page 73. Translated to the groups-within-treatments application, these conditions [1] are as follows:

1) From a population consisting of a very large number of groups, a *set* of groups has been selected strictly at random for each treatment independently.

---

[1] See footnote on page 51.

After administration of the treatments, the groups that received each treatment are regarded as a random sample from a hypothetical treatment population.

2) For all groups in each treatment population, the group means are normally distributed.

3) The variance of this distribution of group means is the same for each treatment population.

4) The (unweighted) mean of the group means is the same for each treatment population.

Before he may reject the hypothesis of equal treatment means (Condition 4) on the basis of a significant F, the experimenter must satisfy himself that Conditions 1–3 have been met — at least closely enough that the sampling distribution of the mean square ratio will not be appreciably affected by the failure to satisfy them exactly.

The first condition, that of random selection of groups, is one which often cannot definitely be shown to have been satisfied. This is particularly true in educational experiments in which the groups correspond to classes or schools. In such cases, the experimenter would usually like to test some hypothesis about a real and specified population of schools, but very seldom is he able to select the experimental schools strictly at random from that population. Ordinarily, he must solicit the necessary cooperation on a personal basis, or on the basis of institutional relationships. For example, a research student may induce some personal friends who are school superintendents or principals to give him the necessary experimental facilities in their schools as a personal favor; or a research professor in a university may seek cooperation among schools known to have a sympathetic attitude toward research in general, or to his university in particular. In such situations, there may frequently be quite marked differences, on the average, between the schools accessible to the experimenter and those not accessible. The experimenter may be able to make a random selection from the list of accessible schools, but the sample is, of course, still a biased sample so far as the whole population is concerned. He may be able to reduce much of this bias by selecting from the accessible schools a sample that, with reference to certain control variables such as size and type of school, geographical location, annual per pupil expenditures, etc., is approximately *representative* of the whole population in which he is interested. If the group of schools used with each treatment is thus made representative for each treatment independently, Condition 1 will clearly be violated, even though the bias may have been reduced. To avoid such bias, and at the same time to satisfy Condition 1, the experimenter may make his total experimental sample representative of the whole population as indicated above, but then assign these *selected* schools at random to the various treatments. He could then resort to the device of defining a hypothetical population that will fit his sample, the population being defined roughly as schools of the type accessible for experimental work in general, but otherwise representative in certain respects of schools in general. The schools assigned to the various treatments may then be regarded as random samples from this hypothetical population. The experimenter should consequently restrict any statistical inferences drawn from the experiment to this hypothetical population. If any further inferences are drawn concerning the real population, these will be drawn without the usual safeguards of the logic of statistical inference, and must rest on the subjective judgment and experience of the individual drawing the inferences.

In most educational experiments of the type just considered, the mean obtained for any given treatment in the experiment must be regarded as a decidedly biased estimate of the corresponding mean for the real population, and any estimate of the standard error of the obtained mean will be a dubious basis for testing any hypothesis concerning the (real) population mean for that treatment. Fortunately, however, in most experiments we are not so much interested in estimating the population mean for the given treatment, as in estimating the *rank order* of the treatments on the basis of their effectiveness for the whole (real) population. For this purpose, it does not matter if all obtained treatment means are biased, so long as all are equally biased in the same direction. In other words, what really matters is whether or not there is any *interaction* between *treatments* and the *differences* between the real and hypothetical populations, or between treatments and the differences in accessible and non-accessible schools. All the treatments may do better with the accessible schools than they would with non-accessible schools, but there may be no reason to suppose that any one treatment will do *relatively* better than any other for either group of schools. That is, if the null hypothesis may be retained for the hypothetical population, one might reasonably contend that it may also be retained for the real population. The crucial question, then, is whether or not any of the possible differences between the selected schools and those not selected are likely to affect the responses to some of the treatments more than to others. If not, Condition 1 need not cause serious concern.

In certain other types of experiments, Condition 1 may often be regarded, for all practical purposes, as completely satisfied. In the illustrative experiment with rats (page 173), for example, the rats may originally have been drawn at random from a homogeneous and well-defined stock of rats, and may have been assigned to the cages on a strictly random basis. The various sources of systematic differences between cages (Type G errors), such as positions of cages in the rat room, could then be strictly randomized with reference to cages and treatments. The particular cages under each treatment could then be fairly regarded as strictly a random sample from a hypothetical population of cages — consisting of an indefinitely large number of rats from the given stock thus assigned to cages and given the specified treatment. In such an experiment, a significant F could hardly be attributed to any failure to satisfy Condition 1 in the experiment.

So far as Conditions 2 and 3 (normality and homogeneity of variance of group means) are concerned, the considerations are almost exactly the same as those reviewed on pages 73–78. In most educational and psychological experiments of this type, the distribution of group means will at least *roughly* approximate the normal distribution. Results from wide-scale testing programs have shown repeatedly that the distributions of mean scores (by schools) on psychological and educational tests usually show a roughly bell-shaped distribution for large numbers of schools. Furthermore, general experience indicates that distributions of randomized *errors*, such as those exemplified in the rat experiment, are typically distributed in an approximately normal form. Finally, means of random samples almost always tend to be more nearly normally distributed than the individual measures on which they are based. Thus, Condition 2 (normality of group means) could be closely satisfied even though the individual measures in each group show markedly skewed or otherwise non-normal distributions.

Whether or not Condition 3 (homogeneity of variance of group means) is satisfied depends on the relative effects of each treatment upon the mean and variance of the distribution of criterion measures. As was suggested on pages 76–77, the induced differences in the treatment means in many experiments are small when measured in terms of the σ of the distribution. In such cases it is reasonable to suppose that since the treatments did not result in marked changes in the population means, neither could they bring about any marked differences in the variances of the group means. Condition 3, however, should never be taken for granted. Sometimes the criterion measures are such that before administration of the treatments, or at the beginning of the experiment, both the mean and variance of the group means of the criterion variable are zero or near zero. This might happen in a learning experiment in which the "treatments" really represent different durations of the *same* treatment, or different amounts of practice with the same procedure, or different numbers of applications of the same treatment, and in which the criterion measure is *gain* or improvement on a criterion test. In this case, there is likely to be a marked correlation between the means and variances of the group means for the various treatments, and the assumption of homogeneity of variance may be far from satisfied.

In the general situation, then, Conditions 1, 2, and 3 are likely to be only approximately satisfied — how closely the experimenter may be unable to say with much accuracy. The more extreme the departure from these conditions, of course, the less accurate, and possibly the more biased, are the probabilities read from the F-table. The minimum level at which the obtained F must be "significant" before the null hypothesis concerning treatment means is rejected should therefore depend on the experimenter's judgment as to the extent to which these conditions have been satisfied. The less his confidence in these conditions, the higher should be the level of significance demanded. Unfortunately, no clear-cut rules can be offered to guide the experimenter in his selection of this level of significance, but considerable help should be secured from the Norton study (see pages 78–86).

The Groups Considered as Random Samples from Corresponding (Hypothetical) Subpopulations

Thus far in this chapter we have regarded the populations in which we are interested as consisting of a large number of *groups*. While each group is finite (and usually small), the population has been considered as consisting of so large a number of groups that, for purposes of error analysis, it may be regarded as of infinite size. The sampling has been by groups rather than by individuals, each group having been used intact. That is, we have not regarded the group itself as a random sample, and have made no assumptions about the form or variance of the distribution of criterion measures for the individual groups.

In many practical applications of the groups-within-treatments design, however, it is possible and plausible to regard each group as itself a random sample from a corresponding subpopulation. For example, the pupils *now* enrolled in the sixth grade in a particular Iowa public school might be regarded as a random sample from a hypothetical subpopulation corresponding to this school, the subpopulation consisting of an indefinite number of "similar" pupils who might pass through the sixth grade in this particular school under essentially the same (stable) conditions. If the pupils in each school are thus regarded as a random sample from a corresponding hypothetical subpopulation, then the "population" of pupils *now* enrolled in the sixth grades in all Iowa public schools would itself become a representative sample from a hypothetical population comprised of the various hypothetical subpopulations corresponding to the schools.

As we shall see, the test of significance (42) already described (page 178) remains valid whether we regard the entire population as consisting of small and finite groups (which are drawn intact) or as consisting of a large number of hypothetical and infinite subpopulations. The latter way of viewing the population, however, does present certain advantages which we shall consider in the following sections.

The Expected Values of ms_A and ms_{GwA}

Let us first consider the case in which $n_{ij} = n$ is a constant. For any given one of the treatments, say Treatment j, the obtained mean (M_{ij}) of any group may be regarded as consisting of two parts — the true mean (μ_{ij}) of the corresponding subpopulation, and an error $(M_{ij} - \mu_{ij})$ due to random sampling from the subpopulation. Thus, for Subpopulation i in Treatment j

$$M_{ij} = \mu_{ij} + (M_{ij} - \mu_{ij}).$$

Subtracting μ_j, the true mean for Treatment j, from both sides of this expression, we get

$$(M_{ij} - \mu_j) = (\mu_{ij} - \mu_j) + (M_{ij} - \mu_{ij}).$$

Squaring both sides, summing for all values of i and dividing by u_j, (the number of groups in set j), we get

$$\frac{\sum_{i=1}^{u_j}(M_{ij} - \mu_j)^2}{u_j} = \frac{\sum_{i=1}^{u_j}(\mu_{ij} - \mu_j)^2}{u_j} + \frac{2\sum_{i=1}^{u_j}(\mu_{ij} - \mu_j)(M_{ij} - \mu_{ij})}{u_j} + \frac{\sum_{i=1}^{u_j}(M_{ij} - \mu_{ij})^2}{u_j}.$$

Letting u_j approach infinity, we note that the left-hand term above becomes the true variance of the group means for Treatment j, which we will represent by $\sigma_{g_j}^2$. The first right-hand term becomes the true variance of the subpopulation means for Treatment j, which we will denote by $\sigma_{\bar{g}_j}^2$. The second right-hand term becomes zero, since there can be no correlation between $(\mu_{ij} - \mu_j)$ and $(M_{ij} - \mu_{ij})$. Finally, the last term becomes the error variance of a single group mean, which, if all subpopulations have the same variance (σ^2), becomes equal to σ^2/n. Accordingly, the preceding expression may be written

$$\sigma_{g_j}^2 = \sigma_{\bar{g}_j}^2 + \sigma^2/n. \tag{43}$$

Let us now assume that $\sigma_{g_j}^2$ is the same for all treatments, and that $\sigma_{\bar{g}_j}^2$ is also constant. We will let σ_g^2 and $\sigma_{\bar{g}}^2$ represent these common variances for the treatment populations. It then follows from (43) that

$$\sigma_g^2 = \sigma_{\bar{g}}^2 + \sigma^2/n. \tag{44}$$

If n were variable, the last term of (44) would be $\sigma^2/\tilde{n}_{ij}$ in which $\tilde{n}_{ij}$ is the harmonic mean of all the group n's.

Now we know that in any experiment, $\sum_{i=1}^{u_j}(M_{ij} - M_j)^2/(u_j - 1)$, for treatment A_j alone, is an unbiased estimate of σ_g^2, or that σ_g^2 is its expected value. Hence, when $n_{ij} = n$ is a constant,

$$ms_{GwA} = \frac{\sum_{i=1}^{u_j} n_{ij}(M_{ij} - M_j)^2}{u_j - 1}$$

is an unbiased estimate of $n\sigma_g^2$. That is,

$$E(ms_{GwA}) = n\sigma_g^2 = n\sigma_{\bar{g}}^2 + \sigma^2(= \tilde{n}_{ij}\sigma_{\bar{g}}^2 + \sigma^2). \tag{45}$$

Thus we see that the "error" term (ms_{GwA}) used in the test of significance (42) suggested on page 178 takes into consideration two types of sources of error: differences among groups or subpopulations as measured by $\sigma_{\bar{g}}^2$, and differences among individual subjects as measured by σ^2.

We already know (see page 60) that ms_{wG} provides us with an unbiased estimate of σ^2. That is,

$$E(ms_{wG}) = \sigma^2. \tag{46}$$

We are thus provided from (45) and (46) with a way of estimating σ_g^2 from the results for a single experiment, as follows:

$$\text{est'd } \sigma_g^2 = \frac{ms_{GwA} - ms_{wG}}{n}. \tag{47}$$

This expression has been obtained for the case in which $n_{ij} = n$ is constant for all groups. When n_{ij} is variable, an estimate of σ_g^2 is given by

$$\text{est'd } \sigma_g^2 = \frac{ms_{GwA} - ms_{wG}}{\tilde{n}_{ij}} \tag{48}$$

in which

$$\tilde{n}_{ij} = \frac{1}{k-1} \left(\sum_{j=1}^{a} \sum_{i=1}^{u_j} n_{ij} - \frac{\sum_{j=1}^{a} \sum_{i=1}^{u_j} n_{ij}^2}{\sum_{j=1}^{a} \sum_{i=1}^{u_j} n_{ij}} \right), \tag{49}$$

k being the total number of groups used with all treatments $\left(k = \sum_{j=1}^{a} u_j \right)$.

In a manner similar to that employed in the preceding proof, it may be shown (proof will not be given here) that

$$E(ms_A) = \sigma^2 + \tilde{n}_{ij}\sigma_g^2 + \tilde{n}_j \frac{\sum_{j=1}^{a}(\mu_j - \mu)^2}{a-1} \tag{50}$$

in which $(\mu_j - \mu)$ represents the deviation of the true mean (μ_j) of Treatment A_j from the mean (μ) of μ_j's, and in which $\tilde{n}_j$, the harmonic mean of the n_j's, is estimated (when a is large) by

$$\tilde{n}_j = \frac{1}{a-1} \left(\sum_{j=1}^{a} n_j - \frac{\sum_{j=1}^{a} n_j^2}{\sum_{j=1}^{a} n_j} \right). \tag{51}$$

When both ms_A and ms_{GwA} have their expected values, we may write

$$\frac{E(ms_A)}{E(ms_{GwA})} = \frac{\sigma^2 + \tilde{n}_{ij}\sigma_g^2 + \tilde{n}_j \dfrac{\sum_{j=1}^{a}(\mu_j - \mu)^2}{a-1}}{\sigma^2 + \tilde{n}_{ij}\sigma_g^2}, \tag{52}$$

which makes it apparent that $F = ms_A/ms_{GwA}$ tests the hypothesis that $\sum_{j=1}^{a}(\mu_j - \mu)^2 = 0$. It is apparent from (52) also that the "treatment effect" (ms_A) is due in part to sampling fluctuations resulting from the random selection of subjects from individual subpopulations (σ^2), in part to sampling fluctuations resulting from the random selection of subpopulations or groups

(σ_g^2), and possibly also in part to real differences among the treatments
$$\sum_{j=1}^{a} (\mu_j - \mu)^2.$$

Meaning of $F = ms_{GwA}/ms_{wG}$

By regarding each group as a random sample from a corresponding (hypothetical) subpopulation, we may also attach a useful probability meaning to ms_{GwA}/ms_{wG}.

We have already noted that, by disregarding treatments and considering only *groups*, the total sum of squares for within-treatments in a groups-within-treatments design may be analyzed into two components, those for groups-within-treatments and within-groups [see (39), page 175].

It may be readily shown in the same manner as with the simple-randomized design (see page 53), that the ratio between the mean squares for groups-within-treatments and within-groups is distributed as F on the conditions stated below. The last of these conditions constitutes the hypothesis to be tested, and others represent the assumptions underlying the test.

1) The distribution of the criterion measures for each subpopulation is normal.

2) The variance of this distribution is the same for all subpopulations.

3) The "group" taken from each subpopulation is a random sample from that subpopulation.

4) Within each treatment set, the subpopulation means are the same.

The important considerations in the interpretation of this F are the same as those discussed on pages 73–78. In most situations, it may be safely assumed that Conditions 1 to 3 are satisfied within limits close enough to leave the F-distribution essentially undisturbed. Accordingly, a significant F usually means that Condition 4 is false, or that there are real differences among the subpopulations in one or more of the populations (treatments).

We may observe from (45) and (46) on pages 183–184, that if Conditions 1 to 3 are satisfied and both ms_{GwA} and ms_{wG} have their expected values,

$$F = \frac{ms_{GwA}}{ms_{wG}} = \frac{\sigma^2 + n\sigma_g^2}{\sigma^2}. \tag{53}$$

Hence, this ratio is a test of the hypothesis that $\sigma_g^2 = 0$, which is of course the same as the hypothesis that within each treatment the true subpopulation means are identical.

In general, with groups-within-treatments designs, there should be little interest in this hypothesis, since the choice of this design is presumably based on the knowledge that there *are* real differences among subpopulations (either due to the treatments or to extraneous factors whose effects are systematic for all subjects in the same group). If differences between groups or subpopulations could not be assumed, the total sample for each treatment might as well be regarded as a simple random sample, and the method of analysis for simple-randomized designs employed. However, in some situations, the groups-within-treatments design might be used initially because differences between groups are suspected but not known to exist. The test $F = ms_{GwA}/ms_{wG}$ might then be made. If this F proved nonsignificant, we might then, on the *assumption* of no group differences, regard the design as a simple-randomized design. However, the assumption of no group differences should be supported by *a priori* considerations as well as shown tenable by the test based on the ratio ms_{GwA}/ms_{wG}. In this case, the sums of squares for groups-within-treatments and for within-groups could be added together to give the sum of squares for within-treatments, and the sum of these sums of squares could be divided by the sum of their degrees of freedom to give the mean square for within-treatments. This mean square would then be used as the error term in testing the significance of the treatment differences.

It may be well to emphasize at this point that if, in the groups-within-treatments design, we regard the entire experimental sample as consisting of a number of randomly selected intact finite groups, rather than as a number of random samples drawn from randomly selected subpopulations, the test of significance given by (42) is valid even though the conditions stated on page 185 do not apply. That is, these conditions need not be regarded as assumptions underlying the test of significance of the treatments effect.

Precision of Individual Means and of Differences in Pairs of Means

The error variance $(\sigma_{M_j}^2)$ of a treatment mean is given by

$$\sigma_{M_j}^2 = \frac{\sigma_g^2}{u_j}.$$

For a constant n_{ij}, ms_{GwA} (see page 183) is an unbiased estimate of $n\sigma_g^2$. Hence,

$$\text{est'd } \sigma_{M_j}^2 = \frac{ms_{GwA}}{nu_j} = \frac{ms_{GwA}}{n_j}, \; df = k - a.$$

If n_{ij} is variable, but all group means are to be given equal weight, $\sigma_{M_j}^2$ may be estimated by

$$\text{est'd } \sigma_{M_j}^2 = \frac{ms^*_{GwA}}{u_j}, \; df = k - a,$$

ms^*_{GwA} computed as shown on page 177.

Given either of these estimates of $\sigma_{M_j}^2$, it is possible, by procedures already familiar to the student, to establish confidence intervals for individual treatment means or to test the significance of differences for individual pairs of treatment means.

If n_{ij} is variable and the treatment means are *weighted* means of the group means, other procedures [1] must be followed for these purposes.

General Advantages and Limitations of the Groups-
Within-Treatments Design

Attention has already been drawn to one very marked advantage of the groups-within-treatments design over the simple-randomized design and the other designs thus far considered. This advantage is that the error term $(ms_{GwA}$ or $ms^*_{GwA})$ takes into consideration not only the fluctuations resulting from random sampling of subjects (Type S errors) but also the result of extraneous factors having a systematic effect on all subjects within the same group. This is apparent from (45) on page 183, which shows that ms_{GwA} depends in part on differences among subjects (σ^2) and in part on differences among groups $(\sigma_{\bar{g}}^2)$. The differences among groups $(\sigma_{\bar{g}}^2)$ may be due in part to extraneous factors, such as differences in teachers employed with the same method in different schools, that is, to Type G errors, and in part to differences among subpopulations which are really characteristic of the treatments, that is, to Type R fluctuations. In the process of taking a random sample of schools, a random sample is also taken of each of these types of error. Thus, the "error term" (ms_{GwA}) used in the groups-within-treatments design takes into consideration all three types of error. Furthermore, the use of this design avoids any possibility of "contamination" of any one treatment by another. These are extremely important advantages of the groups-within-treatments design. Unfortunately they are accompanied by the serious disadvantage of relatively low efficiency, particularly if the differences between groups $(\sigma_{\bar{g}}^2)$ are large, or if ms_{GwA} is very much larger than ms_{wG}. For this reason, when "contamination" is not a serious issue, a much better design is that in which all treatments are simultaneously or successively administered within each group or subpopulation selected. This design will be considered in the following chapter.

STUDY EXERCISES [2]

1. Mohr [3] carried out an investigation to compare the effectiveness of three methods of introducing third-grade pupils to the use of a separate answer sheet with a multiple-choice test. Method A_1 consisted of oral explanatory directions, followed by a practice lesson in the use of the answer sheet, fol-

---

[1] Hanson and Hurwitz, *Journal of American Statistical Association*, vol. 37 (1942), pp. 89 ff.

[2] See second paragraph on page viii.

[3] Richard H. Mohr. *A Study of the Effects of Differential Directions for Teaching the Use of the Separate Answer Sheet at the Third Grade Level*, M. A. Thesis, State University of Iowa; August, 1951.

lowed by a practice test with the answer sheet, followed by a criterion test. Method A_2 was like Method A_1, except that the practice test was omitted. Method A_3 involved no special preparation of any kind; under this "method" the criterion test was self-administered (with printed directions only). The criterion test was a twelve-minute, 20-item test of reading comprehension administered with a separate answer sheet. The score on this test constituted the criterion measure in the experiment.

For various reasons, some of which should be readily apparent, only one method was used in each school. Twenty-seven schools in north central Iowa were selected for the experiment. None of these schools was in a multiple-building system, all had between 30 and 40 pupils in the third grade, and none was currently involved in other experimental work. Twenty-one of the selected schools agreed to participate in the experiment. These schools were randomly assigned, seven to each of the three methods. Detailed instructions were sent to each participating teacher. All experiments were carried out (on one day) during the sixth week of the fall term. The criterion measure for each school was the mean score on the twenty-item reading comprehension test (answer sheet test).

Methods

(School means on answer sheet test)

A_1		A_2		A_3	
1. Manly	13.2	1. Quimby	13.5	1. Gowrie	12.4
2. Postville	11.1	2. Northwood	10.7	2. Williamsburg	12.8
3. New Sharon	12.0	3. Roland	12.4	3. Lake Mills	11.6
4. Rockford	11.5	4. New Hampton	15.2	4. Sheffield	14.3
5. Holstein	11.1	5. Keota	11.5	5. Belmond	11.8
6. Lakota	10.5	6. Forest City	11.7	6. Osage	13.1
7. Humboldt	14.3			7. St. Ansgar	13.5
M_j	11.95		12.5		12.79
$\overset{u_j}{\underset{ij}{\Sigma}} M_{ij}^2$	1011.65		950.68		1149.75

a) Complete the analysis and prepare a summary table.

b) Describe the *parent* population in detail. Describe the methods populations.

c) May the hypothesis of equal methods population means be rejected at the 5% level? May one conclude that the methods are equally effective? Explain. Comment on the danger of a serious Type II error in this situation.

d) Do the restrictions on the selection of schools seriously limit the generality of the results of this experiment? Explain. How does the fact that one school failed to return the results affect the interpretation?

e) The number of pupils actually tested in individual schools varied from 19 to 39. Why is the analysis nevertheless based on unweighted school means? Justify this procedure in terms specific to this experiment.

f) Suppose several of the selected schools had (without the knowledge of the experimenter) already used separate answer sheet tests with their third graders. Would the F-test of (b) remain valid? Explain. How is the validity of this F-test affected by the fact that the pupils in some schools are on the average much better readers than those in other schools?

g) The F-test of (b) involves the assumption that what measures are normally distributed? Is there any serious danger that the distribution is sufficiently non-normal to invalidate the F-test? Explain.

h) Must the pupils in each school be regarded as a random sample from their "school population" in order for the test based on $F = ms_A^*/ms_{GwA}^*$ to be valid? Explain.

i) What types of error are considered in the F-test of (b)? Why? Cite specific illustrations of each type.

j) What specific form does the assumption of homogeneity of variance take in this situation? Is it conceivable that these methods will create sufficient heterogeneity of variance to invalidate the F-test of (b)? Does an inspection of the data suggest an extreme degree of heterogeneity?

k) How would you test the hypothesis that there are no systematic differences among *schools* in the ability measured by this reading test? What new assumptions underlie this test of significance? If this hypothesis proved tenable, what test of the methods effect could one use as an alternative to that of (b)? Does this alternative test have any *important* advantage over that of (b)? Explain.

Source	df	SSq	Msq	F
Treatments	2	2	1	<1
Groups w/A	17	29.92	1.76	
Total	19	31.92		

8

The Random Replications Design

The Generalized Case of the Random Replications Design

When a population consists either of a number of finite groups or of infinite subpopulations, only a few of which may be represented in any single experiment, it is sometimes possible to duplicate the experiment for each of the selected groups or subpopulations independently. The design employed in each replication may be the simple-randomized design, or the treatments × subjects design, or the treatments × levels design, or any of a number of other designs to be considered later. In any case, disregarding any classifications (such as levels) other than *treatments* and *replications*, the criterion measures may be tabulated in a double-entry table, the columns corresponding to the treatments and rows to the replications, that is, to the selected groups or subpopulations.

The Random Replications ($A \times R$) Design When the
Population Consists of Finite Groups

We shall consider first the case in which the population is regarded as consisting of a number of finite groups, and in which the sampling is by intact groups. Each of the r groups selected for the experiment is divided into a number of subgroups, one for each treatment. The analysis is based on the subgroup means, all being given the same weight. There is, therefore, only one entry in each cell of the table. Thus the total sum of squares (ss_T^*) may be analyzed into its *treatments* (ss_A^*), *replications* (ss_R^*), and *treatments × replications* (ss_{AR}^*) components. The asterisks will distinguish sums of squares based on an analysis of cell means from those (without the asterisk) based on individual measures. The computational procedures in the random replications design are in this case exactly the same as in the treatments × subjects design (page 157), replications (R) taking the place of subjects (S).

The analysis may be presented in table form as follows:

Source	df	ss	ms
Treatments(A)	$(a-1)$	ss_A^*	$ss_A^*/(a-1)$
Replications (R)	$(r-1)$	ss_R^*	$ss_R^*/(r-1)$
Treatments $\times$ Replications (AR)	$(a-1)(r-1)$	ss_{AR}^*	$ss_{AR}^*/(a-1)(r-1)$
Total	$ar-1$		

Test of the Significance of the Treatments Effect: With this design, the treatments effect is tested by $F = ms_A^*/ms_{AR}^*$. The conditions [1] under which m_A^*/ms_{AR}^* is distributed as F are essentially the same as those listed on pages 157–158 for the treatments $\times$ subjects design (groups, or replications, taking the place of subjects). These conditions, phrased in terms appropriate to this design, are listed below. As in previous instances, the last of the conditions represents the hypothesis to be tested; the other conditions constitute the assumptions underlying the test.

1) The replications (groups) represented in the experiment are a simple random sample from a real or hypothetical population of such replications.

2) In each replication, the subgroups (together with all associated extraneous factors) are randomly assigned to the treatments. (After administration of the treatments, the subgroups may be regarded as randomly selected from hypothetical treatment populations.)

3) The treatments $\times$ replications (AR) interaction effects are normally and independently distributed in each treatment population (except when $a = 2$, in which case the t-test of page 19, assuming normal distribution of differences, applies.)

4) The distribution of interaction effects has the same variance for each treatment population (not necessary when $a = 2$).

5) The (unweighted) mean of the subgroup means is the same for all treatment populations.

The proof that under these conditions ms_A^*/ms_{AR}^* is distributed as F is exactly similar to the proof presented on page 158 for the treatments $\times$ subjects design. The student should review this proof carefully and translate it into the terms of this particular design.

In any particular experiment, if Conditions 1 to 4 are met, this F-ratio may be used to test the hypothesis expressed in Condition 5. In any application,

---

[1] See footnote on page 51.

$SS_{W/A} = SS_R + SS_{T \times R}$

careful consideration should be given to each of the four conditions essential to the validity of the F-test.

The important considerations so far as Condition 1 is concerned are essentially the same as those presented on pages 179–181 in the discussion of the groups-within-treatments design. The reasons for regarding the treatment subgroup as the unit of analysis, or for giving all subgroups the same weight regardless of size, are the same as those given on pages 173–174. Again, the student should review these discussions carefully with this particular design in mind.

Since Condition 2 is subject to the control of the experimenter, there is generally no reason why it should not be completely satisfied in any particular application. It should be noted that the individual subjects need not necessarily be randomly assigned to the treatment subgroups. There are a number of different possibilities for constituting these subgroups. One is to assign the subjects at random to the subgroups, in which case each replication represents an experiment of the simple-randomized type. Another possibility is to design each replication as a treatments $\times$ levels experiment, that is, to "match" the subjects in the various subgroups on the basis of some control variable. Another possibility is to administer all treatments in succession to the entire group, so that each replication is an experiment of the treatments $\times$ subjects type, and the various subgroups within a replication are different sets of observations on the same subjects. Sometimes the groups are already organized into subgroups, and the experimenter must use the subgroups as he finds them. For example, in an educational experiment with methods of instruction, each group may represent the pupils in a given grade in a given school, and these pupils may already be organized into *classes* for instructional purposes. The experimenter may not be permitted to reorganize these classes for the purposes of his experiment, but may be required to use them as they are, with the teachers, classrooms, hours, etc., already assigned to them. Even so, he can still apply a valid test of significance to the differences among the general treatment means, if he can *randomize* the classes in each school with reference to the experimental treatments. Still other ways of constituting the treatment subgroups in each replication will be considered in later chapters.

While there are many possible ways of constituting the treatment subgroups in each replication, it is highly desirable that whatever method is employed be the *same* for all replications. If the subjects are assigned at random to the subgroups in one replication, they should be similarly assigned in all. If the subjects are matched on a certain basis in one replication, they should be matched on the same basis in all replications. In any case, of course, whatever the manner in which the subjects are assigned to the subgroups, the subgroups (together with all extraneous factors associated with them) should be *independently* randomized with reference to the treatments. For example, in an instructional methods experiment conducted in a number of schools, the pupils may be assigned to the experimental classes on a random basis. Each class may then be assigned a teacher, a classroom, a recitation period, and all other administrative arrangements may be completed that will affect the subgroups during the course of the experiment. Then, as a *final* step, the treatments may be assigned at random to the classes. In this fashion, *all* extraneous factors, such as teachers, classrooms, etc., will simultaneously be randomized with reference to the treatments. This procedure is *essential* if all extraneous factors are to be taken adequately into consideration in the test of significance.

When the analysis is based upon the unweighted means of the treatment subgroups, it is *not* essential, even though it may be desirable, that all treatment subgroups in any replication be the same size. In this situation, if any subjects are "lost" during the course of the experiment, no special problem is raised so far as the analysis of results is concerned, unless there is reason to believe that these losses result in a systematic bias with reference to treatments, which would very rarely be the case.

So far as the requirement of normal distribution of interaction effects is concerned, the considerations are much the same as those discussed on page 181. If the subgroups are the same or nearly the same size from replication to replication, if a uniform control is maintained over Type S and Type G errors in all replications, and if these errors are completely randomized with reference to treatments in each replication, it seems reasonable to assume that in most situations the interaction effects will be normally distributed for each treatment. As has been previously noted, these interaction effects are in part intrinsic (due to treatments only) and in part extrinsic (due to error). That part of the interaction which is extrinsic may be attributed either to Type S or to Type G errors, or to both. It is possible that extraneous factors operating systematically on treatment subgroups (Type G errors) have been effectively equalized, so that the interaction effects are due primarily to Type S errors resulting from the random assignment of subjects to subgroups. In that case if the subgroups differ markedly in size from replication to replication, there may be some tendency toward peakedness in the distribution of the interaction effects for each treatment. This will happen because the corrected means of the large subgroups will tend to have a normal distribution with a small variance, while the corrected means of the small subgroups will tend also to have a normal distribution, but one with a large variance. When these two distributions are thrown together, the combined distribution will tend to be more peaked than a normal distribution.

With subgroups of varying sizes, departure from normality is particularly likely if there is any correlation between the subgroup means and the sizes of the subgroups (such as is sometimes found between means of achievement test scores and sizes of schools — the larger schools usually making the higher average scores).

Failure to exercise uniform control over Type G errors in all replications will tend to have much the same effect as differences in size of subgroups. If for some replications these errors are normally distributed with a large variance, while for others they are normally distributed with a small variance, the combined distribution will again tend to be more peaked than a normal distribution. It is highly desirable, therefore, that both the size of the subgroups and the control over extraneous factors be as uniform as possible from replication to replication.

What form of distribution the intrinsic interaction effects (Type R errors) will take is more difficult to say. However, in many experiments, the extrinsic interaction will be very much larger than the intrinsic interaction, and any lack of normality in the distribution of the intrinsic interaction effects will tend to be "covered over" by the normality of the predominant extrinsic interaction effects.

As has been previously noted (pages 78–86), the assumption of normality is, fortunately, in general not a very critical requirement for an F-distribution of the ms_A^*/ms_{AR}^* ratio. Granting reasonably uniform error control, plus randomization of errors in all replications, it would seem that Condition 3 need not cause the experimenter much concern in most applications of this design.

The requirement of homogeneous interaction between treatments and replications will be particularly difficult to evaluate in many specific applications. However, there is good reason to believe that, in general, the interaction will not be sufficiently heterogeneous to disturb seriously the validity of the F-test of the treatment effects. We may note first that the interaction is always in part an extrinsic interaction, but that in some instances it may also be due in part to intrinsic interaction between treatments and groups (replications). It is quite possible that in some situations the intrinsic interaction may be markedly heterogeneous. For instance, in a treatments $\times$ schools experiment one of the treatments may depend to a marked degree on factors which differ markedly from school to school — such as environmental factors in the school and community, or the nature and adequacy of school facilities (e.g., laboratory equipment and library), or curriculum differences which may predispose the pupils in some schools to more effective use of certain treatments than the pupils in other schools. The effectiveness of other treatments may be quite independent of such factors. Thus, some treatments may be essentially additive in their effects on the school means while others may not, and the intrinsic interaction may be quite heterogeneous.

That part of the interaction due to error, however, should rarely be heterogeneous, granting only that the errors have been randomized with reference to treatments in each replication independently. The extent to which the total observed interaction is heterogeneous, therefore, usually depends on the extent to which the intrinsic or the extrinsic interaction predominates over the other. If the extrinsic interaction, which is usually homogeneous, is much larger than the intrinsic interaction, which may be markedly heterogeneous, the total interaction will show only a moderate degree of heterogeneity — possibly not of sufficient degree to disturb seriously the validity of the F-test. If the intrinsic interaction predominates and is markedly heterogeneous, then the total interaction will be markedly heterogeneous also, and the F-test of the treatment effects may be vitiated.

If the interaction is known to be markedly heterogeneous, a useful interpretation of the F-ratio may still be made. The effect of marked heterogeneity of interaction on the F-test is to result in a larger number of "significant" F's than would otherwise be obtained. According to Cochran and Cox, an allowance can be made for the most extreme of such effects by regarding the ms_A^*/ms_{AR}^* ratio as having 1 and $r - 1$ degrees of freedom, rather than $a - 1$ and $(a - 1)(r - 1)$ degrees of freedom.[1] If the obtained F is "significant" at the desired level when regarded as having these reduced degrees of freedom, one may quite confidently reject the null hypothesis of equal treatment means, even though the interaction is heterogeneous. If the obtained F lies between the significant values for $(a - 1)/(a - 1)(r - 1)$ and $1/(r - 1)$ degrees of freedom, the result is much more difficult to interpret. In this case, if marked heterogeneity is suspected, perhaps the best procedure is to resort to separate tests of treatment effects for individual pairs of treatments. In an experiment involving only two treatments, no assumption of homogeneity of interaction is necessary. Accordingly, if $F = ms_A^*/ms_{AR}^*$ is computed independently for each of the important comparisons of two treatment means, the assumption of homogeneous interaction may be obviated.

Replications of the Simple-Randomized Design with Subgroups of the Same Size (Random Sampling from Randomly Selected Subpopulations)

In some applications of the random replications design, it is possible to regard the subjects in each replication as a simple random sample from a corresponding subpopulation (real or hypothetical), and also to regard the subpopulations represented in the experiment as having been randomly selected from a population consisting of a very large number of such subpopulations. For instance, in an experiment with methods of school instruction, it is possible to regard the pupils in each school as a random sample from a subpopulation corresponding to that school, and to regard the schools in the experiment as a random sample from a population of schools.

In such cases, if the simple-randomized design is used in each replication, and if the subgroups are the same size for all replications, it may be desirable to base the analysis on the criterion measures for the *individual subjects* rather than on the subgroup means. The total sum of squares (ss_T) may then be analyzed (as in any double-entry table with proportional cell frequencies) into four components — in this case the treatments (ss_A), replications (ss_R), treatments $\times$ replications (ss_{AR}), and within-subgroups (ss_w) components. Each of the first three components is n times as large as the corresponding components when the subgroup mean is the unit of analysis $(ss_T = n \cdot ss_T^*, ss_A = n \cdot ss_A^*,$ etc.).

The test of significance of the treatment effects is again based on $F = ms_A/ms_{AR}$ (which in this case equals ms_A^*/ms_{AR}^*) and the considerations

---

[1] See W. G. Cochran and G. M. Cox, *Experimental Designs* (New York: John Wiley and Sons, 1950), pp. 396–401.

underlying the interpretation of this F are exactly the same (with one exception to be considered later) as those discussed on pages 191–195.

The principal advantage of using the subject as the unit of analysis is that it makes possible a test of the significance of the interaction, $F = ms_{AR}/ms_w$. The conditions under which this mean square ratio is distributed as F have been previously presented (pages 138–141). These should be carefully reviewed by the student with specific reference to this design.

Should the interaction prove nonsignificant, and should other considerations permit, we might assume that there is *no* interaction (either intrinsic or due to Type G errors). On this assumption, another test of the treatment effects is available. Let us suppose that in the double-entry table corrections have been applied to the measures within each replication (row) so as to make the mean for each replication equal to the general mean. In this corrected table, the sum of squares for between-cells-within-columns is the same as the sum of squares for interaction in the original table. Accordingly, if there is no interaction, all differences among cell means within any column of the corrected table are due to random Type S errors only. This is equivalent to saying that the measures in any column may be regarded as a simple random sample, or that the once-corrected table may be regarded as representing a simple-randomized design. In this case, ms_A'/ms_{wA}' for the once-corrected data is distributed as F. But

$$ms_A' = ms_A$$

and

$$ms_{wA}' = (ss_{AR} + ss_w)/(df_{AR} + df_w).$$

Hence,

$$F = ms_A \bigg/ \frac{ss_{AR} + ss_w}{df_{AR} + df_w} \qquad (54)$$

may, on the assumption of no interaction, be used to test the treatment effects.

On the assumption of no interaction, ms_{AR} and ms_w are both unbiased estimates of the common within-cells variance (σ^2). Hence, on this assumption, either $F = ms_A/ms_{AR}$ or ms_A/ms_w may be used to test the treatment effects, but (54) is preferable because of the larger number of degrees of freedom available for this test.

The assumptions underlying (54) do not require that the treatment subgroups be the same size in all replications, although they do require that corresponding treatment subgroups be proportional from replication to replication.

It is important to note that if the subgroups differ in size from replication to replication (even though they are proportional), the ratio ms_A/ms_{AR} *is not distributed as F*. When the subgroups vary in size, therefore, the test of the treatment effects should, if other considerations permit, be based on the *unweighted* subgroup means. That is, $F = ms_A^*/ms_{AR}^*$ should be used rather than $F = ms_A/ms_{AR}$. A number of texts have wrongly suggested that, even though the subgroups vary in size from replication to replication, ms_A/ms_{AR} is distributed as F under the same conditions that ms_A^*/ms_{AR}^* is distributed as F. The student should be on guard against this error.

pure replication

The Special Case of "Simple" Replications

"Simple" replications may be regarded merely as a special case of random replications in general. Replications in an $A \times R$ design may be called "simple" replications, if, instead of having been drawn from different subpopulations, the subjects in the various replications are all drawn at random from the *same* population. An example of a design involving simple replications was given on pages 18–20.

In the case of simple replications, there can, of course, be no intrinsic AR interaction. The significance of the observed AR interaction can be due only to Type G errors which vary from replication to replication. The AR interaction is then a valid error term for testing the treatment effects only if the Type G errors have been independently randomized for each replication (see Condition 2, page 191).

The object of providing for simple replications of a simple-randomized or a treatments × levels design is to provide an error term for testing treatment effects that will take Type G as well as Type S errors into consideration. Because of the relative importance of Type G errors in educational and psychological experiments in general, the use of simple replications is an important device in educational and psychological research.

Testing the AR Interaction in Random Replications of Treatments × Levels or Treatments × Subjects Designs

When the simple-randomized design has been used in each replication, the AR interaction may be tested by $F = ms_{AR}/ms_w$. This test may not be employed, however, when the treatments × levels or treatments × subjects design is replicated, since in that case the various treatment subgroups within each replication are not independent random samples. Under certain conditions it is still possible to test the significance of the AR interaction in replications of the treatments × levels design, but the appropriate test can more conveniently be considered in a later chapter (Chapter 10, pages 238–239).

Testing Differences in Individual Pairs of Treatment Means

We have seen that the random replications design is, so far as the computational procedures and the tests of significance are concerned, essentially the same as the treatments × subjects design. In the treatments × subjects design, the rows in the double-entry table correspond to randomly selected subjects; in the random replications design, they correspond to randomly selected replications; in both cases, the error mean square for testing the treatment effects is the interaction mean square. Accordingly, see (36), page 165, the estimated error variance of the difference between two treatment means in a random replications design is

$$\text{est'd } \sigma^2_{(M_{.1}-M_{.2})} = \frac{2ms^*_{AR}}{r} = \frac{2ms_{AR}}{rn}, \ df = (a-1)(r-1), \tag{55}$$

and the critical difference is given by

$$d = t\sqrt{\frac{2ms^*_{AR}}{r}} = t\sqrt{\frac{2ms_{AR}}{rn}},$$

the t representing that for the selected level of significance and the given degrees of freedom. The differences among the treatment means are then classed as significant or non-significant, just as in the example on pages 93–94.

These tests assume homogeneous interaction for all pairs of treatments as well as normal distributions of interaction effects. If homogeneity of interaction is in serious doubt, the safest procedure is to employ as the error term for each pair of treatments the mean square for interaction computed from the data for those treatments only, in which case no assumption of homogeneity is involved.

Establishing a Confidence Interval for the True Mean
for a Given Treatment

In establishing a confidence interval for the population mean for any treatment, the reasoning is the same as in the case of the treatments × subjects design (see pages 166–167). The estimated error variance for a given treatment mean is given by

$$\text{est'd } \sigma^2_{M_{.j}} = \frac{ms^*_{wA_j}}{r}$$

or, if $n_{ij} = n$ is constant, by

$$\text{est'd } \sigma^2_{M_{.j}} = \frac{ms_{wA_j}}{rn}$$

in each case with $(r-1)$ degrees of freedom.

Important Precautions in the Planning and Administration of a
Random Replications (A × R) Experiment

In the preceding discussion of the F-test of the treatment effects, we have noted a number of important implications of the assumptions underlying this

test.   In view of the importance of these implications, it may be well, even at
the cost of some repetition, to restate them in the form of the specific precau-
tions to be taken in planning and administering an experiment of the random
replications type, as follows:

1) Make certain that the replications represented in the experiment are (or
   may be regarded as) a simple random sample from a meaningful population of such replications.   In the $A \times R$ design, the R stands not only
   for "replications," but for "random" replications as well.   In some instances, the population must be defined to "fit" the sample actually
   taken; but unless this population is meaningful and closely related to
   some real population, the experiment will be of little value.

2) Insure that as many as possible of the errors affecting the subgroup
   means are completely *randomized* in each replication.   In general, this
   means that the random assignment of treatments to subgroups should be
   made *after* completing *all* administrative arrangements affecting the
   subgroups during the course of the experiment.

3) Provide for *uniform* error control in all replications.   Give separate consideration to the control of Type S and Type G errors.   Uniform control
   over Type S errors usually implies that the subgroups should be approximately the *same size* for all replications.   If subgroup n's vary from replication to replication, the appropriateness of basing the analysis on unweighted subgroup means should be carefully considered.

4) Provide for the closest possible control over errors of all types in all
   replications.   This is *not* essential to the *validity* of the F-test, but it is
   essential if the treatment comparisons are to be precise, and if the experiment as a whole is to be efficient.   Sometimes close control is impracticable — as when, in a methods of instruction experiment, the
   experimenter must use classes already organized in the schools, must use
   teachers of widely differing abilities, etc.   In this case, a satisfactorily
   valid test is still possible with complete randomization, but each replication is certain to be low in precision; high precision in the total experiment can then be secured only through the use of a large number of
   replications.   In general, the more precise and efficient the design used in
   each replication, the more precise and efficient the entire random replications experiment will be.   Many possible designs, in addition to those
   already considered, will be suggested in later chapters.

5) Employ a sufficient number of replications to provide a substantial number of degrees of freedom for the error term (ms^*_{AR} or ms_{AR}).   Otherwise,
   the sensitivity of the test and the efficiency of the experiment will be
   seriously impaired.   Since the number of degrees of freedom for the error
   term depends on the number of treatments as well as on the number of

replications, fewer replications will be needed if the number of treatments is large than if it is small.

6) Make a careful, logical analysis of all factors that might result in a *heterogeneous* intrinsic interaction. Weigh as carefully as possible, also, the probable relative importance of intrinsic interaction and extrinsic interaction. If the extrinsic interaction appears to predominate strongly, the total interaction will probably be sufficiently homogeneous for the purposes of the *F*-test, even though the intrinsic interaction is heterogeneous. If a predominant and markedly heterogeneous intrinsic interaction is suspected, it may be well to break the entire experiment up into more homogeneous comparisons (unless the *F* is still significant when regarded as having the reduced number of degrees of freedom suggested earlier).

7) Select the minimum level of significance at which you will reject the null hypothesis in terms of your judgment of the degree to which the underlying assumptions have been satisfied in the experiment.

Advantages and Limitations of the Random Replications Design

The outstanding advantage of the random replications design over the simple-randomized, treatments × levels, and treatments × subjects designs is that it takes Type G and Type R errors, as well as Type S errors, into consideration in the test of significance. This is an extremely important advantage of this design, particularly in situations in which, for practical reasons, it is impossible to employ close control over various types of errors in individual replications, or in which there is a substantial interaction between treatments and replications. For this reason, the random replications design is almost *essential* to the conduct of satisfactory experiments with methods of school instruction.

Another very important advantage of the random replications design, closely related to that just considered, is that it often permits the use, in each individual replication, of a design for which *no test of the significance of the treatment effect is available* so far as that replication alone is concerned.

One instance of this kind has just been mentioned, that in which the subgroups in an experiment with methods of school instruction consist of classes already organized in the school, and in which all the experimenter can do is to assign these classes at random to the treatments. In any one such replication considered alone, of course, no test of significance of the treatment effects is possible, because the treatment groups are not random. This characteristic of the random replications design deserves special emphasis, and will be given separate consideration later in the following section.

Due to the control over differences among *groups*, the random replications design is usually much more precise than the groups-within-treatments design.

In the groups-within-treatments design, all group differences are contained in the error term. In the random replications design, a large part of these differences (as measured by ms_R^*) is taken out of the error term; only the interaction effects remain in it. The advantage of the random replications design over the groups-within-treatments design is therefore essentially the same as that of the treatments $\times$ subjects design over the simple-randomized design. In experiments with methods of school instruction, differences among schools are sometimes of almost the same magnitude as differences among individual pupils in the same school; hence control over school differences adds immensely to the precision of the experiment.

In the situation in which the total interaction is due primarily or entirely to Type S errors, the F-test based on ms_A^*/ms_{AR}^* is less satisfactory than one employing a "within-cells" or a pooled error term, because of the much smaller number of degrees of freedom usually available for the interaction mean square.

The Possibilities of Simple Random Replication

Experimenters have often been far more ingenious in inventing designs to control various sources of error than in finding ways of testing the significance of the treatment effects in designs invented. This has been particularly true with many so-called "counterbalanced" designs in psychological research. The principle of random replication offers a general solution to the problem of evaluating the results obtained with many such designs. If simple replication of the design is possible — that is, if the same experiment can be repeated with independent random samples of subjects, and if the treatments can be completely randomized with reference to the various sources of error in each replication, a valid test of the treatment effect can usually be made by means of ms_A^*/ms_{AR}^*. The crucial requirements are that the interaction be *homogeneous* for all pairs of treatments and that the interaction effects be normally distributed. The possibilities of simple random replication will be more fully explored in Chapters 10 and 13.

The Use of ms_{AL} as an Error Term in Treatments $\times$ Levels Designs

In Chapter 5, page 145, the fact was noted that, under certain conditions in a treatments $\times$ levels design, ms_{AL} may be employed as the error term in testing the significance of the treatments effect. These conditions are:

1) The observed interaction is due to error only, that is, there is no intrinsic interaction.

2) Type G errors have been randomized with reference to treatments at each level independently.

3) These Type G errors may be regarded as a random sample from a hypothetical population of such errors.

If these conditions are satisfied the design is essentially a random replications design so far as Type G errors are concerned, and the interaction (AL) mean square may be used as the error term in testing the significance of the main effect of treatments.

STUDY EXERCISES [1]

1. The following problem is adapted from a study by Porter [2] which was concerned with the relative effectiveness of four methods of studying a given reading passage. The study methods differed primarily in the placement of questions (before or after the reading selection), in the degree of detail of the questions (main or main and subordinate), and in the source of the questions (pupil or experimenter).

Fifteen elementary schools were randomly selected from a list of all elementary schools in Iowa communities of over 20,000 population. Letters were sent to the principals of these schools requesting the co-operation of their eighth-grade classes in carrying out the study. Thirteen principals agreed to participate and sent in copies of their eighth grade enrollment lists. From these lists, the pupils in each class were randomly assigned to four experimental groups of equal size.

The materials, consisting of written directions, the reading selection, question sheets, and a 60-item multiple choice test over the selection, were organized in booklet form. Since different experimental methods were produced by varying the arrangement of these elements, it was possible to administer the experiment at one sitting to *all* the pupils in a given school. Each student received the materials for the particular method to which he had been randomly assigned by the experimenter. The teacher then read several brief paragraphs of general instructions pertaining to the conduct of the experiment, following which she read four paragraphs of specific instructions; one directed at each of the four experimental groups. After questions had been cleared up, the experimental session proceeded, each method involving the same period of time. Immediately upon the conclusion of this period, all pupils took the 60-item test over the reading passage.

The data are as follows: (The measures in the body of this table are subgroup means, M_{ij}.)

---

[1] See second paragraph on page viii.

[2] William P. Porter, *The Relative Effectiveness of Questions and Their Placement in Directed Study*, Ph.D. Thesis, State University of Iowa, 1942.

Study Methods (A)

School (S)	I	II	III	IV	Totals
1	32.8	33.9	35.1	37.1	138.9
2	34.6	37.1	38.1	39.4	149.2
3	34.9	33.2	34.2	34.6	136.9
4	35.5	33.3	34.0	41.0	143.8
5	34.3	27.0	32.2	35.4	128.9
6	38.4	36.5	36.7	37.8	149.4
7	33.1	28.8	30.0	32.5	124.4
8	31.3	31.8	32.1	32.4	127.6
9	36.2	35.6	35.9	34.8	142.5
10	33.1	35.6	38.7	35.8	143.2
11	35.0	33.3	39.0	34.9	142.2
12	33.9	33.3	36.9	38.3	142.4
13	38.1	34.7	40.3	36.8	149.9
Totals	451.2	434.1	463.2	470.8	1819.3
Means	34.7	33.4	35.6	36.2	

Calculations Provided:

$$\sum T_A^2/13 = 63710.1$$

$$\sum T_S^2/4 = 63861.9$$

$$\sum\sum M_{ij}^2 = 64048.1$$

a) Complete the analysis of the data and prepare a summary table.

b) It is obvious that some schools provided more pupils than others — hence the subgroup means within each treatment are based on varying n's. We have calculated our methods means as the simple average of the subgroup means. On what reasoning is this a legitimate procedure?

c) Apply an over-all test of the significance of the differences among the method means, using the 1% level. State carefully the exact hypothesis tested [note (b) preceding].

d) State explicitly the assumptions underlying the test in (c). Discuss the probable extent to which these assumptions are violated, and the probable effect on the validity of the usual F-test.

e) If any very marked heterogeneity of interaction characterized this experiment, how might you detect its presence? That is, what would you look for in the table of means? (See Exercise 2, Chapter 6, page 169.)

f) What advantages accrue from administering the tests simultaneously and on a group basis to all the pupils in one room? How would the results probably have differed if the different methods groups in each school had been tested in different rooms and under different teachers?

g) Discuss the probable relative magnitudes of the intrinsic and extrinsic components of the AS interaction. What may be true of the previous instructional experiences of the pupils in various schools that may give rise to an intrinsic interaction? What are several possible specific sources of extrinsic interaction in this design? Discuss the possibilities of rendering the latter effects negligible through careful experimental control.

h) Suppose the observed interaction in this case is primarily intrinsic. Explain why ms_{AS}^* is nevertheless a valid error term for testing treatment effects?

i) Define the population to which the results of the F-test of (c) may be generalized on the logic of statistical inference. On what basis might you be justified in generalizing to all Iowa schools?

j) How would you analyze the original data in order to test the significance of the interaction? Suppose this interaction had been found to be nonsignificant. Would this mean that the test based on $F = ms_A^*/ms_{AS}^*$ was invalid? Explain.

2. One part of an (hypothetical) experiment (suggested by a study by Sheffield[1]) with albino rats was concerned with the relative effects on resistance to extinction of varying degrees of reinforcement during training in a runway situation. The four experimental treatments differed in the percent of the 32 training trials on which reinforcement (reward) was provided — 25% for A_1, 50% for A_2, 75% for A_3, and 100% for A_4. The pattern of the reinforced trials was cyclic, subject to the restriction that the first, third, and last trials were reinforced under every treatment.

Evidence from previous research suggested that the nature and extent of previous experience of the rats might affect their performance under these experimental conditions. All animals in the available colony were normally kept in living cages of four rats each. The previous experiences of the rats were much the same for rats in the same cage, but was known to have differed considerably from one cage to another. However, the exact "experiential history" of each cage was not available. Therefore, ten *cages* were selected at random from among all cages in the colony and the four rats in each cage were randomly assigned, one to each of the four treatments.

The apparatus consisted of a four-foot alley connecting a starting box and a goal box. Timing devices were arranged so that starting time and running time could be automatically recorded.

After a week of adjustment to a common feeding schedule, all animals were given ten *exploratory* trials in the apparatus. On the following day, each animal received 32 *training* trials, a specified proportion of which were reinforced. Reinforcement was provided by a small amount of wet mash and the animal was allowed to remain in the goal box for ten seconds. The inter-trial interval was held constant at 15 seconds. Immediately following the 32 training trials,

---

[1] Virginia F. Sheffield, "Extinction as a Function of Partial Reinforcement and Distribution of Practice," *Journal of Experimental Psychology*, 39: 511–526; August, 1949.

all animals were fed their normal ration minus the amount received during the training trials.

On the third and last day of the experiment, all animals were given 30 *extinction* trials, similar in all respects to the training trials except for the absence of reinforcement. The response time (sum of starting and running times) was determined for each animal on each extinction trial. The criterion measure for each animal was defined as the *number of extinction trials*, out of the 30, on which its response time was less than the *median* response time for the total group of 40 rats.

It should be noted that rats tend to be less active in a clean runway than in one just used by other rats. In this experiment the runway was cleaned at the beginning of each day, but not during the day.

The criterion measures and some computational results are presented below:

Cage	A_1 (25%)	A_2 (50%)	A_3 (75%)	A_4 (100%)	Total
R_1	10	12	14	9	45
R_2	14	22	18	21	75
R_3	18	20	21	18	77
R_4	20	16	10	17	63
R_5	10	9	13	10	42
R_6	9	15	9	15	48
R_7	15	18	14	11	58
R_8	13	17	14	16	60
R_9	8	13	9	14	44
R_{10}	9	14	12	7	42
Total	126	156	134	138	554
M_j	12.6	15.6	13.4	13.8	
$\sum^{10} X^2$	1740	2568	1928	2082	

a) Complete the calculations and prepare a summary table of the analysis.

b) From the information provided, define the population from which these 10 cages may be regarded as a random sample.

c) State the hypothesis tested by the ratio ms_A/ms_{AR}. May this hypothesis be rejected at the 5% level? Does this test involve the assumption that the four rats in each cage are a random sample from a corresponding subpopulation? Explain.

d) What is presumably the purpose of the 10 exploratory trials? What would presumably be done if one rat failed to respond at all during these preliminary trials?

e) The 10 rats under Treatment A_4 (100% reinforcement) were given their extinction trials first, the 10 rats under Treatment A_1 (25% reinforcement) last. Could this result in an "order" effect which partially cancelled the treatment effects, and hence explain why the F of (c) was not significant? Explain.

f) How might one randomize the "order" effect? If this were done, and assuming that there is a real order effect, would ms_{AR} be larger than if the same order had been employed with each cage? Explain.

g) Suppose that not more than 20 animals could be "run" in a single day, either for the training or for the extinction trials, and that the experiment was therefore broken up into two independent parts — the experiment being completed for 20 of the rats (5 cages randomly selected) before anything was done with the remaining rats. Suppose also that there was a marked day effect (which was thus confounded with the R effect) but assume that there was *no* days × treatments interaction, and that the data were analyzed just as in the situation earlier described. Is the test $F = ms_A/ms_{AR}$ still a valid test of the treatments effect? Explain. (Why is the assumption of no days × treatments interaction necessary?)

h) Suppose that not more than 8 rats could be run in one day, so that the experiment had to be broken up into 5 independent parts, each concerned with 2 randomly selected cages. Suppose also that there was a marked days × treatments interaction, but that the 5 days involved could be regarded as a simple random sample from a population of days. Could the experiment still be regarded as a random replications experiment? How then should the data be analyzed and the treatments effect tested? (See pages 163–164.)

i) The criterion measure used in this experiment was selected because it seemed more likely to be normally distributed than the number of trials to extinction, which was considered as an alternative. Why is it more likely to be normally distributed? Is it otherwise as adequate or valid a criterion as the number of trials to extinction? What generalization does this suggest concerning the choice of a criterion measure in a psychological experiment?

j) Would the experiment have been *more* or *less* precise if the 40 available rats had been randomly assigned four to a cage at the beginning of the experiment and the same analysis employed? Explain.

k) Why, presumably, did the experimenter employ four treatments (degrees of reinforcement) rather than only two or three?

9

Factorial Designs (Two Factors)

The Generalized Case of the Two-Factor (A × B) Design

The basic nature and purposes of the factorial design have already been considered in Chapter 1 (pages 20–23), and these should be reviewed carefully by the student before he proceeds with this chapter. In that introductory discussion, the design was illustrated with an example in which there were only two categories in each treatment classification (two *styles* of type and two *sizes* of type), and in which the number of cases was the same for each treatment group. In the generalized case of the two-factor design, there may be any number of categories in either treatment classification, and the number of cases may differ from cell to cell in the same row or column of the double-entry table, but must be in the same proportion from column to column or from row to row.

In order to refer to a specific example, we will extend the illustration used in Chapter 1 to include four styles and three sizes of type, so that the design is as diagrammed below.

		Style of Type				
		A_1	A_2	A_3	A_4	
		Clarendon	Roman	Gothic	Italic	
Size	$B_1 - $ 8 pt.	M_{11}	M_{12}	M_{13}	M_{14}	$M_{1.}$
of	$B_2 - $ 10 pt.	M_{21}	M_{22}	M_{23}	M_{24}	$M_{2.}$
Type	$B_3 - $ 12 pt.	M_{31}	M_{32}	M_{33}	M_{34}	$M_{3.}$
		$M_{.1}$	$M_{.2}$	$M_{.3}$	$M_{.4}$	

By a "factor" we mean one of the bases on which the treatments are classified. In the illustration, *style* of type is one factor and *size* the other. The number of different "treatments" in a two-factor design is, in one sense, equal to the product of the numbers of categories in the two classifications, or the number of cells in the double-entry table. In this sense, there are twelve "treatments" in the experiment diagrammed above. In this discussion, however, we will use the term "treatments" to represent the various categories in each major classification, and will use the term "treatment-combination" to refer to the treatments applied to the subjects in a single cell of the table. Thus, if there are a columns and b rows there will be a treatments in the column classification, b treatments in the row classification, and ab treatment-combinations.

Sometimes the treatments in one or both of the classifications represent different degrees or amounts of the same factor, in which case the treatments are clearly *ordered*. Sometimes the treatments are categorically described and are non-ordered. In the preceding illustration, style of type is non-ordered, but size is ordered. When the treatments in a classification are ordered, as when the various treatments represent increasing durations of time for the same experimental condition, special interest may be shown in the *pattern* or *trend* of the average scores for those treatments. Such questions may be raised as "Do the averages fall along a straight line?", "Is the trend described by a parabolic curve?", etc. In this chapter we shall not be concerned with the trend of the treatment means, but only with whether or not the treatments differ at all, that is, with tests of null hypotheses. The problem of *trend* analysis will be considered in a later chapter (Chapter 15).

The terms "main effect," "simple effect," and "interaction effect" have the same meanings in a factorial design as in a treatments × levels design (see pages 122-123). However, in the factorial design there is a main effect for each of the two factors, as well as simple effects for each factor at given levels of the other factor.

The computational procedures employed with the factorial design are exactly the same as those employed with the treatments × levels design (see page 123), the categories of the second factor (B) taking the place of levels (L).

The analysis may be presented in table form as follows:

Source	df	ss	ms
A	$a - 1$	ss_A	$ss_A/(a - 1)$
B	$b - 1$	ss_B	$ss_B/(b - 1)$
Cells	$ab - 1$	ss_{cells}	
AB	$(a - 1)(b - 1)$	ss_{AB}	$ss_{AB}/(a - 1)(b - 1)$
Within cells (w)	$N - ab$	ss_w	$ss_w/(N - ab)$
Total	$N - 1$	ss_T	

The Test of the *AB* Interaction and Its Interpretation

Since the evaluation and interpretation of the main and simple effects depends on whether or not one may assume that there is no interaction, we shall consider first the test of the significance of the interaction and its interpretation. In any two-factor design, the significance of the interaction is tested exactly as in the treatments × levels design, and on exactly the same assumptions. These assumptions, given on page 138, should be carefully reviewed at this point. If *A* and *B* represent the column and row factors respectively, and *a* and *b* represent the numbers of *A* and *B* treatments, or the numbers of columns and rows, respectively, the test is

$$F = ms_{AB}/ms_w, \; df = (a-1)(b-1)/(N-ab), \qquad (56)$$

in which ms_{AB} is the interaction mean square, ms_w the within-cells mean square, and N is the total number of cases $\left(N = \sum_{j=1}^{a} \sum_{i=1}^{b} n_{ij} \right)$.

[handwritten margin notes: subgroup random, normality, variance homog.), proport. differ. bt subgroup means is same]

As we have repeatedly noted previously, an observed interaction may be wholly extrinsic (due entirely to Type S and Type G errors), or it may in part be intrinsic (due to the treatments only). A significant $F = ms_{AB}/ms_w$ means only that the observed interaction cannot reasonably be accounted for entirely in terms of random Type S errors, but it does not rule out the possibility that the interaction is wholly extrinsic. What weight should be given to this possibility depends on the extent to which the Type G errors have been controlled or equalized for all treatment combinations in the experiment. The interpretation of a significant $F = ms_{AB}/ms_w$ therefore calls for a judgment on the part of the interpreter concerning the effectiveness of the experimental error controls.

Sometimes it is quite evident that Type G errors are negligible. In the illustrative experiment, for example, all twelve treatment-combinations may have been administered simultaneously and under exactly the same conditions to different members of the same group. The reading-rate test used may have been printed in twelve editions, one for each size-style combination, and may be alike in all other respects. The tests may have been administered in a room large enough to permit testing all subjects simultaneously in a single group. The tests may have been passed out in repeated sequence, 1–2–3– . . . 12, so that if the subjects are seated in a random order, a random twelfth of the group takes each test. In this situation it is very difficult to conceive of any extraneous factor or circumstance that would systematically affect any one treatment-combination differently from any other. Experimental errors may occur; for instance, an unanticipated distraction may arise during the testing period, but presumably it would affect all treatment-combinations alike, and could hardly result in any interaction effect. In such an experiment, the observed interaction would presumably be due only to Type S errors or to an intrinsic interaction, or both. If the test of significance shows that Type S errors could not reasonably account for all of the observed interaction, the inference would be clear that an intrinsic interaction is present.

This illustration, however, is by no means typical of factorial experiments in general. Most often, each treatment-combination must be separately administered, frequently each at a different time and sometimes by different individuals. In such cases, quite obviously, extraneous factors could often systematically affect some treatment-combinations and not others; these Type G errors could then give rise to a large observed interaction.

Assuming that Type G errors are negligible, a significant $F = ms_{AB}/ms_w$ means that there is an intrinsic interaction, or in general that the differences among the population means of the treatment-combinations in one row (or column) of the table are not necessarily the same as the corresponding differences in any other row (or column). In the illustration, for instance, the style of type which produces the fastest reading rate in combination with one size of type may not be that which produces the fastest reading rate in combination with another size of type.

The possibility should always be considered that the interaction is heterogeneous. For instance, differences among the effects of corresponding A-treatments may be very nearly the same for B_1 as for B_2, but may differ considerably from B_2 to B_3. It is conceivable that the interaction in a particular experiment is due entirely to the effect of just one of the treatments in either classification. It is possible, for example, that if Row 3 (B_3) were removed from the table, the rest of the table would show no interaction at all. It is even conceivable that the interaction is due entirely to the effect of just one treatment-combination, and that if the criterion mean could be appropriately changed for just one cell in the table, there would be no interaction. Such outcomes are relatively unlikely, particularly if the various treatments in each classification represent different degrees or amounts of the same factor, but they are always possibilities. It should be noted that the test $F = ms_{AB}/ms_w$ is not very sensitive to an interaction which characterizes only a small part of the entire table. The fact that the total interaction proves non-significant, therefore, does not rule out the possibility that such an interaction exists, but it does render dubious any attempts to identify such interactions from closer inspection of the experimental data (see pages 48–49).

The fact that an interaction is "significant" does not necessarily imply that it is of much practical importance. If the precision of the experiment is high — that is, if the mean for each treatment-combination is based on a very large sample and has a small standard error, a relatively weak interaction may prove significant. If the precision of the experiment is low, even a very potent interaction may fail to prove significant. The implications of these possibilities will be considered more fully in later sections.

If the interaction proves non-significant and if other considerations permit, one is free to *assume* that there is *no* interaction so far as the entire population is concerned (although this has by no means been proved). This is equivalent to assuming that the simple effect of each treatment in either classification is the same for all levels of the other classification. In a sense, the main effect of a treatment or factor is simply the (weighted) *average* of all its simple effects; or each simple effect is simply an *estimate* of the main effect. On the assumption of no interaction, therefore, our interest would be entirely in the more stable main effects; there would be no point at all in inquiring into the simple effects.

A significant interaction, on the other hand, suggests that the differences among the simple effects of the treatments in one classification may be different for each treatment (in the other classification) with which they may be combined. In this case, the main effect of any treatment or factor still has a definite meaning, but ordinarily a much less useful one than when the interaction is negligible or nonexistent. Suppose, for instance, that in our illustrative experiment the interaction had proved significant, but that a comparison was nevertheless made between the main effects of B_1 and B_3. Then suppose it was found that $(M_1 - M_3)$ is significant (using a test to be described later). For what *population* may any inferences be drawn on the basis of this significant difference? If the numbers in all columns are the same, one-fourth of the "population" in this case consists of individuals who received Treatment A_1, one-fourth received A_2, one-fourth A_3, and one-fourth A_4. Quite obviously, there would in general be very little practical interest in any such population. The interest rather would be in the possibility, for instance, that Clarendon type is better than Gothic when used with one size of type, that these styles are about equally good when used with another size of type, but that Gothic may be superior to Clarendon for still another size of type. In this case, also, the interest would be in what combination of size and style results in the most rapid reading, rather than in which size is on the average best for all styles, each style receiving the same amount of use, or in which style is best with all sizes, each size receiving the same amount of use.

We may then summarize the preceding discussion as follows. If the interaction is not significant and if other considerations permit us to assume that there is no interaction (either intrinsic or extrinsic), we will have no interest in "simple" effects, since the simple effects for either factor are presumably the same (except for chance) for all levels of the other factor. In this case, we would be interested only in the main effects, and any conclusions drawn about the treatments in one classification would be equally applicable at all levels of the other classification. If, on the other hand, the observed interaction proves significant, and if we may *assume* that there is an *intrinsic* interaction, we would ordinarily have very little interest in any main effects, but would center our attention on the simple effects or on individual treatment combinations. We thus see that it is usually desirable to test the significance of the interaction before proceeding with any other tests.

Testing the Significance of the Main Effect of Either Factor

The main effects of factors A and B respectively are tested by

$$F = ms_A/ms_w, \ df = (a - 1)/(N - ab), \tag{57}$$

and

$$F = ms_B/ms_w, \ df = (b - 1)/(N - ab). \tag{58}$$

The conditions [1] under which these mean square ratios are distributed as F are listed below. The student will note that there is no essential difference between these conditions and those listed on pages 133–134 for the treatments $\times$ levels designs.

1) The subgroups receiving the various treatment-combinations were, at the beginning of the experiment, all drawn at random from the same population (the available subjects have been randomly assigned to the treatment subgroups).

2) The distribution of criterion measures for the subpopulation corresponding to each treatment-combination is a normal distribution.

3) Each of these distributions has the same variance.

4) The numbers in the corresponding treatment subgroups (cells) are in the same proportion from row to row or from column to column of the table.

5) a) The population mean for each A-treatment (column) is the same.

   b) The population mean for each B-treatment (row) is the same.

Which version of Condition 5 is to be employed depends of course on whether the main effect for A- or B-treatments is being tested.

The proof that under these conditions the mean square ratios in (57) and (58) are distributed as F is exactly the same as that presented on pages 134–135.

In any application of this design, careful consideration should be given to the extent to which the underlying assumptions (Conditions 1 to 3) are satisfied in the experiment.

For reasons already discussed, it is frequently impossible for the experimenter to draw the samples for the various treatment combinations strictly at random from the real population in which he may be interested. In nearly every application, however, it is possible for him to randomize the *available* subjects with reference to cells. Hence, in practice, Condition 1 usually means random assignment of subjects to subgroups. In this case, of course, the population to which inferences may be drawn must be defined to fit the sample of available subjects.

The important considerations, so far as Conditions 2 and 3 are concerned, are the same as those discussed in previous chapters and need not be repeated here.

Condition 4 is nearly always wholly within the control of the experimenter; hence, it should ordinarily cause no concern for the validity of the F-test.

If any of these conditions are only approximately satisfied, the ratios of the mean squares will be distributed only approximately as in the F-distribution, and the usual effect will be to make the ratio of the mean squares appear to be

---

[1] See footnote on page 51.

more "significant" than it really is. If there is any serious doubt concerning Condition 3, it may be well to apply the Bartlett test before proceeding with the analysis.

The "population" referred to in 5a is that for which the measures in any column may be regarded as a *representative* sample with reference to the B-categories. For instance, the population mean for Treatment A_1 is the mean of a population all members of which receive Treatment A_1, but in which a certain proportion receive Treatment B_1 in combination with A_1, another proportion Treatment B_2 in combination with A_1, etc., the proportions being exactly the same as in the experimental sample. A similar statement may be made about the population referred to in 5b. For reasons already suggested, there would ordinarily be very little interest in any such populations, since only very rarely would one propose in practice to administer any treatment to any such population.

If corresponding differences among the A means are the same for all levels of B, it follows that if the null hypothesis concerning the A means is true for one level of B, it is true for every other. So far as the test of the null hypothesis (5a) is concerned then, the distribution among B levels in the population is of no importance. Assuming no interaction, the F-test of (57) may be regarded as a test of the null hypothesis for any or all of the B levels.

Testing the Simple Effects of Either Factor

The simple effect of the A factor for a given level, i, of B, is tested by

$$F = ms_{AwB_i}/ms_w, \ df = (a-1)/(N-ab), \tag{59}$$

or by

$$F = ms_{AwB_i}/ms_{w \text{ (for row } B_i \text{ only)}}, \ df = (a-1)/(n_i.-a). \tag{60}$$

In both expressions above, ms_{AwB_i} is the mean square for between-treatments computed only from the data in the ith row of the table, as in a simple-randomized design. In (59), ms_w is computed from the entire table, while in (60), $ms_{w \text{ (for row } B_i \text{ only)}}$ is computed for within-cells from only the data in Row B_i. The second of these tests (60) would be employed if the assumption of homogeneity of variance were regarded as tenable for Row B_i alone, but untenable for the entire table.

The conditions under which these mean square ratios are distributed as F are the same as those listed on page 73, these conditions having to be satisfied only for the part of the table involved in the test. It will be noted that the test of a simple effect of either factor is of exactly the same character as the test of the treatments effect in a simple-randomized design. That is, so far as the A-comparisons are concerned, the factorial design may be regarded as a number of independent simple-randomized experiments, one conducted for each level of B. A similar statement may be made, of course, with reference to the B-comparisons.

The simple effect of the B factor for level A_j of A is tested by

$$F = ms_{BwA_j}/ms_w, \quad df = (b-1)/(N-ab) \tag{61}$$

or by

$$F = ms_{BwA_j}/ms_{w \text{ (for col. } A_j \text{ only)}}, \quad df = (b-1)/(n_{.j}-b). \tag{62}$$

Individual Comparisons of Row, Column, or Cell Means

The estimated error variance of any cell, row, or column mean is given respectively by

$$\sigma^2_{M_{A_j B_i}} = ms_w/n_{ij} \quad \text{cells}$$

$$\sigma^2_{M_{B_i}} = ms_w/n_{i.} \quad \text{row}$$

$$\sigma^2_{M_{A_j}} = ms_w/n_{.j} \quad \text{column}$$

Given these error variances, the usual procedures may be followed to test the significance of the difference between any two means. The number of degrees of freedom for each of the above error variances is $(N-ab)$. Each of these error variances is based on the assumption of homogeneous error variance throughout the entire table. If this assumption is in serious doubt except for the two means compared, the error variance may be computed only for the data on which the given means are based.

The Meaning of $ms_{A \text{ (or } B)}/ms_{AB}$ When the Interaction Is Significant

If there is an intrinsic interaction between A and B for a population, there is no meaningful hypothesis under which the ratio ms_A/ms_{AB} or ms_B/ms_{AB} is distributed as F. This is because the categories in neither the A nor B classifications may be regarded as randomly selected from a population of such categories, so that the interaction effects may not be regarded as random effects. Nevertheless, if the precision of the experiment is high, that is, if the total number of subjects per treatment-combination is large, these ratios do have a useful meaning (although not a probability meaning).

The fact that the interaction is significant and intrinsic does not necessarily imply that the *true* rank order (that is, the order based on the population means) of the A (or B) treatments is different for each level of B (or A). Even though the interaction is intrinsic and pronounced, it is possible that the main effect of A is so much more pronounced than the interaction effect that the rank order of the A treatments is the *same*, or approximately the same, for each level of B (and likewise for the B treatments). By a reasoning similar to that presented on pages 141–144, the following rule-of-thumb may be justified. If ms_A/ms_{AB} is greater than $4b$, one may fairly safely conclude that the true rank order of the A treatments is approximately the same for all levels of B, even though the differences among the true treatment means for one level of B differ somewhat from the corresponding differences for any other level of B. Similarly, if ms_B/ms_{AB} is greater than $4a$, the true rank order of the B treatments is probably approximately the same for all levels of A.

As is true of any rule-of-thumb, these rules should be used with considerable caution. It should be noted particularly that their validity depends on the precision of the means for individual treatment-combinations, and on the extent to which Type G errors are negligible.

The Conditions Under Which $ms_{A\,(or\,B)}/ms_{AB}$ Is Distributed as F

If there is no *intrinsic* interaction and if Type G errors have been independently randomized for each level of B (or A) and if all the other conditions listed on page 212 are met, with the additional requirement of equal n's in all cells, $ms_{A\,(or\,B)}/ms_{AB}$ is distributed as F. In this case, we may test the significance of the treatment effects by

$$F = ms_A/ms_{AB}, \ df = (a - 1)/(a - 1)(b - 1), \tag{63}$$

or

$$F = ms_B/ms_{AB}, \ df = (b - 1)/(a - 1)(b - 1). \tag{64}$$

Since there is no intrinsic interaction, the interaction effects for the b rows (or a columns) of the table may be regarded as a simple random sample from a hypothetical population of such interaction effects for an indefinite number of rows (or columns).

The trouble with the preceding observation is that if the observed interaction is significant there is no objective or statistical basis upon which one may determine whether the interaction is in part intrinsic or is entirely extrinsic. Hence, the use of the preceding F-test must often be based upon the relatively unsupported *assumption* that there is no intrinsic interaction. Sometimes the nature of the treatments may be such that this assumption is extremely plausible, but there is always the possibility that it is false in spite of its plausibility. In general, as will be made clear later, an interaction mean square should be used as an error term only if it is quite definitely *known* that the observed interaction effects are, or may be regarded as, a simple random sample from a meaningful population of such effects. Even then, of course, it should be used as an error term only if the interaction is homogeneous and if the numbers of cases are the same for all cells of the table, or if the interaction mean square is based on an analysis of the unweighted cell means.

How to Make Comprehensive Tests of Significance When the Interaction Is in Part Intrinsic and in Part Due to Randomized Type G Errors

We have seen that the test $F = ms_A/ms_w$ (or $F = ms_B/ms_w$) takes into consideration random Type S errors only. We have seen also that if Type G errors have been randomized for each row independently and if $n_{ij} = n$ is constant, we may, on the *assumption* of no intrinsic interaction (usually a questionable assumption), test the significance of the main effect of A by means of $F = ms_A/ms_{AB}$ (and similarly for the main effect of B). In this case, the test of significance takes both Type S and Type G errors into consideration. In the event that the interaction is in part real, however, we have, for the simple factorial design, no way of testing the significance of a main effect that takes both Type S and Type G errors into consideration.

The latter is one of the situations to which a solution is provided by the principle of random replication (see page 201). If a two-factor experiment is being planned, if there is reason to believe that an intrinsic interaction may exist, and if Type G errors can be randomized independently in each replication, the thing to do is to provide for a number of random replications of the experiment. That is, the whole experiment should be repeated a number of times, each time with an independent random sample of subjects and with an independent randomization of Type G errors. Tests of significance valid both for Type S and Type G errors can then be made, not only for the main effect of either factor, but also for the interaction and for the simple effects. The manner in which such a design may be analyzed will be considered in the next chapter (pages 230–237). It is particularly important to note that by thus replicating a simple two-factor design, it is possible to test the hypothesis that there is no *intrinsic* interaction — an hypothesis it is impossible to test in a single replication of a two-factor design.

The Use of Transformations

The use of transformations with the two-factor factorial design presents essentially the same problems as with the treatments × levels design (see pages 149–151), the difference being that the second treatment factor (B) takes the place of the control factor (L). As in the case of the treatments × levels design, if there is an interaction on the transformed scale, the hypothesis that the means of the treatment populations are identical cannot be true with reference both to the original and the transformed measures. Unless the main effect of one of the treatments is nil, the hypothesis of no interaction cannot be true for both the original and transformed measures. If one wishes to test the hypothesis of no interaction on the original scale, one must determine what is the *equivalent* hypothesis on the transformed scale and then test this hypothesis, rather than test the hypothesis of no interaction on the transformed scale.

STUDY EXERCISES [1]

1. Teichner [2] carried out an experiment concerned with the effect of intertrial time on the acquisition and extinction of an instrumental response in

---

[1] See second paragraph on page viii.

[2] Warren H. Teichner, *Experimental Extinction as a Function of the Intertrial Time During Conditioning and Extinction*, Ph.D. Thesis, State University of Iowa; February, 1951.

white rats. Three groups of hooded male rats were selected at random from the available colony and each group was randomly divided into four subgroups of equal size. The following diagram indicates the sizes of the groups and subgroups, as well as the intertrial times used with each.

Intertrial Time in Seconds

	Acquisition	*Extinction*	
Group I $(N_1 = 40)$	30	30 45 60 90	$(n_1 = 10$ each$)$
Group II $(N_2 = 100)$	45	30 45 60 90	$(n_2 = 25$ each$)$
Group III $(N_3 = 40)$	90	30 45 60 90	$(n_3 = 10$ each$)$

A side view of the problem box used in the experiment is shown below:

The animals, after a week of adjustment to handling and to a 23-hour feeding schedule, were each given a 10-minute exploratory session in the apparatus. On the following day, each animal in turn was given 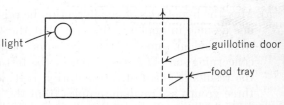 two preliminary trials designed to assure movement toward the food tray during the learning series, followed immediately by 15 training trials under the appropriate intertrial time condition. On each trial, latency was automatically recorded as the time between raising of the door and depression of the tray to obtain a pellet. As soon as the pellet was obtained, the tray returned to normal position, the door was lowered and the rat was allowed to eat. A latency of 10 seconds or more was classed as no response — the door was automatically lowered after this period.

Extinction trials were started immediately after the last training trial, and were exactly like the training trials except that no food was presented. Extinction trials were continued until the animal failed to respond on three successive trials. The criterion measure for each animal was the *number of responses during the extinction series*. The data in the body of the table immediately following are the criterion means for each subgroup.

Intertrial Interval During Extinction (E)

		30 sec.	45 sec.	60 sec.	90 sec.	Means
		10	10	10	10	
Intertrial	30 sec.	6.60	5.40	5.30	6.60	5.98
Interval		25	25	25	25	
During	45 sec.	6.68	8.92	8.00	8.52	8.03
Acquisition		10	10	10	10	
(A)	90 sec.	8.50	8.90	9.90	11.40	9.68
	Means	7.07	8.13	7.82	8.73	7.94

Summary Table

Source	df	ss	ms
Acquisition (A)	2	275.66	137.83
Extinction (E)	3	64.95	21.65
Interaction (AE)	6	72.20	12.03
Within-Cells (w)	168	2236.52	13.31
Total	179	2649.33	

a) May the hypothesis of no interaction be rejected at the 5% level? Must one assume in applying this test that the three original groups of rats were random samples from the same population? What assumption concerning sampling is involved in the test of interaction? To *interpret* the results of this test satisfactorily, is it necessary to assume that the three groups are random samples from the *same* population? Explain.

b) In the test of the hypothesis of no interaction, to what distributions do the assumptions of normality and homogeneity of variance apply? In view of the criterion measure employed, have you any *a priori* reason to question these assumptions? In other experiments, what has usually been the form of the distribution of *trials to extinction*? Is there usually a tendency for the variances and the means of such distributions to be related? How would you justify the usual *F*-test in spite of the failure to satisfy the underlying assumptions? How would you modify the test, if at all?

c) The *F* obtained in (a) was not significant, yet the facts of generalization established in other experiments lead one to expect an intrinsic interaction. How may one reconcile the findings with the hypothesis that there *is* an interaction?

d) In view of the strong *a priori* case for interaction, would you employ a higher or lower level of significance in the test of (a) than if there were no such *a priori* considerations? Explain.

e) On the assumption that there is no interaction, how, in general, would one proceed with the analysis of acquisition and extinction effects? How would one proceed on the assumption that there is an intrinsic interaction?

f) Make a free-hand graph, for each acquisition interval, of the criterion means as a function of extinction intervals (on the abscissa). How can the hypothesis of no interaction be interpreted in terms of these graphs?

A *non-significant* interaction is consistent with the hypothesis that if these graphs were based on population values, they would exhibit what relationship to one another?

g) Test the simple effect of the E factor (extinction intervals) for the 30-second acquisition interval. Define the population involved. Why is ms_w for the whole experiment undesirable for use as an error term here? What is the most appropriate error term for testing $M_{11} - M_{12}$? (The first subscript identifies the A-category, the second the E-category.)

h) The ratio $ms_A/ms_w = 10.36$ is significant at the 1% level, according to the F-table. Why might the risk of a Type I error nevertheless be larger than 1 in 100? According to the results of the Norton study, one may be fairly certain that the true risk of a Type I error does not exceed what value?

i) How do the conditions on which ms_A/ms_w is distributed as F differ from those on which ms_{AE}/ms_w is distributed as F?

j) Which of the following inferences (for the given experimental situation) are justified by the outcome of the test in (h)? Which can be justified only depending on the outcome of other tests in addition to that of (h)? Explain in each case. Suggest, where necessary, changes or qualifications that will make each statement a reasonable statistical inference from the data of this experiment.

1. The longer the intertrial interval during acquisition, the greater is the average resistance to extinction.

2. The average number of responses for all extinction intervals needed to extinguish is not the same for 30-, 45-, and 90-second acquisition intervals.

3. Regardless of what extinction interval is used, a 45-second acquisition interval produces greater average resistance to extinction than does a 30-second acquisition interval.

4. The observed differences among the average number of trials needed for extinction for the various A–E combinations (cells) cannot be attributed to chance assignment of rats to subgroups.

k) What assumptions would be necessary if one wished to extend the conclusions from this experiment to rats in general? Is the use of only male rats a serious limitation of this experiment?

l) What are some of the advantages of the factorial design as used in this experiment?

10

Three-Dimensional Designs

Introduction

A factorial experiment involving two factors ($A \times B$) may itself be replicated in various ways. In some instances, the various replications may be regarded as a random sample from a population of such replications. This design, which was suggested at the close of the preceding chapter, might be denoted an $A \times B \times R$ design. In other instances, each replication may be performed at a different level of some control variable; this might be called a treatments $\times$ treatments $\times$ levels ($A \times B \times L$) experiment. The replications may also represent different levels of a third experimental variable (C) and all replications together may thus constitute a higher order factorial experiment, in this case involving three factors ($A \times B \times C$). In still other instances, a treatments $\times$ levels experiment (in which A represents treatments and L levels) may be replicated on a random basis ($A \times L \times R$).

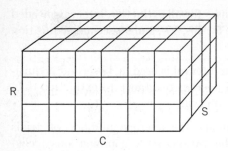

The data from such experiments may always be entered in a triple-entry or three-dimensional table. This table may be geometrically represented as a parallelepiped, consisting of s layers parallel to the front face (or r layers parallel to the top face, or c layers parallel to the side face). The figure to the left illustrates one such parallelepiped in which $r = 3$, $c = 6$, and $s = 4$.

Analysis of Total Sum of Squares

Any parallelepiped of the type suggested above may be regarded as consisting of rc smaller elongated parallelepipeds or *oblongs*, each ending in one of the rc cells in the front (or back) face. One such oblong is shown in the figure below — that ending in the ith cell in the jth column of the front (RC) face.

Each such oblong will consist of s cells, one for each of the s-layers. The parallelepiped may similarly be regarded as consisting of rs oblongs running from side to side (ending in the RS face) or of cs oblongs running from top to bottom (ending in the CS face). We will use the notation obs RC to represent oblongs ending in the RC face, obs RS for those ending in the RS face, etc.

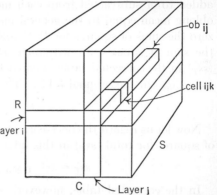

In the notation for this design, the first subscript will always refer to a category in the R classification (a row in the front face of the parallelepiped) the second subscript to a C category (column in the front face) and the third subscript to an S category. Thus, M_{ijk} will represent the mean of the cell which lies in the ith R category, the jth C category, and the kth S category. A dot in the subscript will indicate that all categories in the corresponding classification are represented. Thus, $n_{.j.}$ represents the number of cases in the jth category of C (all cases in the jth layer in the accompanying figure) including all R and S categories represented in that C category; $M_{.jk}$ represents the mean of the oblong formed by the intersection of the jth C layer and the kth S layer; etc. A term with no subscripts applies to the entire table. Thus, T represents the grand total for the entire table.

If the numbers in the corresponding cells are in the same proportion for any two oblongs in the same layer, and if the numbers in corresponding oblongs are proportional for all layers, the total sum of squares may then be analyzed into a number of independent components in the manner explained in the remainder of this section.

Let us first disregard the S classification completely, and regard the parallelepiped as consisting of obs RC ending in the RC face. Let us then think of the data for each oblong as projected into the RC face, so that all of the data are represented in an $R \times C$ table. In this table we may then analyze the total sum of squares into

$$ss_T = ss_R + ss_C + ss_{RC} + ss_{w\ obs\ RC}, \qquad (65)$$

the last term being the sum of squares for within-obs RC.

Similarly, by regarding the parallelepiped as consisting of obs RS, we could write

$$ss_T = ss_R + ss_S + ss_{RS} + ss_{w\ obs\ RS}, \qquad (66)$$

and in the same manner

$$ss_T = ss_C + ss_S + ss_{CS} + ss_{w\ obs\ CS}. \qquad (67)$$

Finally, considering the parallelepiped as consisting of rcs cubicles or cells, we may write

$$ss_T = ss_{\text{cells}} + ss_w, \qquad (68)$$

ss_w representing the within-cells sum of squares.

Now suppose that in each of the *obs RC*, a constant amount (equal to the deviation of the oblong mean from the general mean of the entire table) is added to or subtracted from each measure in the oblong, thus making each oblong mean equal to the general mean. These corrections would reduce to zero the sums of squares for R, C, and RC in the corrected table, leaving only the sum of squares for within-*obs RC*. Thus the sum of squares for total (ss'_T) in the corrected table is equal to the sum of squares for within-*obs RC* $(ss_{w\ obs\ RC})$ in the original table. That is,

$$ss'_T = ss_{w\ obs\ RC}. \tag{69}$$

Now let us regard the once-corrected table as consisting of *obs RS*. The sum of squares for total (ss'_T) in this table may then be analyzed as follows:

$$ss'_T = ss'_R + ss'_S + ss'_{RS} + ss'_{w\ obs\ RS}.$$

In the corrected table, however, ss'_R has been made equal to zero by the corrections in the *obs RC*. Hence,

$$ss'_T = ss'_S + ss'_{RS} + ss'_{w\ obs\ RS}. \tag{70}$$

Now let us apply a correction to the measures within each of the *obs RS* in the corrected table, so as to make the mean of each of these oblongs equal to the general mean for the entire table. In this *twice*-corrected table, the sums of squares for S and RS will each reduce to zero, so that all that is left is the variation within the RS combinations. That is, the sum of squares for total (ss''_T) in the twice-corrected table is the same as $ss'_{w\ obs\ RS}$, or

$$ss''_T = ss'_{w\ obs\ RS}. \tag{71}$$

Let us now regard the twice-corrected table as consisting of *obs CS*. We may then analyze the sum of squares for total in the twice-corrected table as follows:

$$ss''_T = ss''_C + ss''_S + ss''_{CS} + ss''_{w\ obs\ CS}.$$

Because of the two series of corrections

$$ss''_C = 0 \text{ and } ss''_S = 0,$$

and hence,

$$ss''_T = ss''_{CS} + ss''_{w\ obs\ CS}. \tag{72}$$

Now let us apply a third series of corrections, this time to the measures within *obs CS* so as to make the mean of each of these oblongs equal to the general mean. This would reduce to zero the sum of squares for CS, so that the sum of squares for total in the thrice-corrected table would be given by

$$ss'''_T = ss''_{w\ obs\ CS}. \tag{73}$$

In this thrice-corrected table, there would be no differences among the means of R-layers, or of C-layers, or of S-layers, or of any oblongs however viewed. There would, however, still be some residual differences among the cell (cubicle) means, so that the sum of squares for total in the thrice-corrected table could be analyzed into

$$ss_T''' = ss_{\text{cells}}''' + ss_w'''. \tag{74}$$

We may now note that because of the proportionality of cell frequencies, the first correction (within-*obs* RC) would have no effect on ss_S and ss_{RS}. That is,

$$ss_S' = ss_S \text{ and } ss_{RS}' = ss_{RS}. \tag{75}$$

The first two corrections similarly would leave

$$ss_{CS}'' = ss_{CS}, \tag{76}$$

and all three corrections together would leave

$$ss_w''' = ss_w. \tag{77}$$

We will now call the sum of squares for between cells in the thrice-corrected table the sum of squares for "triple" interaction or for RCS. That is, we will let

$$ss_{\text{cells}}''' = ss_{RCS}. \tag{78}$$

Now, substituting from (77) and (78) in (74), we get

$$ss_T''' = ss_{RCS} + ss_w. \tag{79}$$

From (73), (76), and (79) in (72), we get

$$ss_T'' = ss_{CS} + ss_{RCS} + ss_w. \tag{80}$$

From (71), (75), and (80) in (70), we get

$$ss_T' = ss_S + ss_{RS} + ss_{CS} + ss_{RCS} + ss_w \tag{81}$$

and from (69) and (81) in (65), we get

$$ss_T = ss_R + ss_C + ss_S + ss_{RC} + ss_{RS} + ss_{CS} + ss_{RCS} + ss_w. \tag{82}$$

All the right hand terms in this expression may be computed from the original table (see (65), (66), (67), and (68)), but ss_{RCS} may most readily be obtained as a residual. Thus, all the terms on the right of (82) may be computed from the original table without actually having to make any of the arithmetic corrections.

The degrees of freedom for each of the sums of squares computed directly from the original table are determined as in preceding analyses. The degrees of freedom for ss_{RCS} may then be obtained as a residual as follows:

$$df_{RCS} = df_T - df_R - df_C - df_S - df_{RC} - df_{RS} - df_{CS} - df_w,$$

or

$$df_{RCS} = (N - 1) - (r - 1) - (c - 1) - (s - 1) - (r - 1)(c - 1)$$
$$- (r - 1)(s - 1) - (c - 1)(s - 1) - (N - rcs),$$

TABLE 7

Analysis of Total Sum of Squares in Three-Way Table into Eight Components by Successive Applications of the Method of Arithmetic Corrections

Original Table	Once-Corrected Table	Twice-Corrected Table	Thrice-Corrected Table
$(M_{obs\ RC} = M)$	$(M'_{obs\ RC} = M)$	$(M''_{obs\ RS} = M)$	$(M'''_{obs\ CS} = M)$

$$SS_T = \begin{cases} SS_R \\ SS_C \\ SS_{RC} \\ SS_{w\ obs\ RC} \end{cases} = \quad SS'_T = \begin{cases} SS'_R = 0 \\ SS'_S = SS_S \\ SS'_{RS} = SS_{RS} \\ SS_{w\ obs\ RS} \end{cases} = \quad SS''_T = \begin{cases} SS''_C = 0 \\ SS''_S = 0 \\ SS''_{CS} = SS_{CS} \\ SS''_{w\ obs\ CS} \end{cases} = \quad SS'''_T = \begin{cases} SS'''_{cells} = SS_{RCS} \\ SS'''_w = SS_w \end{cases}$$

$$= \quad SS_S + SS_{RS} + \quad SS_{CS} + \quad SS_{RCS} + SS_w$$

$$SS_T = SS_R + SS_C + SS_{RC}$$

$$SS_T = SS_R + SS_C + SS_S + SS_{RS} + SS_{CS} + SS_{RCS} + SS_w$$

which reduces to

$$df_{RCS} = (r-1)(c-1)(s-1).$$

This analysis is summarized in Table 7 on page 224.

Computational Procedures

The procedures for computing the various sums of squares in a three-way table are essentially the same as those employed in the two-way table. The sum of squares for the treatments in the row classification (ss_R), for instance, is obtained just as in a double-entry table by means of the formula

$$ss_R = \sum_{i=1}^{n} T_{i..}^2/n_{i..} - \frac{T^2}{N},$$

in which $T_{i..}$ is the sum of all criterion measures in the ith R-layer (corresponding to the ith row in the front face). The sum of squares for each of the other main effects (C and S) is similarly computed.

The sum of squares for any two-factor interaction is obtained by first computing the sum of squares for between-combinations of those two factors, and then subtracting the sums of squares for the main effects of those factors. We will let $ss_{\overline{RS}}$ represent the sum of squares for between-*obs* RS, or for between-RS-combinations. The sum of squares for between-combinations of the R and S factors is then given by

$$ss_{\overline{RS}} = \sum_{k=1}^{s}\sum_{i=1}^{r} T_{i.k}^2/n_{i.k} - \frac{T^2}{N}$$

in which $T_{i.k}$ is the sum of the criterion measures in one of the *obs* RS. The sum of squares for the RS interaction is then given by

$$ss_{RS} = ss_{\overline{RS}} - ss_R - ss_S.$$

The "triple" interaction sum of squares (ss_{RCS}) is similarly computed by first computing the sum of squares for between-combinations of all three factors (between-cells), given by

$$ss_{\overline{RCS}} = \sum_{k=1}^{s}\sum_{j=1}^{c}\sum_{i=1}^{r} T_{ijk}^2/n_{ijk} - \frac{T^2}{N}$$

and then subtracting the sums of squares for all main effects and for all two-factor interactions.

The formulas for computing the various sums of squares are given in the following summary table:

TABLE 8 Computational Formulas for a Three-Classification ($R \times C \times S$) Design

Source of Variation	df	Sum of Squares
Rows (R)	$r - 1$	$ss_R = \sum_{i=1}^{r} T_{i..}^2 / n_{i..} - \dfrac{T^2}{N}$
Columns (C)	$c - 1$	$ss_C = \sum_{j=1}^{c} T_{.j.}^2 / n_{.j.} - \dfrac{T^2}{N}$
Slices (S)	$s - 1$	$ss_S = \sum_{k=1}^{s} T_{..k}^2 / n_{..k} - \dfrac{T^2}{N}$
RC	$(r-1)(c-1)$	$ss_{RC} = \sum_{j=1}^{c}\sum_{i=1}^{r} T_{ij.}^2 / n_{ij.} - \dfrac{T^2}{N} - (ss_R + ss_C)$
RS	$(r-1)(s-1)$	$ss_{RS} = \sum_{k=1}^{s}\sum_{i=1}^{r} T_{i.k}^2 / n_{i.k} - \dfrac{T^2}{N} - (ss_R + ss_S)$
CS	$(c-1)(s-1)$	$ss_{CS} = \sum_{k=1}^{s}\sum_{j=1}^{c} T_{.jk}^2 / n_{.jk} - \dfrac{T^2}{N} - (ss_C + ss_S)$
RCS	$(r-1)(c-1) \times (s-1)$	$ss_{RCS} = \sum_{k=1}^{s}\sum_{j=1}^{c}\sum_{i=1}^{r} T_{ijk}^2 / n_{ijk} - \dfrac{T^2}{N} -$ $(ss_R + ss_C + ss_S + ss_{RC} + ss_{RS} + ss_{CS})$
Within-cells (w)	$N - rcs$	$ss_w = \sum_{k=1}^{s}\sum_{j=1}^{c}\sum_{i=1}^{r}\sum X^2 - \sum_{k=1}^{s}\sum_{j=1}^{c}\sum_{i=1}^{r} T_{ijk}^2 / n_{ijk}$
Total	$N - 1$	$ss_T = \sum_{k=1}^{s}\sum_{j=1}^{c}\sum_{i=1}^{r}\sum X^2 - \dfrac{T^2}{N}$

Illustration of Computational Procedure: A convenient way of organizing the data from a three-factor experiment for computational purposes is illustrated below for a design involving two levels of factor A, four of B, and three of C, with varying numbers of subjects in the B categories. This may be denoted a $2 \times 4 \times 3$ design, to indicate the numbers of levels of the various factors.

	A_1													A_2										
	B_1			B_2			B_3			B_4				B_1			B_2			B_3			B_4	
	C_1	C_2	C_3	C_1	C_2	C_3	C_1	C_2	C_3	C_1	C_2	C_3		C_1	C_2	C_3	C_1	C_2	C_3	C_1	C_2	C_3	C_1	C_2	C
	9	15	10	14	8	9	18	19	20	16	17	17		13	16	16	17	7	15	29	21	19	30	21	15
	7	10	10	7	6	13	16	13	17	9	16	11		12	10	9	22	16	23	25	18	24	21	15	16
	7	13	15	5	10	7	12	9	13	17	19	15		18	18	14	14	7	16	18	19	15	9	6	17
	14	16	18	15	13	13	16	13	16	9	10	12		18	20	19	17	13	15	25	21	22	13	16	23
	37	54	53	12	13	12	10	7	9	22	21	14		61	64	58	10	16	11	15	15	17	18	18	17
				11	14	8	9	13	14	73	83	69					12	9	13	21	15	17	91	76	88
				64	64	62	11	7	14								92	68	93	18	12	11			
							12	9	12											30	18	24			
				104	90	115														181	139	149			

[handwritten annotations throughout: beside df column "1", "3", "2", "3", "2", "6", "6", "138-24 / 114", "138-1 / 137"; beside data tables "144", "190", "909", "225", "183", "23", "469", "255"]

This table indicates that for the four subjects receiving treatment $A_1B_1C_1$ the criterion measures were 9, 7, 7, and 14, with a total (T_{111}) of 37, etc. The first step is to compute the sums for the various treatment groups. A two-dimensional table should be prepared for each possible *pair* of factors, disregarding the other factor. Such tables for the preceding data are presented below. Thus the entry in the upper left cell of the AC table, 278, is obtained by adding the four A_1C_1 sums, i.e., $37 + 64 + 104 + 73 = 278$; the entry in the lower right cell of the BC table, 157, is obtained by summing the two B_4C_3 sums i.e., $69 + 88 = 157$, etc.

	A_1	A_2	Total			A_1	A_2	Total			C_1	C_2	C_3	Total
	12	12				23	23				8	8	8	
B_1	144	183	327	C_1	278	425	703	B_1	98	118	111	327
	18	18				23	23				12	12	12	
B_2	190	253	443	C_2	291	347	638	B_2	156	132	155	443
	24	24				23	23				16	16	16	
B_3	309	469	778	C_3	299	388	687	B_3	285	229	264	778
	15	15									10	10	10	
B_4	225	255	480	Total	868	1160	2028	B_4	164	159	157	480
Total	868	1160	2028						Total	703	638	687	2028

The subsequent calculations may be indicated as follows:

$$ss_T = 9^2 + 7^2 + \ldots + 23^2 + 17^2 - (2028)^2/138 = 33,260.0 - 29,802.8 = 3457.2$$

$$ss_{\text{cells}} = \left[\frac{37^2 + 54^2 + 53^2 + 61^2 + 64^2 + 58^2}{4} + \frac{64^2 + \ldots + 93^2}{6} \right.$$
$$\left. + \frac{104^2 + \ldots + 149^2}{8} + \frac{73^2 + \ldots + 88^2}{5} \right] - 29,802.8 = 1453.8$$

$$ss_w = 3457.2 - 1453.8 = 2003.4$$

$$ss_A = \frac{868^2 + 1160^2}{69} - 29,802.8 = 617.8$$

$$ss_B = \left[\frac{327^2}{24} + \frac{443^2}{36} + \frac{778^2}{48} + \frac{480^2}{30} \right] - 29,802.8 = 394.1$$

$$ss_C = \left[\frac{703^2 + 638^2 + 687^2}{46} \right] - 29,802.8 = 49.9$$

$$ss_{AB} = \left[\frac{144^2 + 183^2}{12} + \frac{190^2 + 253^2}{18} + \frac{309^2 + 469^2}{24} + \frac{225^2 + 255^2}{15} \right] - 29,802.8$$
$$- 617.8 - 394.1 = 119.1$$

$$ss_{AC} = \left[\frac{278^2 + 425^2 + 291^2 + 347^2 + 299^2 + 388^2}{23} \right] - 29,802.8 - 617.8$$
$$- 49.9 = 92.3$$

$$ss_{BC} = \left[\frac{98^2 + 118^2 + 111^2}{8} + \frac{156^2 + 132^2 + 155^2}{12} + \frac{285^2 + 229^2 + 264^2}{16} + \frac{164^2 + 159^2 + 157^2}{10} \right] - 29,802.8 - 394.1 - 49.9 = 110.1$$

$$ss_{ABC} = 1453.8 - 617.8 - 394.1 - 49.9 - 119.1 - 92.3 - 110.1 = 70.5$$

(Note that in every case the divisor is the number of *measures* on which each squared term is based. If these n's are not the same for all terms involved, separate divisions must be performed before summation.)

Summary Table

Source	df	ss	ms
A	1	617.8	617.80
B	3	394.1	131.36
C	2	49.9	24.95
AB	3	119.1	39.70
AC	2	92.3	46.15
BC	6	110.1	18.35
ABC	6	70.5	11.75
w cells	114	2003.4	17.56
Total	137	3457.2	

Meaning of Triple Interaction

The *observed* triple interaction is measured by the residual variability in the *cell* means after corrections have been applied that make the means of all *oblongs* (in any direction) equal to the general mean. In a table so corrected, the sums of squares for all main effects and for all two-factor interactions will be equal to zero, but there will still be differences among the cell (cubicle) means. If these differences are too large to be reasonably attributed to random Type S fluctuations in the cell means, we say that the observed triple interaction is significant.

To say that there is a *triple* interaction also means that corresponding interaction effects (see page 118) of two of the factors differ in magnitude from level to level of the third factor. For instance, if corresponding interaction effects for the various R–C combinations (cells) are not the same for all s-layers, then there is a triple interaction in the table. This is also equivalent to saying that there is a simple interaction between the S factor and the RC interaction, $(ss_{RCS} = ss_{(RC)S})$, or between the R factor and the CS interaction, $(ss_{RCS} = ss_{R(CS)})$, etc. It does not matter in what order the factors are arranged in the subscript, that is, $ss_{RCS} = ss_{CSR} = ss_{SCR}$, etc.

The meaning of triple interaction is perhaps most readily understood in the case of a $2 \times 2 \times s$ table, such as that diagrammed below. Let μ_{111},

μ_{121}, etc. represent the true means corresponding to M_{111}, M_{121}, etc., respectively. If $(\mu_{11k} - \mu_{12k}) - (\mu_{21k} - \mu_{22k}) \neq 0$ for any given value of k, we would say that there is an interaction between the R and C factors so far as the corresponding level of S is concerned. If $(\mu_{11k} - \mu_{12k}) - (\mu_{21k} - \mu_{22k})$ differs for different values of k, that is, if it differs from s-layer to s-layer, then a triple interaction is present. To test the hypothesis that there is no triple interaction, one would ascertain whether the observed variance of $D = (M_{11k} - M_{12k}) - (M_{21k} - M_{22k})$ for the various values of k is significantly larger than the variance which would be expected as the result of sampling fluctuations in the cell means. This, as we shall see later, is what is accomplished by the F-test based on the ratio ms_{RCS}/ms_w.

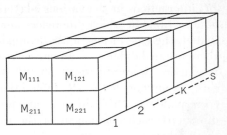

From any $r \times c \times s$ table one can select a number of $2 \times 2 \times s$ tables, each of which consists of *obs RC* ending in the corner cells of a rectangle drawn on the RC face (see the accompanying drawing). If, in any $2 \times 2 \times s$ table, there is a triple interaction as just defined, then there is a triple interaction in the entire table. The F-ratio ms_{RCS}/ms_w for the entire table tests the hypothesis that there is no triple interaction in *any* $2 \times 2 \times s$ or $2 \times 2 \times r$ or $2 \times 2 \times c$ table taken from the entire table. [This F-test, however, is not very sensitive to a triple interaction affecting only a small part of the whole table (see page 140)].

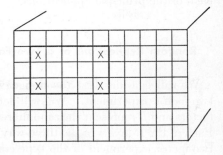

It should be apparent that the triple interaction may be much more pronounced in one of the component $2 \times 2 \times s$ tables than in others, or that there may be no triple interaction in some such tables and some triple interaction in others. It is possible, in other words, that the triple interaction for the whole table is not homogeneous. Heterogeneity of triple interaction, however, may be quite independent of heterogeneity of any two-factor interaction, either for the table as a whole or for any layer.

In the *twice-corrected* table of page 222, in which all *obs RC* and *obs RS* means equal the general mean, the triple interaction may also be regarded as measured by the differences among cell means within *obs CS*. If corrections have made all *obs RS* and *obs CS* means equal to the general mean, the triple interaction would similarly be measured by differences among cell means within *obs RC*. It is also measured by differences among cell means within *obs RS* after differences among *obs RC* and *obs CS* have been eliminated.

Each of the interactions is independent of each of the others. It is quite possible, for instance, that there is no RC interaction for the entire table even though there is a triple interaction. This would mean that the differing RC interactions in the various s-layers tend to "average out" to zero. That is, in a table in which differences among $obs\ RS$ and $obs\ CS$ have been eliminated, the true means of $obs\ RC$ might all have the same value, even though there are real differences among cells within $obs\ RC$. However, if the true RC interaction were the same for all s-layers, the RCS interaction would be zero, even though the RC interaction is pronounced. In a table in which corresponding cell frequencies are proportional from layer to layer (in any direction), each component of the total sum of squares (82) is *independent* of all others.

Applications of Three-Dimensional Designs

As noted earlier (page 220), there is a variety of experimental designs for which the data may be presented in a three-way table, and in which the total sum of squares may be analyzed in the manner just considered. We will now consider the various tests of significance and their interpretation for each of the principal applications.

Random Replications of a Two-Factor Experiment ($A \times B \times R$ Designs)

We will consider first the design which involves random replications of a two-factor experiment. We will let A and B represent the experimental factors and R represent the random replications of the basic $A \times B$ experiment. Each of the R-layers in the three-way table will then represent an independent two-factor experiment of the type considered in Chapter 9, while the r-layers or replications represented in the entire experiment will be regarded as a simple random sample from a hypothetical population of such layers or replications. The replications may be "simple" replications, in the sense that the subjects involved in each replication are a random sample from the same population. On the other hand, the entire population may consist of a very large number of subpopulations. A relatively small number (r) of these may have been selected at random for the purposes of the experiment, and from each of these selected subpopulations a number of subjects may have been drawn at random.

Testing the ABR Interaction: In general, in experiments involving random replications of a two-factor experiment, there is relatively little interest in a test of the triple interaction. In many such instances it may be taken for granted that either experimental errors (Type G) which vary from replication to replication, or differences among the subpopulations sampled, or both, will result in a non-chance triple interaction. In general, also, the significance or non-significance of the ABR interaction will have little bearing on the rest of the analysis. However, the significance of the triple interaction may be tested by means of

$$F = ms_{ABR}/ms_w, \, df = (a - 1)(b - 1)(r - 1)/(N - abr). \tag{83}$$

The conditions under which this mean square ratio is distributed as F are as follows:

1) The measures in each cell of the table are a simple random sample from a corresponding subpopulation.

2) The distribution of criterion measures for each of these subpopulations is normal.

3) Each of these distributions has the same variance.

4) The triple interaction (ABR) is zero for the entire population.

Since proportionality of cell frequencies is required in the analysis of the total sum of squares into its components, this requirement will not be repeated for each of the tests here considered, but is always actually one of the underlying requirements.

To prove that under these conditions ms_{ABR}/ms_w is distributed as F, we may note first that in the thrice-corrected table on page 223, the total sum of squares may be analyzed into

$$ss_T''' = ss_{\text{cells}}''' + ss_w'''.$$

Accordingly, under Conditions 1, 2, and 3, the design in the thrice-corrected table may be regarded as a simple-randomized design. We know that in any simple-randomized design, $ms_{\text{groups}}/ms_{w \text{ groups}}$ is distributed as F. In this case, $ms_{\text{groups}} = ms_{\text{cells}}'''$ and $ms_{w \text{ groups}} = ms_w'''$. We know also that $ms_{\text{cells}}''' = ms_{ABR}$ and that $ms_w''' = ms_w$. Accordingly,

$$F = ms_{\text{ groups}}/ms_{w \text{ groups}} = ms_{ABR}/ms_w.$$

In deciding to what extent Conditions 1 to 3 are satisfied in a particular experiment, the important considerations are essentially the same as those discussed in Chapter 3, pages 72–90, and again in subsequent chapters.

Testing the AB Interaction: As noted in the preceding section, there is usually little interest in the triple interaction in an $A \times B \times R$ experiment. Usually the existence of a triple interaction is taken for granted, and the mean square for this triple interaction is used as the error term in testing the AB effect. The use of the ABR interaction as an error term, however, requires either that the number of observations be the same for all cells in the table or that the analysis be based on the unweighted cell means. If the number of cases per cell is constant, the ratios used in the tests of significance are the same as when the analysis is based on the individual measures, since any sum of squares based on the individual measures is n times the corresponding sum of squares based on the unweighted cell means. Since the proofs may thereby be simplified, the discussion from this point on will be concerned primarily with the case in which the analysis is based on the unweighted cell means. As in preceding chapters, we will employ an asterisk to indicate that a sum of squares or a mean square is based on the unweighted cell means.

The hypothesis that there is no interaction of A and B in the population from which the particular replications involved in the experiment are a random sample may be tested by

$$F = ms^*_{AB}/ms^*_{ABR}, \; df = (a-1)(b-1)/(a-1)(b-1)(r-1). \qquad (84)$$

The conditions under which this mean square ratio is distributed as F are as follows:

1) The replications represented in the experiment are an independent simple random sample from a hypothetical population of such replications.

2) The triple interaction effects are normally and independently distributed in the population for each treatment-combination.

3) The triple interaction in the population is homogeneous (has the same population variance for all $2 \times 2 \times r$ tables in the entire table).

4) The AB interaction for the entire population is zero.

It should be noted that if n_{ijk} is variable, even though these n's are in the same proportion from row to row within each replication, ms_{AB}/ms_{ABR} is not distributed as F.

To prove that ms^*_{AB}/ms^*_{ABR} is distributed as F, let us suppose that in the three-way table corrections have been applied within $obs\, AR$ and $obs\, BR$ independently, so as to make their means equal to the general mean. Let us regard this twice-corrected table as consisting of $obs\, AB$. Each of these $obs\, AB$ is divided into r cells, corresponding to the r replications. In this twice-corrected table, there will be no within-cells component of the total sum of squares, since the analysis is based on the cell means. Accordingly, the total sum of squares in the twice-corrected table may be analyzed (see page 222) into

$$ss''^*_T = ss''^*_{obs\, AB} + ss''^*_{w\, obs\, AB} \qquad (85)$$

in which $ss''^*_{w\, obs\, AB} = ss^*_{ABR}$, since $ss^*_w = 0$.

From (85) it is apparent that the design in the twice-corrected table may be regarded as a simple-randomized design, in which $ms^*_{groups}/ms^*_{w\, groups}$ is distributed as F. In this case, $ss^*_{groups} = ss''^*_{obs\, AB} = ss^*_{AB}$ (see Table 7, page

224) and $ss^*_{w\,\text{groups}} = ss''^*_{w\,\text{obs}\,AB} = ss^*_{ABR}$. Hence, $ms^*_{AB}/ms^*_{ABR} = ms_{AB}/ms_{ABR}$. Accordingly we may write

$$F = ms_{\text{groups}}/ms^*_{w\,\text{groups}} = ms^*_{AB}/ms^*_{ABR}$$

If ABR has already been shown to be significant, or if on *a priori* considerations we may take an ABR interaction for granted, we know that there *is* an AB interaction in individual replications, but that it varies from replication to replication. However, it is conceivable that these AB interactions cancel one another so far as the whole population is concerned, or that there is no AB interaction for the population as a whole. If $F = ms^*_{AB}/ms^*_{ABR}$ proves non-significant, we might assume that there is no AB interaction for the population as a whole, unless we are prevented from doing so by other (*a priori*) considerations.

If ABR is due to random Type S and Type G errors only, as it presumably would be in the case of "simple" replications in which Type G errors have been randomized for each replication independently, a significant $F = ms^*_{AB}/ms^*_{ABR}$ would indicate that there is an intrinsic AB interaction. This is the situation referred to at the end of Chapter 9 (page 216). If the replications are not "simple," and if ABR is in part intrinsic, one may still more surely infer from a significant $F = ms^*_{AB}/ms^*_{ABR}$ that there is an intrinsic AB interaction. A very important feature of this design, then, is that the test of significance enables one to test the hypothesis that there is an intrinsic AB interaction — a test which could not be made in a simple $A \times B$ experiment.

It should be noted that the test $F = ms^*_{AB}/ms^*_{ABR}$ is valid whether or not ABR is significant. (This is another reason why there is usually little interest in a test of the ABR interaction.) This test of AB must always be used if ABR is significant, but if the observed ABR is non-significant, and one may assume that there is no intrinsic or extrinsic triple interaction in the population, the AB interaction may be tested by

$$F = ms_{AB}\left/\frac{ss_{ABR} + ss_w}{df_{ABR} + df_w}\right., \quad df = (a-1)(b-1)/[(a-1)(b-1)(r-1) + N - abr]. \tag{86}$$

The conditions under which this mean square ratio is distributed as F are as follows:

1) The measures in each *cell* of the table are an independent simple random sample from a corresponding subpopulation.

2) The distribution of criterion measures for each of these subpopulations is normal.

3) Each of these distributions has the same variance.

4) The ABR interaction for the entire population is zero.

5) The AB interaction for the entire population is zero.

It should be noted that in this case it is not necessary that n be constant, although proportionality of the n's is necessary for computational purposes. It may be noted also that the replications need not be regarded as random replications. This latter feature will be of special consequence in later designs.

To prove that under these conditions the mean square ratio in (86) is distributed as F, let us suppose that for each replication independently arithmetic corrections have been applied within rows and columns so as to make all row means and all column means equal to the general mean for that replication. The only remaining variations within each replication are then those due to between-cells and to within-cells. Each replication thus corrected may therefore be viewed as a simple-randomized design, with the ab "treatments" corresponding to the ab treatment-combinations. The corrected data for the complete experiment may therefore be presented in a two-way table, with ab columns corresponding to treatment-combinations and r rows corresponding to replications. This corrected two-way table may then be regarded as corresponding to a treatments $\times$ random replications design of the type considered in Chapter 8.

We will let ss_R', ss_C', ss_{RC}', and ss_w' represent the components of the total sum of squares in an analysis of the corrected data in this two-way table. It should now be apparent that ms_C' in the corrected two-way table is the same as ms_{AB} in the original table, that $ms_R' = ms_R$, that $ms_{RC}' = ms_{ABR}$, and that $ms_w' = ms_w$. Accordingly, if there is no ABR interaction in the original table, then neither will there be any RC interaction in the corrected two-way table. Therefore, by the reasoning underlying (54) on page 196, the significance of the columns effect may be tested by

$$F = ms_C' \left/ \frac{ss_{RC}' + ss_w'}{df_{RC}' + df_w'} \right. = ms_{AB} \left/ \frac{ss_{ABR} + ss_w}{df_{ABR} + df_w} \right. ,$$

which is what we set out to prove.

Evaluating the AR and BR Interactions: If the observed ABR interaction is significant and there is presumably an intrinsic ABR interaction, neither ms_{AR}/ms_{ARB} nor ms_{BR}/ms_{BRA} is distributed as the ordinary F with $(a-1)(r-1)/(a-1)(b-1)(r-1)$ degrees of freedom, since neither A nor B is a random effect. However, we may use $F = ms_{AR}/ms_w$ to test the hypothesis that in a certain *hypothetical* population the AR interaction is zero (and similarly for the BR interaction). This hypothetical population is first of all restricted to the subpopulations corresponding to the particular replications involved in the experiment, the numbers in the various subpopulations being proportional to the corresponding numbers in the replications of the experiment. In this hypothetical population, some of the members have received Treatment B_1, some Treatment B_2, some Treatment B_3, etc., the members receiving each B-treatment being in the same proportion as in the experimental samples. Since this hypothetical population is nearly always an artificial population unlike any real population in which the experimenter is interested, there is ordinarily little interest in any test of the significance of the AR and BR interactions.

Frequently, in experiments of this kind, the mean squares for AR, BR, and ABR will not differ significantly, and the assumption will be plausible on *a priori* grounds that these interactions are all of the same strength. In that case, a pooled error term may be obtained by adding the sums of squares for AR, BR, and ABR, and dividing by the sum of their degrees of freedom. This pooled error term may then be used to test the significance of the AB interaction. Proof that under these conditions the ratio of ms_{AB} to the pooled error mean square is distributed as F is similar to the preceding and need not be presented here.

Testing the Main Effects of A and B: If the AB interaction has been proved non-significant and if other considerations also permit us to assume that there is no AB interaction in the population, we will then be interested in the main effects of A and B and wish to test their significance. The main effect of either A or B can of course be tested whether or not the AB interaction is significant, although if the AB interaction is significant we would ordinarily be interested only in the simple effects of A and B (see page 213).

Whether or not the AB interaction is significant, the main effects of A and B may be tested by

and

$$F = ms_A^*/ms_{AR}^*$$
$$F = ms_B^*/ms_{BR}^*. \tag{87}$$

The conditions under which ms_A^*/ms_{AR}^* is distributed as F are as follows:

1) The replications represented in the experiment are a simple random sample from a hypothetical population of such replications.

2) The AR interaction effects are normally and independently distributed in the population for each A-treatment.

3) The AR interaction effects in the treatment populations are homogeneous in variance.

4) In the treatment populations the unweighted mean of the subpopulation means is the same for each treatment.

The conditions under which ms_B^*/ms_{BR} is distributed as F are exactly similar. (If the number of cases differs for the various A-R combinations, $F = ms_A/ms_{AR}$ is not distributed as F (and similarly for ms_B/ms_{BR}).)

To prove that under these conditions ms_A^*/ms_{AR}^* is distributed as F, let us assume that arithmetic corrections have been applied to the original data so as to eliminate ms_B^*, ms_{AB}^*, and ms_{ABR}^*. (To eliminate ms_{ABR}^*, for example, one would apply a correction within each A-B-R combination; the correction would be equal to the ABR interaction effect for that combination, and there would then be no interaction effect for the corrected measures.)

These corrections, of course, would leave ms_A^* and ms_{AR}^* unaffected. In any one replication, there would then be only chance differences among the distributions of criterion measures for the various AB combinations in each A-category. Accordingly, in each replication all the observations for Treatment A_1 could be regarded as a simple random sample, and similarly for each of the other A treatments. That is, so far as the corrected measures are concerned, each replication would constitute a simple-randomized experiment. Accordingly, so far as the corrected measures are concerned, the entire experiment constitutes a random replications design, in which, under the hypothesis of equal treatment means, ms_A^*/ms_{AR}^* is distributed as F.

The proof that ms_B^*/ms_{BR}^* is distributed as F is exactly similar to the preceding.

The differences in the interpretation of the main effect of A when the observed AB interaction is significant and presumably partly intrinsic, and when it is non-significant and there is presumably no AB interaction in the population, are the same as in the case of the simpler $A \times B$ design (see pages 209–211).

If the analysis is based on the individual measures rather than on the unweighted cell means, if *all* the observed interactions prove non-significant when tested against ms_w, and if there is presumably no interaction of any kind (either intrinsic or extrinsic) in the population, the main effects of A and B may be tested against an error term obtained as follows:

$$ms_{\text{error}} = (ss_{AB} + ss_{AR} + ss_{BR} + ss_{ABR} + ss_w)/(df_{AB} + df_{AR} + df_{BR} + df_{ABR} + df_w).$$

In this case, all the interactions are presumably due to random Type S errors; hence it is legitimate to pool all these sums of squares to get a more stable error term. The main effects of A and B would then be tested by $F = ms_A/ms_{\text{error}}$ and $F = ms_B/ms_{\text{error}}$, the degrees of freedom for the error term being $N - a - b - r + 2$. There will obviously be very few occasions on which this test of significance may be used.

Testing the Simple Effects of A or B: If ms_{AB}^* is significant and an interaction presumably exists, neither ms_A^*/ms_{AB}^* nor ms_B^*/ms_{AB}^* is distributed as F (see page 214). In this case, these mean square ratios may be evaluated as in a two-factor design (see pages 214–215), but the safest procedure is to test the effect of the A factor for each level or category of B separately, or the effect of the B factor for each level of A separately, and to make no attempt to generalize about A differences for all B categories or about B differences for all A categories. To test the simple effect of the A factor for any given B category, one would use

$$F = ms_A^*/ms_{AR}^*, \quad df = (a - 1)/(a - 1)(r - 1) \tag{88}$$

computed from the data for the particular B category only. In other words, one would regard the data for the selected B category as taken from a simple random replications design, using the test of the treatments effect already proved valid for that design (see page 191).

It should be noted that what we are now calling a "simple" effect of A for a given level of B is also a "main" effect of A with reference to R for the given level of B. We could, if we wished, also compute the "simple" effect of A for a given replication for all levels of B, or for a given replication within a given level of B. Thus there are three kinds of simple effects of A in this three-dimensional design: The average effect of A at a given level of B for all levels of R; the average effect of A in a given replication for all levels of B; and the effect of A for a given BR combination — that is, for a given replication within a given category or level of B. In designs involving more than three dimensions, there is a still larger number of "simple" effects for any given factor. To avoid confusion, it will be best henceforth to specify exactly what effect is intended in each case. In this design, for instance, it would be better to speak of the "average effect of A at a given level of B for all replications" instead of "the simple effect of A for a given level of B" — noting that "average" effect may mean a *weighted* average if the number of cases in the various treatment combinations differs from replication to replication.

The average effect of the B factor, in any given A category, for all replications is similarly tested by

$$F = ms_B^*/ms_{BR}^*, \, df = (b-1)/(b-1)(r-1)$$

computed from the data for the particular A category only.

On the assumption of homogeneous AR interaction for all B categories, one could use ms_{AR}^* computed for the whole table as the error term for testing ms_A^*; and similarly ms_B^*.

If $n_{ij} = n$ is constant, the corresponding F-ratio computed on the basis of the individual measures may be used.

Treatments × Treatments × Subjects (A × B × S) Designs

Sometimes the various treatment-combinations in a two-factor experiment are such that all may be administered in succession to each subject, without introducing any serious order or sequence effects. In this case, a very efficient experiment can be performed, using a random sample of subjects for the population concerning which the inferences are to be drawn. The criterion measures can then be entered in a three-way table, in which we will let A and B represent the treatment classifications, S the subject classification, and s the number of subjects.

Testing the AB Interaction. The significance of the observed AB interaction is tested by means of

$$F = ms_{AB}/ms_{ABS}, \, df = (a-1)(b-1)/(a-1)(b-1)(s-1).$$

The conditions under which this ratio is distributed as F (assuming only one criterion measure in each cell of the three-way table) are as follows:

1) The subjects represented in the experiment are a simple random sample from a specified population of subjects.

2) The ABS interaction effects in the population are normally and independently distributed for each AB combination.

3) The ABS interaction in the population is homogeneous.

4) The AB interaction in the population is zero.

Proof that under these conditions this mean square ratio is distributed as F is exactly similar to the proof of (84) on page 232.

The important considerations in the interpretation of a significant $F = ms_{AB}/ms_{ABS}$ are closely similar to those involved in the interpretation of a significant $F = ms_A/ms_{AS}$ in the simpler $A \times S$ design (see pages 157–160.)

Testing the Main Effects of A and B: We would ordinarily be interested in testing the main effect of A (or B) only if we could assume that there is no AB interaction. Whether or not the AB interaction is significant, the significance of the main effect of A is tested by

$$F = ms_A/ms_{AS}, \ df = (a - 1)/(a - 1)(s - 1).$$

The conditions under which this mean square ratio is distributed as F (assuming one observation per cell) are as follows:

1) The subjects involved in the experiment are a simple random sample from a specified population of subjects.

2) The AS interaction effects in the population are normally and independently distributed for each A treatment.

3) The AS interaction in the population is homogeneous.

4) The population means for the various A treatments are identical.

The important considerations in the interpretation of a significant F are closely similar to those discussed on pages 159–160.

The proof that this mean square ratio is distributed as F is closely similar to the proof of (87) on pages 235–236.

The main effect of B, of course, is similarly tested by

$$F = ms_B/ms_{BS}.$$

Random Replications of Treatments × Levels Designs (A × L × R Designs)

We have noted previously that the analysis and interpretation of a two-factor $(A \times B)$ design (Chapter 9) and of a treatments × levels $(A \times L)$ design (Chapter 5) are very much alike. In the treatments × levels design, the primary interest is in the main effect of only the experimental factor (the treatment classification); in the two-factor design the interest is in the main effects of both factors as well as in the interaction effect. However, the tests of significance and their interpretation are essentially the same for both designs, except that the population for which the experimental sample is representative with respect to levels of a control variable may be a real population, or, if hypothetical, may be closely like some real population in which the experimenter is interested. In the factorial design, however, the population from which the experimental sample may be regarded as representative with respect to the categories of either factor is an artificial population of little practical interest. Hence, main effects in a two-factor design are usually of interest only if the observed interaction between the factors is non-significant and if there is presumably no interaction in the population.

The situation is very much the same with reference to random replications of two-factor $(A \times B \times R)$ designs and random replications of treatments × levels $(A \times L \times R)$ designs. The tests of significance and their interpretation are essentially the same in both instances. However, for the reasons given, the main effect of treatments (A) in random replications of a treatments × levels design will be of interest even though the AL interaction is significant, whereas the main effect of one of the treatments $(A$ or $B)$ in random replications of a two-factor design will be of little interest if the AB interaction is significant.

It is important to note that in random replication of an $A \times L$ design, the levels must be the same for all replications if the mean squares for L, AL, LR, and ALR interactions are to have any clear and useful meaning. This means that if these effects are to be tested, use may *not* be made of the method of constituting levels by "counting off" *na* subjects at a time (see pages 129–132). Instead the method of representative sampling from a real population (pages 128–129) must be used. However, if the levels in each replication are constituted by the "counting off" method, in which case the "levels" will not be the same for all replications, the significance of the *treatment* effect may still be tested by $F = ms_A^* / ms_{AR}^*$, assuming that the AR interaction effects are normally and independently distributed for each treatment, and assuming also a homogeneous AR interaction.

Two-Factor Experiments with Matched Groups (A × B × L Designs)

We may now consider the case in which A and B again represent experimental factors, but in which L represents a control variable introduced to achieve higher precision in the evaluation of A and B. The levels are constituted in the manner described in Chapter 5, pages 129–132, providing for at least two observations in each cell, and a two-factor $(A \times B)$ experiment is then performed at each of these levels. That is, within each level the subjects are randomly assigned to the various A-B combinations (cells). Usually the number assigned to each cell is the same, but this is not necessary so long as the corresponding numbers are proportional from row to row or from column to column within each level.

Testing the ABL Interaction: With this design, the significance of the triple interaction is tested in exactly the same fashion as was the ABR interaction in the $A \times B \times R$ design (see pages 230–231) and under exactly the same assumptions. A significant $F = ms_{ABL}/ms_w$ indicates that differences between corresponding AB interaction effects are not the same from level to level. Whether this variation is *intrinsic* or due to *error* only is a matter for judgment, based on considerations similar to those discussed on pages 123–127.

Testing the AB Interaction: The hypothesis that there is no AB interaction for the population as a whole may be tested by means of

$$F = ms_{AB}/ms_w, \ df = (a-1)(b-1)/(N-abl). \tag{89}$$

The conditions under which this mean square ratio is distributed as F are as follows: [1]

1) The subjects receiving each A-B combination were originally an independent *representative* sample from the same population (representative with reference to the L levels).

2) The distribution of criterion measures is normal for the subpopulation corresponding to each A-B combination in each level (to each *cell* in the three-way table).

---

[1] To prove that under these conditions ms_{AB}/ms_w is distributed as F, let us suppose that within the original three-way table constant corrections are applied within each *level* so as to eliminate the A and B effects for that level. These corrections would of course also eliminate the A and B effects as well as the AL and BL interactions, for the table as a whole. That is, for the corrected measures, $ms_A = ms_B = ms_{AL} = ms_{BL} = 0$. The corrected measures could then be entered in a two-way table with ab columns corresponding to the various A-B treatment combinations and with l rows corresponding to the various levels. The relations between the mean squares in the original three-way table and in the corrected two-way table would then be as follows:

$$ms'_{\text{rows} \times \text{columns}} = ms_{ABL}$$
$$ms'_{\text{cols}} = ms_{AB}$$
$$ms'_{\text{rows}} = ms_L$$
$$ms'_w = ms_w$$

This table might thus be regarded as corresponding to a treatments $\times$ levels design, in which the "treatments" are the various A-B combinations. Accordingly, in the corrected table, the significance of the "treatments" (columns) effect is tested by

$$F = ms'_{\text{cols}}/ms'_w$$

which, according to the equalities listed above, is the same as

$$F = ms_{AB}/ms_w.$$

3) Each of these distributions has the same variance.

4) The AB interaction in the population is zero.

Note that Condition 1 provides for proportionality of cell frequencies, but proportionality is in any case necessary for computational purposes.

The population referred to in Condition 4 is that from which the total experimental sample is *representative* with reference to the L-levels. This is usually a meaningful population and one which, if not real, is at least closely similar to a real population in which the experimenter is interested (see page 131). Any inferences drawn about the hypothetical population may therefore usually be safely extended to the corresponding real population.

A significant $F = ms_{AB}/ms_w$ indicates that the observed interaction may not be attributed to random Type S errors only, but it does not rule out the possibility that the significance of the observed AB interaction is due to experimental (Type G) errors only, with no intrinsic AB interaction in the population as a whole. How a significant F is to be interpreted in this respect, then, depends on the interpreter's judgment and on the extent to which Type G errors have been controlled in the experiment.

A non-significant $F = ms_{AB}/ms_w$ permits one to retain the hypothesis that there is no AB interaction in the population as a whole. A non-significant F, however, does not rule out the possibility that there is an AB interaction at any particular level of L. This possibility could be tested for any given level as in a simple two-factor design, using only the data for that level or (on the assumption of homogeneous error variance) using the error term (ms_w) obtained from the table as a whole. There would be little point in making such tests, however, unless the ABL interaction had first been proved significant for the table as a whole.

If one can assume that the ABL interaction is significant because of experimental errors *only* (no *intrinsic ABL* interaction), and if experimental errors have been *independently randomized* at each level (this would involve independent administration of the treatments at each level separately), then the ABL effect is a random effect. In this case, the interaction may be tested by

$$F = ms_{AB}^*/ms_{ABL}^*$$

on the conditions listed on page 232. If n_{ijk} is constant, the interaction may be tested by $F = ms_{AB}/ms_{ABL}$.

If the observed ABL interaction is non-significant, and if presumably there is no ABL interaction in the population, the AB interaction may be tested as in (86) and on the same conditions.

Testing the AL and BL Interactions: If $A \times B \times L$ is significant and presumably partly intrinsic, neither ms_{AL}/ms_{ABL} nor ms_{BL}/ms_{ABL} is distributed as F, since neither A nor B is a random effect. However, ms_{AL}/ms_w is distributed as F under the following conditions:

1) The subjects receiving each A-treatment at each level of L were originally a *representative* sample from the same population (representative with respect to the B-categories). After administration of the treatments, the subjects in each A-L combination are a representative sample (with reference to B) from a corresponding hypothetical population.

2) The distribution of criterion measures is normal for the subpopulation corresponding to each *cell* in the three-way table.

3) Each of these distributions has the same variance.

4) The AL interaction in the population is zero (that is, the relative effects of the A treatments are the same from one L subpopulation to another).

If ABL is significant and presumably partly intrinsic, the "population" referred to in Conditions 1 and 4 is a population in which some members take Treatment B_1 in combination with each of the A-L combinations, some take Treatment B_2 in combination with the A-L combinations, etc., the numbers taking the various B treatments being in the same proportion as in the experimental sample. This, obviously, is a "population" of little interest. In other words, if the AL interaction depends on which B category is involved, the interest would be in the AL interaction for each B category separately, rather than in the average of the AL interactions for the various B categories.

The test of significance for the BL interaction is similar to that for AL.

Testing Main Effects: If AB is significant and presumably partly intrinsic, then neither ms_A/ms_{AB} nor ms_B/ms_{AB} is distributed as F, since neither A nor B is a random effect. In this case, these mean square ratios may be evaluated as in a two-factor design (see pages 214–215), but the safer procedure is to test the main effect of the A factor for each category of B separately, and the main effect of the B factor for each category of A separately, with no attempt to generalize about A differences for all B categories or about B differences for all A categories. For any given category of B considered alone, the design is an $A \times L$ design of the type considered in Chapter 5, and the main effect of either A or L may be tested in the manner explained on pages 214–215.

If all the two-factor interactions prove non-significant, and if the assumption is tenable on *a priori* grounds that there is no intrinsic triple interaction, but that the observed triple interaction is due entirely to randomized experimental errors plus random sampling fluctuations, the main effects of A and B can be tested by

$$F = ms_A^*/ms_{ABL}^* \text{ or } F = ms_B^*/ms_{ABL}^*.$$

The conditions under which these mean squares are distributed as F and the proofs that they are so distributed are left as an exercise for the student.

If *all* observed interactions are non-significant when tested against ms_w, and one can assume that there is no interaction (either intrinsic or extrinsic) of any kind in the population, then one can use ms_w as the error term in testing main effects, or can pool the sums of squares for all interaction with that for within-cells, and divide by the sum of their degrees of freedom to provide an error term. Proof of this is also left as an exercise for the student.

Three-Factor (A × B × C) Designs

We have noted repeatedly that there are no differences in the analysis and interpretation of a treatments × levels and a treatments × treatments (factorial) design, except that the "populations" concerning which certain inferences are drawn are more meaningful in the case of the treatments × levels than in the case of the treatments × treatments design. We are therefore generally interested in main effects in an $A \times B$ design only if the observed AB interaction is non-significant and if presumably there is no interaction in the population.

Exactly the same situation prevails with reference to the $A \times B \times C$ and $A \times B \times L$ designs. All the tests of significance that can be used in the $A \times B \times L$ design can also be used in the $A \times B \times C$ design, C taking the place of L. In the $A \times B \times C$ design, however, we would generally be interested in any two-factor interaction in the table as a whole only if the observed triple interaction were non-significant and if presumably there was no triple interaction in the population. If the ABC interaction is significant and presumably partly intrinsic, our interest would be in the interaction of two of the factors for each category of the third factor separately.

Testing Differences in Individual Pairs of Means in Three-Dimensional Designs

In general, in complete three-dimensional designs, if $F = ms_A/ms_{error}$ is valid to test the effect of the A factor, whether for the table as a whole or for individual levels or categories or combinations of other factors, then the estimated error variance of the difference between any two corresponding A means, based on n_1 and n_2 cases respectively, is given by

$$\sigma^2_{(A_1-A_2)} = ms_{error}\left(\frac{1}{n_1} + \frac{1}{n_2}\right).$$

This is true regardless of what ms_{error} may represent. In some instances ms_{error} may be ms_{ABR}; in others it may be ms_{AR}, in others ms_w, in others $(ss_{ABC} + ss_w)/(df_{ABC} + df_w)$, etc. The difference is then tested by the ordinary t-test with a number of degrees of freedom equal to that for ms_{error}.

Similar statements, of course, apply to other factors or classifications (including levels, subjects, and replications).

STUDY EXERCISES [1]

1. An experiment [2] was performed to compare the accuracy of visual interpolation in circular coordinate plots differing in size of *scale interval* (*I*), and in the amount of illumination of the viewing field, *field intensity* (*F*).

Each coordinate plot consisted of a number of concentric circles with equal intervals between circles, printed in black on a sheet of very thin, translucent paper. This was placed over a sheet of blueprint paper containing 16 small (2 mm.) white dots more or less randomly distributed. This combination was then fastened to the frosted-glass surface of an inclined projection table which was illuminated from behind. The entire display was "masked down"

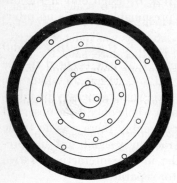

to produce a circular opening 24 inches in diameter, as shown in the following diagram.

Four separate coordinate plots were provided, one each with 1-inch, 2-inch, 3-inch, and 4-inch *scale intervals* (*I*), i.e., linear distance between successive concentric circles. (The scale lines themselves were of negligible width in comparison with the interval.) The projection surface was illuminated from behind with either a 100-watt bulb producing a dark blue background, or with a 300-watt bulb which produced a light blue background. In the former case, the scale lines were somewhat less distinct, but the white dots more conspicuous than in the latter. These two *field intensity* (*F*) conditions will be identified as F_d and F_l, respectively. (Room lighting was maintained at a constant level during every experimental session.)

The subjects, six experienced aircraft radar navigators, were instructed to estimate the distance, along a radius, from the center of the coordinate plot to the center of each of the white dots, starting with the one closest to

---

[1] See second paragraph on page viii.

[2] The experiment described here is hypothetical, but was suggested by a study reported by M. Leyzorek, "Accuracy of Visual Interpolation Between Circular Scale Markers as a Function of the Separation Between Markers," *Journal of Experimental Psychology*, vol. 39 (April, 1949), pp. 270–279. In his study, Leyzorek used several additional scale intervals and a Latin Square design, but did not vary the field intensity. However, the techniques used here and the results obtained are quite consistent with those of Leyzorek.

the center and working counterclockwise around each circle in turn. The subjects were told that the scale interval represented 1000 yards and that they were to make their estimates in those units. The criterion of visual *interpolation* was obtained by expressing the absolute error in the estimate of distance to a given dot as a *percentage of the scale interval* and taking the average of such values for the 16 estimates (dots) made by each subject under each of the eight treatment-combinations. Note that although the subjects were instructed to estimate the total distance to each dot, this criterion is concerned only with the accuracy of interpolation *within* the interval. Thus an absolute error of 20 yards, using any scale interval, represents an interpolation error of 2% (criterion value of 2.00), whether the total distance from the center of the plot was, say, 2100 or 9600 yards.

Each of the six subjects reported for a one-hour experimental session each day for four successive days. Since all of the subjects had recently participated in an experiment using somewhat similar materials, it was assumed that there would be no practice (or order) effect with respect to the scale interval factor. Hence, it was *considered* "safe" to administer the scale intervals in the same order for all subjects. All used the 1-inch scale the first day, the 2-inch scale the second day, etc. With each interval size, however, the order of administration of the field intensity conditions was independently determined for each subject by the flip of a coin. Furthermore, since the two intensity conditions were administered in the same one-hour session with identical scale intervals, it was necessary to use two "equivalent" dot patterns, *A* and *B*. Pattern *A* was always used for a subject's first trial at each session, and Pattern *B* for the second.

The following table presents the *average interpolation error* for each subject under each treatment-combination. Note that the smaller the criterion measure, the "better" the performance.

	I_1 1″ Interval		I_2 2″ Interval		I_3 3″ Interval		I_4 4″ Interval	
	F_d	F_l	F_d	F_l	F_d	F_l	F_d	F_l
S_1	3.48	4.20	4.87	4.03	3.60	3.85	2.75	3.56
S_2	7.86	7.31	5.42	5.36	6.41	6.73	3.98	4.20
S_3	5.08	4.64	7.34	6.82	5.23	5.90	6.26	7.54
S_4	4.47	4.30	5.01	5.48	3.65	4.22	4.60	5.11
S_5	4.23	3.00	2.32	2.29	2.70	2.76	2.17	2.60
S_6	3.03	3.46	4.19	5.00	3.02	3.14	2.45	3.18
ΣX	28.15	26.91	29.15	28.98	24.61	26.60	22.21	26.19
M	4.69	4.49	4.86	4.83	4.10	4.43	3.70	4.37
ΣX^2	146.75	132.07	155.01	151.76	111.13	130.21	94.46	130.15
$T^2/6$	132.07	120.69	141.62	139.97	100.94	117.93	82.21	114.32

The following tables of totals are provided for computational convenience.

Field (F)
(n per cell = 4)

	F_d	F_l	
S_1	14.70	15.64	30.34
S_2	23.67	23.60	47.27
S_3	23.91	24.90	48.81
S_4	17.73	19.11	36.84
S_5	11.42	10.65	22.07
S_6	12.69	14.78	27.47
	104.12	108.68	212.80

Interval (I)
(n per cell = 6)

	1″	2″	3″	4″	
F_d	28.15	29.15	24.61	22.21	104.12
F_l	26.91	28.98	26.60	26.19	108.68
	55.06	58.13	51.21	48.40	212.80

Summary Table

Source	df	ss	ms
Intervals (I)			
Field Intensity (F)			
Subjects (S)		73.62	
IF			
IS		25.50	
FS			
IFS			
Total		108.13	

a) Complete the calculations and fill in the summary table.

b) Explain in terms specific to this experiment what is meant by a triple interaction. By a triple interaction effect. What would it mean to say that this interaction is heterogeneous? What is probably the major source of triple interaction?

c) May the hypothesis of no *IF* interaction be rejected at the 5% level? Define as precisely as possible the population to which this hypothesis applies. In this test, what is assumed to be normally distributed with homogeneous variance?

d) Since "days" is confounded with "intervals" in this design, does it seem likely that the *IF* interaction is really due in part to interaction between Days and Field Intensity? Suggest some reasons for believing that the *IF* interaction is primarily intrinsic.

e) Why does the outcome of the test in (c) direct attention to the simple effects of *I* and *F*, rather than to their main effects?

f) If the *IF* interaction had been non-significant, a test of the main effect of Field Intensity would have been indicated. For that test, what error term should be used? What assumptions are involved?

g) Is the simple effect of Intervals for the dark field condition (F_d) significant at the 5% level? What assumptions are involved in this test?

h) What mean square ratio may be used to test the simple effect of field intensity for the 1-inch interval?

i) Under what assumptions would it be legitimate to pool the *FS* and *IFS* interactions? What test can be applied to determine the tenability of one of these assumptions? What would be gained by such a pooling in this instance?

j) Suppose the assumption of no practice (or order) effect with reference to intervals could not be made. How then should the intervals be administered if the same method of analysis is to be used? How would this affect the apparent precision of the experiment?

2. An experiment was carried out by Wilson [1] to investigate remote associations within serial lists of adjectives as a function of (A) *degree of learning*, (B) *distribution of practice*, and (C) *delay of recall*.

The experimental design was the $A \times B \times C$ design (page 243). The levels of these three factors were as follows: Degrees of learning — 50% (one-half of the words in the list correctly anticipated), 75%, 100%, and 200% (the entire list correctly anticipated in each of two successive trials); Distribution of practice — 6, 30, and 60 seconds between trials during practice; Delay of recall — 0, 2, 5, and 20 minutes from close of learning period to beginning of recall test. The recall test consisted of the same 16 words as in the practice list, but with the words in a different random order. There were thus $4 \times 3 \times 4 = 48$ different treatment combinations.

A different random order of the 16 words was assigned to each treatment combination as the list to be learned under that condition. Still a different random order of the words was later assigned to each treatment-combination as the list to be used during recall. According to Wilson, this procedure re-

---

[1] John T. Wilson, "The Formation and Retention of Remote Associations in Rote Learning," *Journal of Experimental Psychology*, vol. 39 (December, 1949), pp. 830–838.

duced to a minimum the differential effects which might arise due to inherent associations between particular pairs of words.

On the recall test, each word was exposed until a response was elicited. The subject was instructed to respond as quickly as possible with "the first word from the list which comes to mind." A "remote association" was defined as a response word from within the list other than the word following the cue word in the original list. The *criterion measure* for each subject was the *number of remote associations* on the recall test.

The subjects were 144 college students, 40 women and 104 men, from a course in elementary psychology. Three subjects were assigned at random to each of the 48 treatment-combinations. Each subject was given a practice session 24 hours preceding his experimental session, designed to familiarize him with learning and recall instructions and the general procedure of the experiment. During the experimental session the subjects under the 30- and 60-second spacing conditions named colors during the intertrial interval — subjects under the 2-, 5-, and 20-minute delay conditions rated cartoons during the delay period. This was done to reduce extraneous recitation.

The over-all criterion means for the treatment groups are as follows:

A				B			C			
Degrees of Learning(%)				Spacing Interval (sec.)			Delay Interval (min.)			
50	75	100	200	6	30	60	0	2	5	20
7.47	6.44	3.47	3.17	4.60	5.89	4.92	5.50	5.17	5.11	4.77

Summary Table

Source	df	ss	ms
Degree of Learning (A)	3	497.39	165.80
Spacing Interval (B)	2	43.60	21.80
Delay Interval (C)	3	9.44	3.15
Interaction (AB)	6	40.24	6.71
Interaction (AC)	9	112.61	12.51
Interaction (BC)	6	39.18	6.53
Interaction (ABC)	18	161.43	8.97
Within (w)	96	757.33	7.89
Total (tot)	143	1661.22	

a) In interpreting the results of an analysis of this kind in an $A \times B \times C$ design, the first step is usually to test the ABC interaction. Suppose this interaction is found to be significant. In this case, what is likely to be true (in the population) of the AB interactions for the various levels of C? Could there be a strong AB interaction for one level of C and none for another? In that case, would one be more interested in the "simple" AB interactions (those for individual levels of C) or in the "main" AB interaction?

b) If ABC were significant, and one nevertheless tested the "main" BC interaction, to what specific population would the hypothesis tested apply? Why would there usually be little interest in this population?

c) If the ABC interaction in this experiment had been found significant, how would you proceed to test the simple AC interaction for level B_{30} (30-second spacing) of B?

d) If ABC were significant, would you be most interested in the main effect of A, the simple effect of A for a given level of B (or C), or the simple effect of A for a given BC combination? Explain.

e) In this experiment, on how many cases is each of the B means for $A_{75}C_2$ based? Could one then make a very precise test of the simple effect of B for $A_{75}C_2$?

f) If there had been a strong and significant ABC interaction in this experiment, might the whole experiment have proved practically futile? Explain.

g) Fortunately for the purposes of this experiment, the ABC interaction was found to be non-significant, so that the main two-factor interactions could be tested on the assumption that ABC is non-existent in the population. What mean square ratio would you use to test the main AC interaction? State the hypothesis tested by this ratio, specifying the population involved.

h) Suppose the AC interaction had been found to be significant, so that one would probably not be interested in the main effect of A or C. For C_0 alone, on how many cases would each of the A means be based? With AC significant, might the test of the simple effect of A at C_0 be too imprecise to be of much value?

i) Were $A\bar{C}$ significant, on what condition might one still be interested in the main effect of B?

j) Is any interaction in this experiment significant at the 5% level? Is this a desirable outcome if one is primarily interested in the main effects of A, B, and C? Explain.

k) If you had planned this experiment just as described, and had then found reason to believe that all interactions would probably be found significant, would you still go ahead with the experiment? Does the answer to this question depend on what are your major interests in the experiment? Explain.

l) Define one of the treatment populations involved in the test of the main A effect.

m) What explanation can you offer for the fact that several of the mean square ratios are less than that for within-cells?

n) On the assumption that all interactions are non-existent in the population, one could pool the sums of squares with that for within-cells. Compute the pooled error mean square. How many degrees of freedom does it have? Just what is gained by this pooling in this case? Is this gain of much importance? Under what conditions is such pooling most worth while? What risks does it always entail?

o) Do you see any point in using a different order of the words in the learning list for each treatment-combination? Compare Wilson's procedure of randomizing lists with the simplest satisfactory alternative you can suggest.

p) Compute the estimated standard deviation of a cell population. Considering the sizes of the treatment means, do you see any reason to doubt that these populations are normal? Does this in itself cause you to question the validity of the tests of significance used? Explain.

q) Can you see any reason for using different error terms for testing the difference in the A_{50} and A_{75} means and the difference in the A_{100} and A_{200} means? Explain.

3. In an experiment in retroactive inhibition carried out by Haverkamp,[1] each subject: (1) learned by the anticipation method (in 8 trials) a list of 10 stimulus-response pairs of adjectives presented by memory drum, (2) learned another (interpolated) list, with the same stimulus words, but with different response words, and (3) relearned the original list (after an initial warm-up trial). One of the purposes of the study was to determine the effects upon retention of the original list of (1) the degree of synonymity between the response words of the original and interpolated lists and (2) the degree

---

[1] H. J. Haverkamp, "Retroactive Inhibition as a Function of Response Synonymity and Interpolated Learning," Ph.D. Thesis, State University of Iowa; August, 1951.

of learning (number of trials) of the interpolated list. Three different degrees of synonymity and three degrees of learning were represented, thus constituting nine different treatment-combinations. The *criterion measure* for each subject was the difference between the number of correct responses (out of 10) on his first trial of relearning and that on his last trial of original learning. Thus the subject with the "best" performance was the one with the lowest criterion measure.

Two hundred seven volunteer subjects from the course in sophomore psychology in two undergraduate colleges were employed. Each subject reported for one hour on each of three successive days. The first two days were devoted to practice sessions, the last to the experimental session. The "running" of the subjects was done at two different places over a considerable period of time. The $A \times B \times L$ design was used, the nine treatment (AB) groups being matched on the basis of a *control measure*, the number of correct responses on the last original-learning trial.

Subjects with the same control measure were assigned to the same "level." Since the range of this measure was 0–10, there were thus 11 possible levels, or a possible 99 cells in the $3 \times 3 \times 11$ table. Since the control measure for each subject was obtained in the same session as the criterion measure, it was not possible to employ the usual "counting off" method in constituting the levels. Instead, each of the early subjects was assigned at random to one of the treatment-combinations for his own level, the assignment being made immediately after the last original-learning trial, the trial on which the control measure was obtained. This was continued with subsequent subjects until one of the cells in the subject's level was filled with its "quota" of 3 subjects, in which case the subject was assigned at random to one of the unfilled cells in his level. When all cells in a level had been filled, the data for subsequent subjects in that level were discarded. After all 207 subjects had been run, all data in any level for which all nine cells were not filled were discarded. This resulted in the discard of all subjects whose control measures were 0, 1, 8, 9, or 10, as well as of the surplus subjects in the remaining levels. Thus the data for only 162 (out of 207) subjects in six levels were used in the analysis.[1]

The *mean* of the criterion measures (over all levels) for each treatment and treatment-combination group is presented in the following table.

---

[1] This method is described in detail here because it has possibilities in other similar situations. However, Haverkamp discarded more data than was necessary. He might have combined unit intervals with small frequencies; that is, he might have defined his top interval as 8–10 and his bottom interval as 0–1, making a total of 8 levels. He might then have set an initial minimum quota of two per combination, rather than three. As soon as a level was filled at this quota, he could raise the quota for that level to 3 per cell, when filled at this quota to 4 per cell, etc. Had he used this method, Haverkamp would probably have discarded less than 12 cases out of 207, and could probably have retained all 8 levels in the analysis.

Degree of Synonymity

	S_1 (High)	S_2 (Med)	S_3 (Low)	
I_1 (4 tr)	1.28	1.94	2.56	1.93
I_2 (8 tr)	2.33	2.89	2.94	2.72
I_3 (12 tr)	1.83	2.67	3.28	2.59
	1.81	2.50	2.93	

Degree
of Inter-
polated
Learning

N (per cell) = 18

The summary of the analysis is as follows:

Source	df	ss	ms
Syn (S)	2	33.94	16.97
Interpolated Learning (I)	2	19.72	9.86
Levels (L)	5	86.70	17.34
SI	4	3.80	.95
IL	10	22.43	2.43
SL	10	26.21	2.61
SIL	20	29.83	1.49
w	108	190.67	1.76
Total	161	413.30	

a) Define carefully the population about which one may draw strict statistical inferences about the *SI* interaction from this experiment.

b) Test the significance of the *SI* interaction. What error term did you employ? On what assumption could you have used ms_{SIL}? ms_{SL}? On what assumption could you have pooled the sums of squares for "within," *SIL*, and *SL* to provide an error term for this test? Is there sufficient advantage in using a pooled error term to justify making these relatively unsupported assumptions in this case? Explain.

c) The *criterion measure* in this experiment is the difference between the *control* measure (number of correct responses on the last original-learning trial) and the number of correct responses on the relearning trial. In consideration of this fact, explain why the variance of the criterion measures in the lowest (2) level must necessarily be very much smaller than that in the highest (7) level. (Haverkamp does not report the original individual measures, so that this inference cannot be verified from his report.)

d) Test the hypothesis that the *SL* interaction in the population is zero, limiting the risk of a Type I error to 5%. What "apparent" level of significance must you employ to feel reasonably certain that the risk of a Type I error is less than 5%? Explain fully.

e) Test the significance of the *IL* interaction, limiting the risk of a Type I error to 5%.

f) Define a real population to which the experimenter would presumably like to generalize from this experiment. In what important respects does this population differ from that described in (a)? Does the outcome of the tests of (d) and (e) facilitate such generalization? Explain.

g) Describe in general terms the relative advantages and disadvantages of the usual "counting off" method of constituting levels and the method employed in this experiment (with improvements suggested in the footnote).

h) Show that this experiment, based on 162 subjects, is more precise than a simple factorial experiment with all 207 subjects would have been. That is, estimate the error variance of a single mean (such as M_{S_1}) that would have been obtained in a simple factorial experiment, and express the corresponding error variance in the matched group experiment as a percent of this estimated error variance.

i) If you wished to test the difference between the S_1I_1 and S_2I_1 means, what data would you need that have not here been supplied? Explain.

11

Higher-Dimensional Designs

Analysis in Higher-Dimensional Designs

We are now ready to generalize to higher-dimensional designs the principles that have been established for one-, two-, and three-dimensional designs.

We have seen that a simple-randomized (one-dimensional) design may be replicated into a two-dimensional design $(A \times L, A \times S, \text{ or } A \times R)$, and that a two-dimensional design $(A \times B \text{ or } A \times L)$ may be replicated into a three-dimensional design $(A \times B \times R, A \times B \times L, A \times B \times S, A \times B \times C, \text{ or } A \times L \times R)$. In the same fashion, a three-dimensional design may be replicated into a four-dimensional design, in which the replications may be random replications, or levels of a control variable, or categories of a fourth factor, etc. This may be continued without theoretical limit; a design in any dimension may be replicated at will to constitute a design of a still higher order.

The total sum of squares in a simple-randomized (one-dimensional design) may be analyzed into two components: the (main) treatment effect and within-treatments.

The total sum of squares in a two-dimensional design may be analyzed into four components: two main effects, one two-factor interaction, and within-treatment-combinations.

The total sum of squares in a three-dimensional design may be analyzed into eight components: three main effects, three two-factor interactions, one three-factor interaction, and within-treatment-combinations.

The sum of squares in an n-dimensional design may be analyzed into 2^n components: n main effects, $n(n-1)/2$ two-factor interactions, $n(n-1)(n-2)/6$ three-factor interactions, etc. [The successive numbers are the terms in the expansion of $(1+1)^n$, omitting the first term, unity.]

Computational Procedures

The sum of squares for a two-factor interaction (regardless of the number of other factors involved in the design) is always computed (see pages 225–226) by first computing the sum of squares for *between-combinations* of those two factors and subtracting the sums of squares for their main effects. For example, in a five-factor ($ABCDE$) design,

$$ss_{BE} = ss_{\overline{BE}} - ss_B - ss_E,$$

in which $ss_{\overline{BE}}$ is the sum of squares for *between-combinations* of B and E. The sum of squares for between-combinations is computed by

$$ss_{\overline{BE}} = \sum_i \sum_j (T^2_{B_i E_j}/n_{B_i E_j}) - T^2/N$$

in which $T_{B_i E_j}$ is the sum of the criterion measures for a single combination of B and E, $n_{B_i E_j}$ is the corresponding number of subjects, and the summation is for all possible combinations. For example, $T_{B_2 E_3}$ would be the sum of the criterion measures for all subjects who had received the $B_2 E_3$ combination, regardless of the other factors with which this combination may have been combined.

Similarly,

$$ss_{ACD} = ss_{\overline{ACD}} - ss_A - ss_C - ss_D - ss_{AC} - ss_{AD} - ss_{CD}$$
$$= ss_{\overline{ACD}} - \text{(sums of squares for main effects of } A, C, \text{ and } D)$$
$$\quad - \text{(sums of squares for all two-factor interactions of } A, C,$$
$$\qquad \text{and } D)$$

in which $ss_{\overline{ACD}}$ is the sum of squares for *between-combinations* of A, C, and D, without regard to the other factors.

Similarly,

$$ss_{ABDE} = ss_{\overline{ABDE}} - \text{(sums of squares for main effects of } A, B, D, \text{ and } E)$$
$$\quad - \text{(sums of squares for all two-factor and three-factor}$$
$$\qquad \text{interactions involving } A, B, D, \text{ and } E \text{ only)}$$
$$= ss_{\overline{ABDE}} - \text{(sums of squares for all main effects and all lower order}$$
$$\qquad \text{interactions involving only these factors).}$$

This last expression suggests a generalized formula for computing the sum of squares for *any* higher-order interaction. Stated in words, the sum of squares for any higher-order interaction involving certain specified factors is the sum of squares for between-combinations of these factors minus the sums of squares for all main effects and lower-order interactions involving the specified factors only.

Interpretation of Higher-Order Interactions

Any higher-order interaction (in the population) may be interpreted in a manner suggested by the interpretations of two- and three-factor interactions. We have seen that a three-factor interaction may be regarded as the interaction of one of the factors with the interaction of the other two. For instance, the ABC interaction may be regarded as the interaction of the C factor with the AB interaction. This is to say that the AB interaction effects depend on which level of C is involved, or that corresponding AB interaction effects are not the same from level to level of C.

A four-factor interaction may similarly be regarded as the interaction of one of the factors with the triple interaction of the other three. For instance, the $ABCD$ interaction may be regarded as the interaction of the D factor with the ABC interaction. This is to say that corresponding ABC interaction effects are not the same from level to level of D. Similarly, $ABCD$ may be regarded as $(ABD)C$ or $A(BCD)$, etc. A four-factor interaction may also be regarded as the interaction between two two-factor interactions, for instance, $ABCD = (AB)(CD) = (AC)(BD)$, etc. That is, the AB interaction depends on which combination of factors C and D is involved, or the BD interaction depends on which combination of factors A and C is involved, etc.

A Notation for Factorial Designs

For convenience in reference, it is common practice to identify factorial or higher-dimensional designs in terms of the product of the numbers of categories involved in the classifications. For example, a "3×5" design is one which involves three treatments or categories in the first classification and five in the second. A $2 \times 2 \times 3 \times 3$ design is one involving two treatments in each of the two first classifications and three treatments or categories in each of the others, etc. A 2^3 design is a $2 \times 2 \times 2$ design.

Practical Limitations of Higher-Dimensional Designs

A "complete" factorial design is one in which all possible treatment combinations are administered. Complete experimental designs of four or more dimensions are rarely employed in educational and psychological research. With so many factors or classifications, the experiment becomes so unwieldy that administrative difficulties and other practical considerations often outweigh whatever theoretical advantage the designs may have over simpler lower-dimensional designs. Even with only three or four dimensions, the organization and administration of the experiment often present serious practical difficulties. This is especially true if there are several treatments in each treatment classification, and if the higher order interactions are significant. In a $4 \times 3 \times 2 \times 3$ design, for example, there would be 72 different treatment-combinations. Obviously, unless some of the treatments could be administered to the same subjects, such an experiment would require at least 72 subjects — preferably at least 144 — in order to provide a within-combinations error term. The number of subjects required for higher-dimensional designs, therefore, often prohibits their use. Furthermore, unless many or all of the treatments may be *simultaneously* administered on a group basis, the administrative problems involved may also prohibit the use of such complex designs. Finally, if the higher-order interactions prove significant, no very useful interpretations may be made of the main effects or of the lower-order interactions; the analysis must be broken down into a complex pattern of simple effects. For example, in a four factor $(A \times B \times C \times D)$ design the "simple" effects of A include the average effect of A

— with all combinations of C and D at a given level of B
— with all combinations of B and D at a given level of C
— with all combinations of B and C at a given level of D
— with a given CD combination at all levels of B
— with a given BD combination at all levels of C
— with a given BC combination at all levels of D

and the effect of A for a given BCD combination. For this reason, higher-dimensional designs in general are of dubious advantage unless one may be fairly certain in advance that the higher-order interactions will prove non-significant.

"Complete" and "Incomplete" Factorial Designs

For the reasons just given, complete factorial designs involving four or more factors are rarely employed in educational and psychological research. However, considerable use is made of what may be described as "incomplete" factorial designs, in which only a portion of the possible combinations are administered. Under certain conditions, almost as much of the *desired* information can be secured from a properly planned incomplete design as from a complete design involving the same factors. The possibilities of incomplete factorial designs will be considered in the succeeding chapters (12 and 13).

12

Latin Square and Graeco-Latin
Square Designs

Introduction

A serious disadvantage of complete factorial designs involving several factors with several levels of each factor is that the number of treatment-combinations or the number of different groups to which treatment-combinations must be administered may become so large as to make the experiment administratively unmanageable or impracticable.

In a^3 experiments of this character (that is, $a \times a \times a$ experiments in which the number of treatments, a, is the same for each factor), the procedure is sometimes followed of including in the experiment only a^2 of the a^3 possible treatment-combinations, giving each treatment-combination to an independent random sample of the same size. The treatment-combinations are so selected that each treatment in one classification is combined *once and only once* with each treatment in each of the other classifications. The comparison of overall treatment means for any one classification would then *appear* to be completely balanced so far as the effects of superimposed treatments from other classifications are concerned.

For example, in an experiment involving three levels of each of three factors (A, B, and C), the 27 possible combinations of treatments (all of which would be included in a complete factorial design) are

$A_1B_1C_1*$	$A_2B_1C_1$	$A_3B_1C_1$
$A_1B_1C_2$	$A_2B_1C_2$	$A_3B_1C_2*$
$A_1B_1C_3$	$A_2B_1C_3*$	$A_3B_1C_3$
$A_1B_2C_1$	$A_2B_2C_1*$	$A_3B_2C_1$
$A_1B_2C_2*$	$A_2B_2C_2$	$A_3B_2C_2$
$A_1B_2C_3$	$A_2B_2C_3$	$A_3B_2C_3*$
$A_1B_3C_1$	$A_2B_3C_1$	$A_3B_3C_1*$
$A_1B_3C_2$	$A_2B_3C_2*$	$A_3B_3C_2$
$A_1B_3C_3*$	$A_2B_3C_3$	$A_3B_3C_3$

Suppose, however, that only the starred (*) combinations are administered in the experiment. The results could then be entered in a table like the following,

	B_1	B_2	B_3
A_1	C_1	C_2	C_3
A_2	C_3	C_1	C_2
A_3	C_2	C_3	C_1

in which the combination $A_1B_1C_1$ corresponds to the left cell in the first row, $A_2B_2C_1$ to the middle cell in the second row, etc. In the comparison of A (row) means, for instance, since each of the three B treatments and each of the three C treatments appears once in each row, the A comparisons would *seem* to be balanced so far as B or C effects are concerned, and similarly for the B comparisons and C comparisons.

This type of design is known as a simple Latin square design. It derives its name from an ancient puzzle, that of determining in how many different ways Latin letters may be arranged in a square table so that each letter appears once but only once in each row and each column. The following are examples of Latin squares.

a	b
b	a

a	b	c
c	a	b
b	c	a

b	a	c
c	b	a
a	c	b

a	b	c	d
b	c	d	a
c	d	a	b
d	a	b	c

a	b	c	d
b	d	a	c
c	a	d	b
d	c	b	a

It may be shown, for instance, that there are two different ways of arranging the letters in a 2 × 2 square, 12 different ways in a 3 × 3 square, 576 in a 4 × 4, and 161,280 in a 5 × 5, etc.

The "simple" Latin square experimental design is one in which a different and independent random sample of n subjects corresponds to each cell of the table. As an illustration of a simple Latin square design, let us suppose that we wish in a single experiment to compare the effects on reading rate of three *styles* of type (A), three *sizes* of type (B), and three *widths* of column (C). In a complete factorial design of the type suggested on page 243, this would require the printing of 27 different editions of the rate-of-reading test, each with a different combination of size, style, and width of columns. Suppose, however, that we printed only nine editions, combining each style of type only once with each size and only once with each width of column, and also combining each size only once with each width of column. We might then administer the nine editions simultaneously, each to one of nine different randomly selected groups of subjects. The main effect of styles would then be independent of the main effects of size and width, and similarly for the main effect of size or of width.

However, for reasons that will be made clear later, this is a defective design unless one can assume that there are no interactions of the factors involved.

Analysis in Simple Latin Square Designs

In a simple Latin square design with a levels of each factor and n subjects receiving each treatment-combination (n subjects in each cell), the analysis of the total sum of squares is

$$ss_T = ss_A + ss_B + ss_C + ss_w + ss_{res}. \tag{90}$$

The corresponding analysis of the degrees of freedom is

$$(N - 1) = (a - 1) + (a - 1) + (a - 1) + (N - a^2) + (a - 1)(a - 2).$$

The sums of squares for the main effects are computed as in any factorial design; for example,

$$ss_C = \sum_i (T^2_{c_i}/n_{c_i}) - \frac{T^2}{N}.$$

The sum of squares for within-cells is computed by subtracting the sum of squares for between-cells from the sum of squares for total, and the last term in (90) is obtained as a residual. The usual procedure in an experiment like the size × style × width experiment described above has been to test the main effects against ms_w as an error term. For instance, the main effect of C has been tested by $F = ms_C/ms_w$. In some applications, the *residual* sum of squares has been used as the error term — necessarily so when there has been only one observation per cell. These tests, however, are valid only under special and rather unusual conditions to be explained later, and the tests are not generally recommended.

In contrast with (90), the analysis of the total sum of squares in the complete factorial design involving the same factors would be

$$ss_T = ss_A + ss_B + ss_C + ss_{AB} + ss_{AC} + ss_{BC} + ss_{ABC} + ss_w.$$

If a is large, say, larger than 10, the sums of squares for A, B, and C, and for within-cells would have very nearly the same meaning in an incomplete as in a complete design with the same number of cases per cell, and ss_{res} in the Latin square would be interpreted in the same way as the pooled sums of squares for all the interactions in the complete design. This is true, however, only when a is large — larger than would usually be the case in any psychological application. It is apparent, then, that there is no possibility of identifying or testing individual interactions in the Latin square. Also the use of the "residual" mean square as an error term for testing main effects would be open to exactly the same objections as the use of a pooled error term in a complete design (see page 236).

When a is small, however, the problem of interpreting and evaluating main effects is considerably more involved. The difficulties encountered in this situation are fully considered in the following section.

Confounding in Latin Square Designs

It may be noted that in the introductory section preceding, the statements were made that the comparisons of overall treatment means in any classification would "appear" or would "seem" to be completely balanced with reference to the other factors. This phrasing was used advisedly. Actually the comparisons are not truly balanced.

Consider the following 2×2 Latin square.

	A_1	A_2
B_1	C_1	C_2
B_2	C_2	C_1

In this Latin square, the mean for column 1 is $1/2(M_{A_1B_1C_1} + M_{A_1B_2C_2})$ and for column 2 is $1/2(M_{A_2B_1C_2} + M_{A_2B_2C_1})$. Hence the sum of squares for "columns," on which the estimate of the main effect of A will be based, depends on the difference between the sums of the means of the following pairs of cells:

Column 1	Column 2
$A_1B_1C_1$	$A_2B_1C_2$
$A_1B_2C_2$	$A_2B_2C_1$

Obviously, the B and C effects are each counterbalanced and hence have no effect on this difference. It is clear that any interaction of A and C or of A and B would also be equalized or counterbalanced. If the AC interaction effects (deviations of twice-corrected cell means from the general mean) were, for example,

	C_1	C_2
A_1	$+3$	-3
A_2	-3	$+3$

these interaction effects would cancel and would not affect the column difference, as indicated below.

Column 1	Column 2
$+3$	$+3$
$A_1C_1B_1$	$A_2C_2B_1$
-3	-3
$A_1C_2B_2$	$A_2C_1B_2$
$3 - 3 = 0$	$3 - 3 = 0$

Also, if the AB interaction effects were, for example,

	B_1	B_2
A_1	-5	$+5$
A_2	$+5$	-5

these effects would again cancel, as shown below:

Column 1	Column 2
-5	$+5$
$\overbrace{A_1B_1C_1}$	$\overbrace{A_2B_1C_2}$
$+5$	-5
$\overbrace{A_1B_2C_2}$	$\overbrace{A_2B_2C_1}$
$-5 + 5 = 0$	$5 - 5 = 0$

However, if the BC interaction effects were, for example,

	C_1	C_2
B_1	$+2$	-2
B_2	-2	$+2$

these effects would be completely *confounded* (inextricably intermingled) with the A effect in the column difference. That is, the full effect of these interactions would be included in the column difference, as follows:

Column 1	Column 2
$+2$	-2
$\overbrace{A_1B_1C_1}$	$\overbrace{A_2B_1C_2}$
$+2$	-2
$\overbrace{A_1B_2C_2}$	$\overbrace{A_2B_2C_1}$
$2 + 2 = 4$	$-2 - 2 = -4$

Thus, even though Treatments A_1 and A_2 were equally effective at each level of B or C separately, the A_1 mean would be higher than the A_2 mean in this comparison, due only to the fact that Treatment B_1 works better with C_1 than C_2, and B_2 works better with C_2 than C_1.

The triple interaction effects are the same in both columns and do not affect the differences between the columns. For instance, the triple interaction effects may be

	C_1	C_2
A_1B_1	2	-2
A_2B_1	-2	2
A_2B_2	2	-2
A_1B_2	-2	2

In this case, the effect of the triple interaction effects on the column means would be as follows:

Column 1	Column 2
$+2$	$+2$
$\overbrace{A_1B_1C_1}$	$\overbrace{A_2B_1C_2}$
$+2$	$+2$
$\overbrace{A_1B_2C_2}$	$\overbrace{A_2B_2C_1}$
$2 + 2 = 4$	$2 + 2 = 4$

In general, then, the BC interaction effect, but only this effect, is completely confounded with the A effect in the column difference. Similarly, the AC interaction effect is confounded with the B effect and the AB interaction effect is confounded with the C effect.

In 3×3 (or larger) squares, the BC interaction is, in general, only partially confounded with the A effect in ss_{rows}. That is, the interaction effects are partly but not completely cancelled out. For example, in the Latin square design

	A_1	A_2	A_3
B_1	C_1	C_3	C_2
B_2	C_2	C_1	C_3
B_3	C_3	C_2	C_1

if the BC interaction effects are

	C_1	C_2	C_3
B_1	6	-3	-3
B_2	-1	-4	5
B_3	-5	7	-2

the column (A) means in the Latin square design are affected as follows:

Col 1	Col 2	Col 3
6	-3	-3
$\overbrace{A_1B_1C_1}$	$\overbrace{A_2B_1C_3}$	$\overbrace{A_3B_1C_2}$
-4	-1	5
$\overbrace{A_1B_2C_2}$	$\overbrace{A_2B_2C_1}$	$\overbrace{A_3B_2C_3}$
-2	7	-5
$\overbrace{A_1B_3C_3}$	$\overbrace{A_2B_3C_2}$	$\overbrace{A_3B_3C_1}$
$6 - 4 - 2 = 0$	$7 - 3 - 1 = 3$	$-3 + 5 - 5 = -3$

It is easy to show, similarly, that the AB and AC interactions do not affect differences among column means. Similarly, also, the AC interaction may be shown to be partially confounded with the row (B) effect, etc.

In general, in 3×3 or larger squares, each main effect is partially confounded with the interaction of the other two factors and with the triple interaction. However, the larger the square, the more completely will these interactions tend to cancel out in the comparisons for main effects. This is why the statement was made earlier that when a is large the sum of squares for any main effect will tend to be the same in the incomplete (Latin square) as in the complete design.

Because of this confounding of interactions with main effects, and because of the ambiguous character of the "residual" which must often be employed as the "error" term in testing main effects, experimental designs based on a single "simple" Latin square will perhaps seldom be useful in educational and psychological research. In general, they may be safely used only when the intrinsic interactions may be assumed to be negligible and the Type G errors have been completely randomized with reference to cells (in this case ms_{res} is the appropriate error term) or when both intrinsic and extrinsic interactions may be assumed negligible (in which case ms_w or ms_{res}, or both pooled, is an appropriate error term). More complex Latin square designs, however, involving the administration of several treatments or treatment-combinations to the same subject, should prove quite useful. These are considered in Chapter 13 following.

Graeco-Latin Squares

A Graeco-Latin square design is one involving four factors or treatment classifications with the same number of levels of each, in which each treatment in any classification is combined once and only once with each treatment in each other classification. This design may be pictured below with rows corresponding to one treatment classification, columns to another, Latin letters to another, and Greek letters to the last.

$A\alpha$	$B\beta$	$C\gamma$
$C\beta$	$A\gamma$	$B\alpha$
$B\gamma$	$C\alpha$	$A\beta$

In the "simple" Graeco-Latin square design (a different random sample in each cell), each main effect is partially confounded with the first-order interactions of the remaining factors and with all higher order interactions. This design is therefore as limited in usefulness as is the simple Latin square design.

The Graeco-Latin square will be used in certain of the designs in the following chapter. A Graeco-Latin square consists of two superimposed Latin squares, one formed with Greek and the other with Latin letters, such that the same Latin letter is never paired more than once with the same Greek letter. Latin squares that may thus be superimposed to form Graeco-Latin squares are called "orthogonal" Latin squares. Complete sets of orthogonal 3×3, 4×4, and 5×5 Latin squares are given below. By superimposing three or more orthogonal Latin squares "hyper-Graeco-Latin" squares may be formed. No orthogonal 6×6 Latin squares exist. Sets of orthogonal Latin squares for larger squares may be found in R. A. Fisher and F. Yates, *Statistical Tables for Biological, Agricultural and Medical Research*, Third Edition (London: Oliver and Boyd, 1948), pp. 62–63, and examples concerning their use on pages 15–18.

TABLE 9

Complete Sets of Orthogonal Latin Squares

3×3

I	II
1 2 3	1 2 3
2 3 1	3 1 2
3 1 2	2 3 1

4×4

I	II	III
1 2 3 4	1 2 3 4	1 2 3 4
2 1 4 3	3 4 1 2	4 3 2 1
3 4 1 2	4 3 2 1	2 1 4 3
4 3 2 1	2 1 4 3	3 4 1 2

5×5

I	II	III	IV
1 2 3 4 5	1 2 3 4 5	1 2 3 4 5	1 2 3 4 5
2 3 4 5 1	3 4 5 1 2	4 5 1 2 3	5 1 2 3 4
3 4 5 1 2	5 1 2 3 4	2 3 4 5 1	4 5 1 2 3
4 5 1 2 3	2 3 4 5 1	5 1 2 3 4	3 4 5 1 2
5 1 2 3 4	4 5 1 2 3	3 4 5 1 2	2 3 4 5 1

13

Controlling Individual Differences in Factorial Experiments Through the Use of "Mixed" Designs

Introduction

Differences among individuals or subjects are a major source of variation in psychological experiments. Usually this source of error (Type S errors) is very much more potent than any other. In general, the most precise and efficient experimental designs are therefore those in which the effects of individual differences are held constant or counterbalanced, rather than merely randomized.

If the number of treatments is small and it is both possible and feasible to administer all treatments to each of the subjects, the effect of individual differences can be completely equalized in all comparisons. This is done by using the treatments × subjects design, in which every subject takes *all* of the treatments. The possibilities of thus completely controlling individual differences, however, are extremely limited. In many factorial experiments the number of treatment-combinations is so large that it is not practicable to administer all of them to each subject. In other instances, one (or more) of the treatment classifications may be such that more than one of the treatments in the same classification cannot possibly be satisfactorily administered to the same subject. This is because the subject is so changed by the administration of the first treatment that the results of the later administration of another treatment are not comparable or meaningful for purposes of evaluation. For example, having learned how to perform a certain task under certain conditions, the same subject cannot "learn" to do the *same* task again under a second set of conditions. In still other factorial experiments, the criterion measure employed may be such that it cannot meaningfully be secured more than once for the same subject. For example, the criterion measure may be the time required to read a certain passage. Obviously the time required to read the same passage a second time would not have the same meaning, nor

266

would the time required to read a different passage of possibly different difficulty. Finally, in some factorial experiments one of the "factors" to be investigated or controlled is the *order* in which the experimental treatments have been administered. Quite clearly, the same subject cannot take more than one treatment in the same rank order in the same series of treatments.

In factorial experiments of the types just described it may nevertheless be possible to control individual differences in some but not all of the treatment comparisons. This may be done by administering some of the treatment-combinations to some of the subjects and other treatment-combinations to other subjects. That is, the experiment may be so designed that in comparisons involving only one of the factors, the effects of the other factors are counter-balanced or equalized, and so that these comparisons are still unbiased.

Experimental designs of the type just suggested, in which each subject takes more than one but not all of the combinations, will be referred to in this discussion as "mixed" designs. A "mixed" design may be defined as one in which some of the treatment comparisons are *inter*-subject and some are *intra*-subject comparisons. In the simple-randomized design of Chapter 3, and in the simple factorial design of Chapter 9, all of the comparisons are inter-subject comparisons. In contrast, in the $A \times S$ design of Chapter 6 and in the $A \times B \times S$ design of Chapter 10, all treatment comparisons are intra-subject comparisons. "Mixed" designs may be regarded as mixtures of the simple-randomized and the treatments $\times$ subjects designs. In designs of this mixed type, of course, the inter-subject comparisons are usually much less precise than the intra-subject comparisons. However, the experiment may sometimes be designed so that individual differences are controlled in all of the more important comparisons, and so that precision is sacrificed only in the less important ones.

For convenience in the subsequent discussions, we will identify each mixed design by a Roman numeral, since any truly descriptive name would be too cumbersome.

Type I Designs

The simplest type of mixed design is a two-factor $(A \times B)$ design in which each of the A treatments in combination with any one B treatment is administered to the same subjects, but with each B treatment administered to a different group of subjects. For convenience in later reference, we will call this a Type I design. An example of this type of design is diagrammed below for the case in which $a = 4$ and $b = 3$. The subjects are divided at random into three groups, not necessarily of the same size. The first group is given all combinations of A with B_1, that is, the first group is given treatment-combinations A_1B_1, A_2B_1, A_3B_1, and A_4B_1. The second group is given all combinations of A with B_2, etc. The total experiment may thus be regarded as consisting of three treatments $\times$ subjects experiments, one with B held constant at the B_1 level, another at the B_2 level, etc.

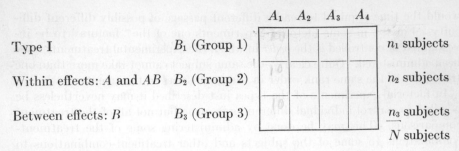

Type I

Within effects: A and AB

Between effects: B

The total sum of squares in this table may be analyzed into two or more components on each of several different bases, as follows:

(Disregarding both A and B) $ss_T = ss_S + ss_{wS}$ (91)

(Disregarding B only) $ss_T = ss_A + ss_S + ss_{AS}$ (92)

(Disregarding A only, see page 175) $ss_T = ss_B + ss_{SwB} + ss_{wS}$ (93)

(Disregarding S only) $ss_T = ss_A + ss_B + ss_{AB} + ss_{w\text{ cells}}$ (94)

From (91) and (92) we get

$$ss_{wS} = ss_A + ss_{AS}, \qquad (95)$$

and from (91) and (93)

$$ss_S = ss_B + ss_{SwB}. \qquad (96)$$

Thus, as is otherwise evident, the A effect is a "within" subjects effect and the B effect is a "between" subjects effect.

We may next note that if for each subject a constant correction were applied to all of his measures so as to make their mean equal to the general mean, that is, if the between-subjects sum of squares (ss_S) were eliminated by arithmetic corrections, the sum of squares for A and for AB would remain unaffected. Obviously, therefore, ss_{AB} cannot be contained in ss_S, and by (94), neither is it contained in ss_A. Accordingly, by (95), ss_{AB} must be contained in ss_{AS}. For reasons to be explained later, we will call the remainder of ss_{AS} the sum of squares for "error within." That is,

$$ss_{\text{error } (w)} = ss_{AS} - ss_{AB}. \qquad (97)$$

We will also let $ss_{SwB} = ss_{\text{error } (b)}$, which we will call the "error between" sum of squares. Then

$$ss_{wS} = ss_A + ss_{AB} + ss_{\text{error } (w)}. \qquad (98)$$

From (96), (97), (98), and (91) we find that we have thus analyzed the total sum of squares into five components, two of which are based upon between-subjects comparisons and three on within-subjects comparisons, as follows:

$$ss_T = \underbrace{ss_B + ss_{\text{error } (b)}}_{\text{"between components"}} + \underbrace{ss_A + ss_{AB} + ss_{\text{error } (w)}}_{\text{"within components"}}.$$

It is very important to note that, because of proportionality of cell frequencies, each of these components is unaffected by changes in the magnitude of any other. The student should satisfy himself of this by noting that arithmetic corrections applied to the data to eliminate any of these components will leave all other components unaffected.

The degrees of freedom for ss_B, ss_A, and ss_{AB} are $(b-1)$, $(a-1)$ and $(a-1)(b-1)$, respectively; a representing the number of A treatments and b the number of B treatments. The degrees of freedom for $ss_{\text{error }(b)}$ is obtained by subtracting the degrees of freedom for B from the degrees of freedom for S. The degrees of freedom for $ss_{\text{error }(w)}$ is similarly obtained as a residual.

It may be helpful to regard $ss_{\text{error }(b)}$ as the sum of squares for "between-subjects-within-groups" and to note that $ss_{\text{error }(b)}$ could be obtained by computing the sum of squares for between-subjects for each group separately, and then summing these sums of squares for all groups. That is, $ss_{\text{error }(b)} = \sum_{i=1}^{b} ss_{SwG_i}$. For a single group, the degrees of freedom for $ss_{SwG_i} = n_i - 1$, and hence the degrees of freedom for $ss_{\text{error }(b)}$ is $\sum_{i=1}^{b}(n_i - 1) = N - b$.

We may note also that the Type I design consists essentially of a number of treatments $\times$ subjects $(A \times S)$ experiments, one for each level of B. For any one level of B the A effect is tested by $F = ms_{A(B_i)}/ms_{AS(B_i)}$, in which $ms_{AS(B_i)} = ss_{AS(B_i)}/(a-1)(n_i-1)$. The sum of squares for error (w) may be regarded as the sum of the sums of squares for AS computed for the various levels of B, that is,

$$ss_{\text{error }(w)} = \sum_{i=1}^{b} ss_{AS(B_i)},$$

with

$$df_{\text{error }(w)} = \sum_{i=1}^{b}(a-1)(n_i-1) = (a-1)(N-b).$$

The analysis in the general case may be summarized as in Table 10. In this table, N refers to the total number of subjects.

TABLE 10

Analysis of Type I Designs

Source	df	Sums of Squares	Mean Squares
Between-Subjects	$N-1$	ss_S	
B	$b-1$	ss_B	ms_B
error (b)	$N-b$	$ss_{\text{error }(b)} = ss_S - ss_R$	$ms_{\text{error }(b)}$
Within-Subjects	$N(a-1)$	$ss_{wS} = ss_T - ss_S$	
A	$a-1$	ss_A	ms_A
AB	$(a-1)(b-1)$	$ss_{AB} = ss_{\overline{AB}} - ss_A - ss_B$	ms_{AB}
error (w)	$(a-1)(N-b)$	$ss_{\text{error }(w)} = ss_{wS} - ss_A - ss_{AB}$	$ms_{\text{error }(w)}$
Total	$aN-1$	ss_T	

Test of the B Effect: The significance of the B effect is tested by $F = ms_B/ms_{\text{error }(b)}$. To prove that this mean square ratio is distributed as F, let us suppose that within each row of the table (page 268) constant corrections have been applied to the measures within each cell, so as to make the cell mean equal to the row mean. It should be clear that these corrections would eliminate both the A effect and the AB interaction effect, or would make both ms_A' and ms_{AB}' equal to zero. The other mean squares, however, would remain unaffected. That is, ms_B' in the corrected table would be the same as ms_B in the original table, and likewise $ms_{SwB}' = ms_{SwB} = ms_{\text{error }(b)}$. So far as the corrected measures are concerned, the design would then be a groups-within-treatments design, the a observations for each subject constituting a "group," so that S would take the place of G and B that of A in the analysis on page 177. In this groups-within-treatments design, since the number of observations (a) is the same for each "group" (subject), the treatments (b) effect is tested by $F = ms_B'/ms_{SwB}' = ms_B/ms_{\text{error }(b)}$. The degrees of freedom for $ms_{SwB}' = (N - b)$, which is the same as that for $ms_{\text{error }(b)}$. The assumptions underlying this test are that, for the population as a whole, the subject *means* are normally distributed with the same variance for each B treatment (see pages 178–179), and that the subjects involved in the experiment are a simple random sample from the population concerning which inferences are to be drawn. The hypothesis tested is that for this population the mean of the subject means is the same for each treatment. The error variance of the difference between two individual B means, say for B_1 and B_3, is

$$ms_{\text{error }(b)} \left(\frac{1}{an_1} + \frac{1}{an_3} \right).$$

Test of the A Effect: The significance of the A effect is tested by $F = ms_A/ms_{\text{error }(w)}$. To prove that this ratio is distributed as F, let us again suppose, in the manner of preceding proofs, that constant corrections have been applied to the measures in each row of the table (page 268) so as to make each row mean equal to the general mean. Let us suppose that within each column of the table subsequent corrections have also been applied to the measures in each *cell*, so as to make each cell mean equal to the column mean. These corrections would eliminate both the B effect and the AB interaction effect, rendering $ss_B' = 0$ and $ss_{AB}' = 0$. It follows from (97) that $ss_{AS}' = ss_{AB}' + ss_{\text{error }(w)}' = ss_{\text{error }(w)}'$, so that $ms_{AS}' = ms_{\text{error }(w)}'$. These corrections, however, would leave the other mean squares unchanged; that is, $ms_A' = ms_A$, $ms_{\text{error }(b)}' = ms_{\text{error }(b)}$, and $ms_{\text{error }(w)}' = ms_{\text{error }(w)}$. In the table of (twice) corrected measures, other-than-chance differences between rows have been eliminated, so that the entire table may be regarded as corresponding to a simple treatments $\times$ subjects $(A \times S)$ design, with a treatments and $s = N$ subjects. With this $A \times S$ design, the appropriate test of the treatments (A) effect is made by $F = ms_A'/ms_{AS}' = ms_A/ms_{\text{error }(w)}$. The assumptions underlying this test are that in the corrected table the AS interaction effects are normally and independently distributed with the same variance for each of the A treatments. This is equivalent to assuming for the original table that the AS interaction effects in the population are normally and independently distributed for each A treatment at each level of B, and that the variances of these distributions are the same for all levels of B. The error variance of the difference between the means for A_2 and A_3 is $2ms_{\text{error }(w)}/N$.

Test of the AB Interaction: The significance of the AB interaction is tested by $= ms_{AB}/ms_{\text{error }(w)}$. The proof that this ratio is distributed as F is similar to the preceding. We will first suppose that constant corrections have been applied to the a measures for each subject so as to make the mean for each subject equal to the general mean. These corrections would of course eliminate both of the between-subjects effects; that is, they would render $ms_B = 0$ and $ms_{\text{error }(b)} = 0$. Let us suppose that other constant corrections have subsequently been applied to the measures in each column so as to make each column mean equal to the general mean, thus eliminating ms_A. From Table 10, it is apparent that this would leave AB and error (w) as the only remaining sources of variation in the corrected table. On the assumption that the AS interaction effects are normally and independently distributed for each treatment at each level of B, with the same variance throughout, the measures in the corrected table may then be regarded as derived from a simple-randomized design, in which the various A-B combinations represent the "treatments." In this design, the "treatments" effect would be the AB interaction, and "within treatments" would be the same as error (w). The "treatments" (AB) effect would then be tested by the F-ratio of the mean square for "treatments" to that for "within treatments," which in this case is the same as $F = ms_{AB}/ms_{\text{error }(w)}$.

Tests of Simple Effects: The simple effects of A are "within" effects, and should be tested against error (w). This is on the assumption that error (w) is homogeneous for all levels of B. If this assumption is questionable, the A effects for any given level of B may be tested against the AS interaction mean square computed for that level of B only, as in a simple $A \times S$ design. For computing the significance of the difference between two A means at any given level of B, the appropriate error term is also $ms_{\text{error }(w)}$ [see (36), page 165].

The simple effects of B in this design cannot be tested as is the main effect of B. So far as any one A-level alone is concerned, the design is a simple-randomized design. Accordingly, an appropriate error term for testing the B effect at any given level of A is the mean square for within-treatments (within-cells) computed for that level of A only. This error term may be used in an over-all F-test to test the (simple) effect of B, and also in t-tests of differences between individual B-means at the given level of A. The only objection to this error term is the loss of degrees of freedom involved by using the data from a part of the table only. If the number of degrees of freedom for this error term $\left[\sum_{i=1}^{a}(n_i - 1)\right]$ is small, say, less than 20, it may be desirable to use a more stable error term based on all of the experimental data. Assuming that the mean square for "within-cells" is homogeneous for all levels of A, this more stable error term may be secured by averaging these mean squares for all levels of A. This average is the same as the mean square for within-cells for the entire table. The sum of squares for within-cells for the whole table is the residual left when the sums of squares for A, B, and AB are subtracted from the sum of squares for total. It is evident from Table 10 that

$$ss_{w\text{ cells}} = ss_{\text{error }(b)} + ss_{\text{error }(w)}.$$

Accordingly, for the case in which the number of cases is constant for all B categories, the mean square for within-cells for the entire table is

$$\frac{ss_{w\text{ cells}}}{ab(n-1)} = \frac{ss_{\text{error }(b)}}{ab(n-1)} + \frac{ss_{\text{error }(w)}}{ab(n-1)} = \frac{ms_{\text{error }(b)} + (a-1)ms_{\text{error }(w)}}{a}.$$

It does not follow from this, however, that the simple effect of B for any given level (j) of A may be tested by means of $F = ms_{B(j)}/ms_{w\text{ cells}}$ with $(b-1)$ and $ab(n-1)$ degrees of freedom. The sum of squares for within-cells for a single level of A is a χ^2 distributed variable with $b(n-1)$ degrees of freedom, but the sum of these sums of squares for the a levels is not distributed as χ^2 with $ab(n-1)$ degrees of freedom, since these sums of squares are not independent — the same subjects being involved in all levels of A. Nevertheless, according to W. G. Cochran, an *approximate* t-test for testing the significance of the difference between two B means for the same level of A may be obtained by employing the procedure described on page 98. For example, suppose we wish to test the difference between the means for B_1 and B_3 at the second level of A by

$$t = \frac{M_{12} - M_{32}}{\sqrt{2ms_{w\text{ cells}}/n}}.$$

If we let t_b and t_w represent the values of t which are significant at the selected level for the degrees of freedom corresponding to $ms_{\text{error }(b)}$ and $ms_{\text{error }(w)}$, respectively, the value of t which is significant at the selected level may be taken as

$$t' = \frac{ms_{\text{error }(b)}\, t_b + (a-1)ms_{\text{error }(w)}\, t_w}{ms_{\text{error }(b)} + (a-1)ms_{\text{error }(w)}}.$$

From the expression for t it is, of course, possible to compute the "critical difference" which may be applied to any simple B-comparison in the entire table (granting that n is constant).

It should be noted that this procedure has the disadvantage that it does not permit an over-all F-test of any simple effect of B. Unless the number of degrees of freedom is too small, therefore, it may be better as well as simpler to use the error term computed from the data for the given level of A only.

For establishing a confidence interval for a single B mean for all levels of A (independently of other B means) the appropriate error term is est'd $\sigma_{M\,i.}^2 = \frac{ms_{\text{error }(b)}}{N}$, with $N - b$ degrees of freedom. For a single A mean over all levels of B the error term is est'd $\sigma_{M\,.j}^2 = ms_{w\text{ cells}}/nb$, and the critical value of t is computed in the manner shown above. For a single cell mean, the error term is either est'd $\sigma^2_{M_{ij}} = ms_{w \text{ cells}}/n$ (the critical value of t being found in the manner already explained), or the mean square for "within cells" computed only for the particular level of A involved.

An Important Use of the Type I Design: Among the most important applications of the Type I design are those in which each of a number of groups of subjects is given a different "training series," or is trained in a certain function under a different set of conditions. Observations of the function under training (criterion measures) are taken at regular or stated intervals during the learning or training series, these intervals being the same for all series. In the Type I design, these intervals correspond to the A categories and the different training series correspond to the B categories. The object of the experiment may be to determine whether or not there are any characteristic differences in the "learning curve" or in the *trend* of the A means for the various levels of B. Other purposes may be to determine whether any given training series has *any* effect on the function involved, or whether the different series differ in their final effect. In many experiments, each series is an "extinction" series rather than a "training" series — the object being to eliminate the effects of previous training series. How the various tests of significance just considered may be interpreted in relation to these purposes will be explained in Chapter 15.

Type II Designs

If the number of treatments (a) is the *same* for both treatment classifications, it is possible to control individual differences in evaluating the main effects of both treatments (A and B), without having to administer more than a of the a^2 treatment-combinations to any one subject.

The subjects are divided at random into a groups; each group takes a treatment combinations, but no group or individual takes more than one treatment in any A category or more than one treatment in any B category. To draw up the design, one selects any $a \times a$ Latin square, letting the columns correspond to the various A categories and the rows to the groups. The B factor is then the Latin square factor. This has been done for the case in which a equals 4 in the left-hand diagram below. It is then readily apparent which treatment combinations are to be administered to each group. The design to the right represents an alternate way of representing exactly the same design.

		A_1	A_2	A_3	A_4		A_1	A_2	A_3	A_4
Type II	G_1	B_1	B_3	B_4	B_2	B_1	G_1	G_2	G_3	G_4
$a = b$	G_2	B_3	B_1	B_2	B_4	B_2	G_4	G_3	G_2	G_1
Within effects: A and B	G_3	B_4	B_2	B_1	B_3	B_3	G_2	G_1	G_4	G_3
Mixed effect: AB	G_4	B_2	B_4	B_3	B_1	B_4	G_3	G_4	G_1	G_2

If there are only two levels of each factor ($a = 2$), the AB interaction is completely confounded with the G factor (group differences) as was pointed out on page 262, and is therefore a "between" effect (see page 268). If there are three or more levels per factor ($a > 2$), the AB interaction is a "mixed" effect, being based partly on intra-subject and partly on inter-subject comparisons. Since the intra-subject differences are usually less variable than the inter-subject differences, the AB interaction is usually a heterogeneous interaction.

The AB interaction is heterogeneous in this case in a somewhat different sense than in the instances previously considered. We have noted (page 34) that the sum of the squared deviations of a number of measures from their mean depends upon the sum of the squares of all possible differences among the measures taken two at a time. Accordingly, the sum of squares for between-cells in a double-entry table depends on the differences for all possible pairs of cells in the table. Some of these differences are differences between cells in the same row but in different columns; some are differences between cells in the same column but in different rows. The rest of the differences are based upon "cross comparisons," that is, upon comparisons between cells that are neither in the same row nor the same column. The differences between cells in the same row but different columns account for the sum of squares for between-columns, which in the case of the Type II design is ss_A. The differences between cells in the same column but different rows account for the sum of squares for between-rows, which in this case is ss_B. We know that $ss_{\text{cells}} = ss_A + ss_B + ss_{AB}$. It is apparent, therefore, that the remaining differences, that is, the differences based upon cross comparisons, account for the interaction sum of squares (ss_{AB}). It is apparent from the diagram above, however, that some of the cross comparisons are based upon the *same* group and hence are intra-subject comparisons, while some are based upon *different* groups and hence are between-subject comparisons. The between-subject cross comparisons account for one component of ss_{AB}, which we will call $ss_{AB(b)}$. The within-subject cross comparisons account for the remaining component, which we will call $ss_{AB(w)}$. The between-subject differences will of course be more variable than the within-subject differences, and $ms_{AB(b)}$ will be larger than $ms_{AB(w)}$. It is in this sense that the AB interaction is heterogeneous in the Type II design.

The meaning of $AB(b)$ and $AB(w)$ may be further clarified by viewing the AB interaction mean square in still another light. We may note first that, in general, in any square table the sum of squares for "between-cells," with ($a^2 - 1$) degrees of freedom, can be analyzed into ($a + 1$) independent components, each of which is the sum of squares for "between-sets" in an arrangement of a sets of a cells each. One such arrangement is that in which each set consists of the cells in a single column of the table. The sum of squares for "between-sets" in this case is what we have called ss_{cols}, or ss_A if the A categories correspond to columns. Another such arrangement is that in which each set consists of the cells in a given row of the table, the sum of squares for between sets in this case being ss_{rows} or ss_B. The sums of squares for between sets in the remaining arrangements are components of the sums of squares for interaction.

Consider a 2×2 table, in which the cells are numbered as follows:

1	2
3	4

The possible arrangements of two sets of two cells each, with the corresponding sums of squares and degrees of freedom, are as follows:

Arrangement	Sets	ss	df
A	$(1+3)$ and $(2+4)$	ss_A	1
B	$(1+2)$ and $(3+4)$	ss_B	1
AB	$(1+4)$ and $(2+3)$	ss_{AB}	1
between cells		ss_{cells}	3

The sums of squares for between sets in the last arrangements is what we have known as ss_{AB}. In the 2×2 table, then, ss_{AB} is based on the difference in the means for 2 sets or pairs of cells, one of which consists of cells 1 and 4 and the other of cells 2 and 3, as numbered above.

In the 3×3 table

	A_1 A_2 A_3		
B_1	1	2	3
B_2	4	5	6
B_3	7	8	9

the possible independent arrangements are

Arrangement	Sets	ss	df
A	$(1+4+7)$, $(2+5+8)$ and $(3+6+9)$	ss_A	2
B	$(1+2+3)$, $(4+5+6)$ and $(7+8+9)$	ss_B	2
AB_1	$(1+5+9)$, $(2+6+7)$ and $(3+4+8)$	ss_{AB_1}	2
AB_2	$(3+5+7)$, $(1+6+8)$ and $(2+4+9)$	ss_{AB_2}	2
between cells		ss_{cells}	8

In this case, one component of ss_{AB} is based on the comparisons among three sets, one of which consists of cells 1, 5, and 9; another of 2, 6, and 7; and the third of cells 3, 4, and 8. This component is denoted ss_{AB_1}, in the table above. If the design is a Type II design in which cells 1, 5, and 9 are assigned to Group 3, the between-sets comparisons are clearly "between-subjects" comparisons, since different subjects constitute each set. In this case, ss_{AB_1} may also be written $ss_{AB(b)}$. The between-sets comparisons in the last arrangement (AB_2) above are clearly "within-subjects" comparisons, since each of the sets in this arrangement consists of the same subjects. Consequently, the last component may in this case be written $ss_{AB(w)}$.

In the 4×4 table

1	2	3	4
5	6	7	8
9	10	11	12
13	14	15	16

five possible arrangements of five sets of four cells each are as follows:

Arrangement	Sets	ss	df
A	$(1+5+9+13)$, $(2+6+10+14)$, $(3+7+11+15)$ and $(4+8+12+16)$	ss_A	3
B	$(1+2+3+4)$, $(5+6+7+8)$, $(9+10+11+12)$ and $(13+14+15+16)$	ss_B	3
AB_1	$(1+6+11+16)$, $(2+5+12+15)$, $(3+8+9+14)$, and $(4+7+10+13)$	ss_{AB_1}	3
AB_2	$(1+7+12+14)$, $(2+8+11+13)$, $(3+5+10+16)$ and $(4+6+9+15)$	ss_{AB_2}	3
AB_3	$(1+8+10+15)$, $(2+7+9+16)$, $(3+6+12+13)$ and $(4+5+11+14)$	ss_{AB_3}	3
between cells		ss_{cells}	15

If this design is a Type II design and if cells 1, 6, 11, and 16 are assigned to Group 1; cells 2, 5, 12, and 15 to Group 2; cells 3, 8, 9, and 14 to Group 3; and cells 4, 7, 10, and 13 to Group 4, the sum of squares for between sets in this arrangement corresponds to $ss_{AB_1} = ss_{AB(b)}$, while $ss_{AB(w)} = ss_{AB_2} + ss_{AB_3}$, with 6 degrees of freedom. It should be apparent to the student from an inspection of the preceding diagram and table that the between-sets comparisons of any one of the five arrangements are independent of those in any other, since each set in any one arrangement is represented in every one of the sets in each of the other arrangements.

Importance of the Type II Design: The Type II design finds many important applications in psychological research. The most obvious application is that already suggested, in which A and B represent two experimental factors or treatment classifications. A less obvious but quite important application is that in which the design is used to counterbalance the effects of the *order* in which the treatments are administered to the subjects in what would otherwise be a simple treatments × subjects design. If there are four treatments, for example, the subjects are divided at random into four groups of the same size. Group 1 takes Treatment A_1 first, Treatment A_2 second, A_3 third, and A_4 fourth; Group 2 takes A_2 first, A_3 second, A_4 third, and A_1 fourth; Group 3 takes A_3 first, A_4 second, A_1 third, and A_2 fourth; and Group 4 takes A_4 first, A_1 second, A_2 third, and A_3 last. The diagram on page 273 again describes the design, if we let B_1, B_2, etc., each represent the rank *order* in which a treatment is administered. If the order in which a treatment is administered has any effect on the criterion measures, this effect is rendered the same for all treatments, since each treatment is administered in each possible rank order. This design would make possible not only a study of the effects of *order* upon the main effects of *treatments*, but also of the interaction of order and treatments.

Another important application is that in which the design is used to counterbalance the effect of differences in the tests or other devices employed to secure the criterion measures, in what would otherwise be a simple treatments × subjects design. We will henceforth refer to this source of error as the "criterion" factor. Suppose, for example, that it is desired to control individual differences in an experiment concerned with the effect of size of type upon reading rate. Obviously, the purposes of this experiment could not be served by having the same subjects read the same passage four times in four different sizes of type. If individual differences are to be controlled, a different passage must be used with each size of type. It may not be practicable to use passages that have been experimentally equated for difficulty. Instead, the passages may be selected so that, in the subjective opinion of qualified observers, they are *nearly* or approximately of the same difficulty. What differences in difficulty do exist among the passages, however, can be *counterbalanced* in the experiment by using the Latin square design that has just been described. Each passage would be printed in all four sizes of type, so that there would be 16 tests in all. In the diagram on page 273, the four different passages would correspond to B_1, B_2, B_3, and B_4, and A would represent the treatment (size of type) factor. Group 1 would read all four passages, each in a different size of type, as would Groups 2, 3, and 4, but the combinations of *size of type* and *passage* would differ for each group. Thus each treatment would be administered to each group, and each passage would be used an equal number of times with each treatment and with each group, but no passage would be used more than once with any treatment or any group. Any differences among passages, as well as any differences among groups, would then be completely counterbalanced so far as their effect on treatment means is concerned. (To avoid any possible bias due to the *order* in which the passages are read by the same subject, the order could be randomized for each subject independently. Another possibility would be to counterbalance both *order* and *passages*, using one of the designs to be considered later.)

Analysis of Total Sum of Squares: The total sum of squares in the Type II design may be analyzed (see diagram on page 273) into independent components in a number of different ways as follows:

$$ss_T = ss_S + ss_{wS} \tag{99}$$

$$ss_T = ss_A + ss_B + ss_{AB} + ss_{wC} \tag{100}$$

$$ss_T = ss_G + ss_{CwG} + ss_{wC} \tag{101}$$

in which ss_{wC} represents the sum of squares for within-cells, and ss_{CwG} represents the sum of squares for "between-cells-within-groups."

It is evident that if differences among subjects were eliminated by arithmetic corrections, the mean squares for A and B would remain unaffected. It is clear, therefore, that the sums of squares for A and B are both a part of ss_{wS}. Elimination of subject differences, however, would also mean elimination of group differences (G). Hence, ss_G is clearly a part of ss_S.

From (100) and (101) it is evident that

$$ss_A + ss_B + ss_{AB} = ss_G + ss_{CwG}.$$

Now since both the ss_A and ss_B are "within" components, and ss_G is a "between" component which cannot be contained in either ss_A or ss_B, it follows that ss_G must be contained in ss_{AB}, or that ss_{AB} is partly a "between" subjects effect. As previously noted, $ss_{AB(b)} = ss_G$ represents the "between" subjects component of ss_{AB}, and $ss_{AB(w)}$ represents the "within" component. That is,

$$ss_{AB(w)} = ss_{AB} - ss_G.$$

We will finally let $ss_{\text{error }(b)}$ represent the residual obtained when ss_G is subtracted from ss_S, and $ss_{\text{error }(w)}$ represent the residual obtained when ss_A, ss_B, and $ss_{AB(w)}$ are subtracted from ss_{wS}; that is,

$$ss_{\text{error }(w)} = ss_{wS} - ss_A - ss_B - ss_{AB(w)}.$$

The entire analysis is presented in Table 11, n representing the number of subjects in each group.

TABLE 11

Analysis of Type II Designs

Source	df	Sums of Squares
Between-Subjects	$an - 1$	ss_S
AB (b)	$a - 1$	$ss_{AB(b)} = ss_G$
error (b)	$a(n-1)$	$ss_{\text{error }(b)} = ss_S - ss_G$
Within-Subjects	$an(a-1)$	$ss_{wS} = ss_T - ss_S$
A	$a - 1$	ss_A
B	$a - 1$	ss_B
AB (w)	$(a-1)(a-2)$	$ss_{AB(w)} = ss_{AB} - ss_G$
error (w)	$a(a-1)(n-1)$	$ss_{\text{error }(w)} = ss_{wS} - ss_A - ss_B - ss_{AB(w)}$
Total	$a^2 n - 1$	ss_T

Tests of Significance of the Main Effects of A and B: Let us suppose that constant corrections have been applied to the *a* measures for each subject so as to make each subject mean equal to the general mean. This would of course render $ms_{AB(b)}$ and $ms_{\text{error}(b)}$ both equal to zero, since both are "between" effects. Let us suppose that subsequent corrections have been applied to the measures in each row so as to make the row mean equal to the general mean, thus rendering ms_B equal to zero. Let us suppose, finally, that within each column of the table further corrections have been applied within each cell so as to make each cell mean equal to the column mean. This would eliminate the remainder of the *AB* interaction — its "within" component — or would render $ms_{AB(w)}$ equal to zero. The total sum of squares in the corrected table, then, consists only of ss'_A and $ss'_{\text{error}(w)}$, so that $ss'_{wA} = ss'_{\text{error}(w)}$. Let us now assume that the *AS* interaction effects are normally and independently distributed with the same variance for each cell in the table. On this assumption, since there are no systematic differences among cells in the same column, the design, so far as the corrected measures are concerned, is a simple-randomized design, in which ms'_A/ms'_{wA} is distributed as *F*. However, $ms'_A = ms_A$ and $ms'_{wA} = ms_{\text{error}(w)}$. Hence, in the original table, $ms_A/ms_{\text{error}(w)}$ is distributed as *F*.

The assumptions that were necessary in this proof are equivalent to the assumptions that in a simple $A \times S$ experiment involving the same *A* treatments and the same subjects, but performed for any given level of *B* alone, the *AS* interaction effects would be normally and independently distributed with the same variance for each treatment, and that this variance would be the same for any level of *B*. The important considerations in judging the extent to which these assumptions are satisfied are essentially the same as those presented on pages 159–160 in Chapter 6.

The proof that $ms_B/ms_{\text{error}(w)}$ is distributed as *F* is exactly similar to the preceding.

Test of the AB Interaction: To test the hypothesis that there is no interaction between *A* and *B*, each of the components of *AB* must be tested separately, each against its own appropriate error term. If both components are non-significant, the hypothesis of no interaction may be retained. If either component is significant, the hypothesis must be rejected. When this procedure is followed, however, the risk of a Type I error is not that indicated by the level of significance at which the separate components are tested. Rather, it is almost twice that amount. If the hypothesis of no *AB* interaction is true, the within-component of *AB* will be "significant" at the 5% level five percent of the time. The between-component of *AB* will also be "significant" five percent of the time. But since the two components are entirely independent of one another, the times that one component is "significant" will rarely (5% of 5% of the time) coincide with the times when the other is "significant." Under a true null-hypothesis, one or the other or both of the components will be "significant" at the 5% level almost ten percent of the time, so that if the null-hypothesis is rejected when either or both components is or are significant at the 5% level, a true null-hypothesis will be rejected almost ten percent of the time. Accordingly, if in testing the hypothesis of no interaction in the Type II design, one wishes the risk of a Type I error to be less than $X\%$, one should test each component at the $X/2\%$ level. (Strictly the rule should read "... at the $\frac{1}{2}\left(X - \frac{X^2}{100}\right)$ level," but when X is small, $\frac{X^2}{100}$ becomes negligible, and the term reduces to an approximate $X/2$.) The same rule applies in the testing of a mixed interaction in any of the designs described subsequently in this chapter.

The "between" component of AB is tested by $F = ms_{AB(b)}/ms_{\text{error }(b)}$. To prove that this ratio is distributed as F, let us again suppose that corrections have been applied to the data so as to eliminate all other mean squares. In an analysis based on the subject *means*, the design would then reduce to a simple-randomized design in which ms'_G/ms'_{wG} is distributed as F. In this case, $ms'_G = ms_G = ms_{AB(b)}$, and $ms'_{wG} = ms_{\text{error }(b)}$ $(= ms_{SwG})$. The underlying assumptions are that the distribution of subject means is fundamentally normal for each *group*, that these distributions are homogeneous in variance for all groups, and that each group was originally a random sample from the same population.

The "within" component of AB is tested by $F = ms_{AB(w)}/ms_{\text{error }(w)}$. To prove that this ratio is distributed as F, we again suppose that corrections have been applied to the data so as to eliminate all other mean squares. It may then be shown that the corrected data may be regarded as coming from a simple-randomized experiment, in which the between-treatments mean square corresponds to $ms_{AB(w)}$, and the within-treatments mean square corresponds to $ms_{\text{error }(w)}$. The underlying assumptions are the same as those involved in the tests of the main effects of A and B.

It will be noted that when there are only two treatments in each classification, that is, when $a = 2$, the degrees of freedom for $ms_{AB(w)}$ becomes equal to zero, which means that the corresponding sum of squares vanishes. This is equivalent to saying what has been pointed out earlier (page 274), that when $a = 2$, the AB interaction is completely confounded with G, or that the interaction effect is entirely a "between" subjects effect.

Tests of Simple Effects: The simplest way to test the simple effect of A at a given level of B is to use the data from the given level of B only. For a single level of B, the design is a simple randomized design, and the appropriate error term for testing the (simple) A effect is $ms_{\text{within cells}}$ computed for the given level of B only. Either an over-all F-test or specific t-tests may be employed at the given level of B. The procedure for testing simple B effects, using the data from only a single column (level of A) is exactly the same.

If one wishes to employ an error term based on all of the experimental data, an *approximate* t-test for testing the significance of the difference between two different A (cell) means at the same level of B may be applied by the method described on page 272. Again, $ss_{w \text{ cells}} = ss_{\text{error }(b)} + ss_{\text{error }(w)}$. The denominator of the t is $2ms_{w \text{ cells}}/\sqrt{n}$, and the critical value of t is determined as before. For testing simple effects of B at a selected level of A, exactly the same procedure is employed.

The Control of Criterion Differences: Among the more important applications of the Type II design are those in which it is desired to equalize the effects of the differences (usually small) in difficulty among the non-equivalent criterion tests (B) employed, such as lists, reading passages, and alternate forms of achievement tests. In such cases there is often no good *a priori* reason to suppose that there is any intrinsic AB interaction, and the experiment may sometimes have been administered so as to render unlikely any AB interaction due to varying Type G errors. Suppose, for example, that in the experiment concerned with effect of size of type upon reading rate described on page 277, all subjects (and all groups) were tested simultaneously in the same room. That is, all four groups would read their B_1 passages (in a different size of type for each group) simultaneously, all would then read their B_2 passages simultaneously, etc. — "order" being confounded with "passages." In that case, it would be very difficult to conceive of specific differences in the administration of the 16 criterion test forms that would bias the results on any particular form with reference to any particular treatment. In such an experiment, therefore, if $AB(w)$ did not differ significantly from error (w), one might safely assume that the observed AB interaction is due only to random Type S errors, and include it in the error terms. In that case, the sums of squares for the pooled error terms are

$$ss_{\text{error } (b)} = ss_S, \text{ and } ss_{\text{error } (w)} = ss_{wS} - ss_A - ss_B.$$

The number of degrees of freedom for the pooled error term $df_{\text{error } (b)}$ is $an - 1$, and for $df_{\text{error } (w)}$ is $an(a - 1) - (a - 1) - (a - 1) = (an - 2)(a - 1)$. The $ms_{\text{error } (b)}$ would be needed as the error term if one wanted, for example, to test $M_{A_1B_1} - M_{A_2B_1}$, or if one wanted to establish a confidence interval for the mean for a given A treatment, independent of the other A treatments.

In Type II designs employed to counterbalance the effect of the rank order in which the treatments are administered to the subjects, the interaction of treatments and order may likewise frequently prove non-significant. If there is no good *a priori* reason to suppose that there is an interaction, either intrinsic or due to Type G errors, the sums of squares for $AB(b)$ and $AB(w)$ may, as suggested above, be pooled with the corresponding error terms. In general, however, such poolings should not be resorted to until tests of the separate components of AB have failed to reveal a significant interaction.

Type III Designs

Suppose that a factorial experiment is to be performed with three factors, A, B, and C, with a possible total of abc treatment-combinations. In such situations, one of the treatment classifications (A) may sometimes be such that all treatments in that classification are administrable to the same subjects, but this may not be true of the other (B and C) classifications. In that case, an experiment may be designed in which the main effect of A and all interactions involving A will be "within" effects, but the main effects of B and C and the BC interaction will be "between" effects.

The subjects are divided at random into bc groups of the same size. Each group takes one of the B-C combinations in combination with each level of A; that is, each group takes a of the possible abc combinations. The design is diagrammed below in two different ways for the case in which $a = 4$, $b = 2$, and $c = 3$. The numbers on the faces of the parallelepiped identify the groups. As seen in the diagram, Group 1 takes treatment-combinations $A_1B_1C_1$, $A_2B_1C_1$, $A_3B_1C_1$, and $A_4B_1C_1$, etc.

Type III

Within Effects:
A, AB, AC, ABC

Between Effects:
B, C, BC

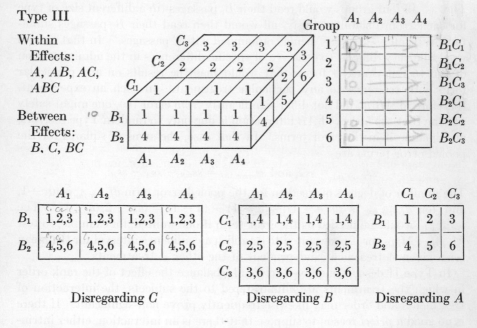

Disregarding C Disregarding B Disregarding A

Analysis of Total Sum of Squares: Disregarding the A, B, and C classifications, the total sum of squares may be analyzed into its between-subjects (S) and within-subjects (wS) components.

In any three-way table, regardless of the meaning of the classifications corresponding to the three dimensions, the total sum of squares may always be analyzed into components in the manner of Chapter 10. In the Type III design, therefore, the total sum of squares may be analyzed into the A, B, C, AB, AC, BC, ABC, and within-cells components. It is evident from the preceding diagrams which of these components are "between" and which are "within" components.

Disregarding the C classification, the design is clearly a Type I design (page 268) in which A and AB are "within" components and B is a "between" component. Disregarding the B classification, the design is again a Type I design, in which A and AC are "within" components and C is a "between" component. Disregarding the A classification, the design is a simple factorial design of the type considered in Chapter 9, in which all components — B, C, and BC — are "between" components. When the design is viewed as represented in the upper right-hand diagram preceding, it is apparent that the design is still of Type I. In this case, the row classification is the B–C cross classification, and $ss_{\text{rows}} = ss_B + ss_C + ss_{BC}$. From this it follows that $ss_{\text{rows} \times \text{columns}} = ss_{AB} + ss_{AC} + ss_{ABC}$. Since the rows $\times$ columns interaction is clearly a "within" effect, it follows that ABC is a within effect also.

The analysis of the total sum of squares for this design is summarized in Table 12. This table indicates also how the various sums of squares may be computed.

Tests of Significance: The main effects of B and C and the BC interaction are tested against $ms_{\text{error }(b)}$ as follows:

$$F = ms_B/ms_{\text{error }(b)},$$

$$F = ms_C/ms_{\text{error }(b)},$$

$$F = ms_{BC}/ms_{\text{error }(b)}.$$

That these mean square ratios are distributed as F is evident from the fact that if we disregard the A classification and base the analysis on subject *means*, leaving only between-subjects differences, the design reduces (see lower right-hand diagram) to a simple two-factor $(B \times C)$ design, in which $ms_{\text{error }(b)}$ is the within-cells mean square.

The error variance for the difference between the means of two individual B categories is $2ms_{\text{error}(b)}/acn$. That for a difference between the means of two individual B–C combinations is $2\ ms_{\text{error }(b)}/an$.

The main effect of A and all interactions involving A are tested against $ms_{\text{error }(w)}$. Suppose that we eliminate all effects involving B (B, BC, AB, and ABC) through arithmetic corrections, and regard all of the corrected data as projected into the AC face of the three-way table (see the middle-lower diagram preceding). The design then reduces to a Type I design in which the mean squares for A, C, and AC based on the corrected data are the same as those in the original table. In this Type I design, the mean square for "within A–C combinations" ($ms'_{\text{error }(w)}$) is the same as that for "within A–B–C combinations" ($ms_{\text{error }(w)}$) in the original table, since all B differences have been eliminated within each A–C combination. In this Type I design, then, A is tested by $F = ms'_A/ms'_{\text{error }(w)} = ms_A/ms_{\text{error }(w)}$ and AC is tested by $F = ms'_{AC}/ms'_{\text{error }(w)} = ms_{AC}/ms_{\text{error }(w)}$. By eliminating all effects involving C (lower left-hand diagram) it may similarly be shown that AB may be tested by $F = ms_{AB}/ms_{\text{error }(w)}$. The error variance for the difference between the means of two individual A categories is $2\ ms_{\text{error }(w)}/bcn$.

The procedures to follow in testing simple effects of differences among individual treatment means can readily be inferred from the discussions of the simple factorial design (Chapter 9) and the Type I and Type II designs of this chapter. For instance, simple effects of B at a given level of C are tested against error (b). Simple effects of B at a given level of C, or simple effects of C at a given level of B, are tested against error (b). Simple effects of A at a given level of B or C, or for a given BC combination, and the simple AC or AB interactions for given levels of A and C respectively, are tested against error(w). Simple effects of either B or C at a given level of A, or the simple BC interaction at a given level of A, or simple effects of B for a given AC combination, or simple effects of C for a given AB combination, may be tested as in a simple factorial design $(B \times C)$ by using the data from the given level of A only — the error term being the mean square for "within cells" computed only for that level of A. For t-tests of differences in individual pairs of means within a given level of A, one may use the data from the entire table by applying the approximate t-test described on page 272. The Type III design is particularly useful in experiments involving comparisons of learning curves or of trends in training or extinction series for different groups, since it permits the use of matched groups in such experiments. In this case, the intervals in the training or extinction series correspond to the A categories, the different training or extinction series correspond to the B categories, and the levels of the control variables correspond to the C categories. The interpretation of the data for applications of this type is discussed in Chapter 15, pages 351 ff.

TABLE 12

Analysis of Type III Designs

Source	df	Sums of Squares	
Between-Subjects	$bcn - 1$	ss_S	
B	$b - 1$	ss_B	
C	$c - 1$	ss_C	
BC	$(b-1)(c-1)$	$ss_{BC} = ss_{\overline{BC}} - ss_B - ss_C$	
error (b)	$bc(n-1)$	$ss_{\text{error }(b)} = ss_{\text{res }(b)}$	
Within-Subjects	$bcn(a-1)$	$ss_{wS} = ss_T - ss_S$	
A	$a - 1$	ss_A	
AB	$(a-1)(b-1)$	$ss_{AB} = ss_{\overline{AB}} - ss_A - ss_B$	
AC	$(a-1)(c-1)$	$ss_{AC} = ss_{\overline{AC}} - ss_A - ss_C$	
ABC	$(a-1)(b-1)(c-1)$	$ss_{ABC} = ss_{\overline{ABC}} - ss_{\overline{AB}} - ss_C$	
		$\quad - ss_{AC} - ss_{BC}$	
error (w)	$bc(a-1)(n-1)$	$ss_{\text{error }(w)} = ss_{\text{res }(w)}$	
Total	$abcn - 1$	ss_T	

Type IV Designs

If the number of levels is the same for two of the factors in a three-factor experiment, it is possible to control individual differences in evaluating the main effects of both of these factors, as well as the interaction of either of these factors with the third, without having to administer all treatments to each subject. That is, if $a = b$, it is possible to control individual differences in evaluating A, B, AC, and BC, leaving C as a between-effect and AB and ABC as mixed effects. The design consists essentially of c replications of the Type II design, one for each level of C. For the purposes of the experiment, the subjects are divided at random into ac groups of the same size (n).

To diagram this design for any given level of C, one proceeds exactly as with the Type II design; that is, one selects an $a \times a$ Latin square, letting A be the column factor, G (groups) the row factor, and B the Latin square factor. The diagram for each of the other levels of C is exactly the same, except that a different set of groups corresponds to the columns for each C level. A design of this kind is represented in the top pair of Latin squares below, for the case in which $a = b = 3$ and $c = 2$. The parallelepiped to the right in the top row constitutes an alternate way of representing exactly the same design. From either of these diagrams, it is apparent that group 1 takes $A_1B_1C_1$, $A_2B_2C_1$, and $A_3B_3C_1$, etc.

Type IV: $a = b$

Within Effects: A, B, AC, BC

Between Effects: C

Mixed Effects: AB, ABC when $a > 2$. (When $a = 2$, these are "between" effects.)

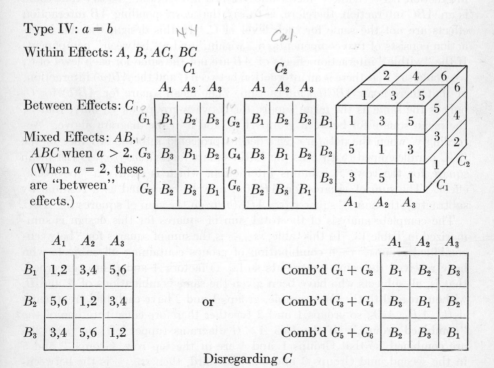

Disregarding C

	A_1	A_2	A_3
C_1	1,3,5	1,3,5	1,3,5
C_2	2,4,6	2,4,6	2,4,6

Disregarding B

	C_1	C_2
B_1	1,3,5	2,4,6
B_2	1,3,5	2,4,6
B_3	1,3,5	2,4,6

Disregarding A

Analysis of the Total Sum of Squares: The total sum of squares may be analyzed as before into its S and wS components as well as into its A, B, C, AB, AC, BC, ABC, and within-cells components. To classify the latter components, we note first that this design is a combination of the Type I design and the Type II design. Disregarding the C classification, the design is a Type II design, in which A and B are "within" effects and AB is partly a "within" effect and partly a "between" effect. Disregarding the B classification, the design is a Type I design, in which A and AC are "within" effects and C is a "between" effect. Disregarding the A classification, the design is again a Type I design, in which B and BC are "within" effects and C is a "between" effect.

We have seen that in general the ABC interaction may be regarded as the interaction between the C factor and the AB interaction. To say that there is an ABC interaction, therefore, is to say that corresponding AB interaction effects are not the same for each level of C. In this design, the AB interaction consists of two components, a "within" and a "between" component. If the "within" interaction effects of AB are not the same for each level of C, we would say that there is an interaction between C and the $AB(w)$ interaction, or that there is an $ABC(w)$ interaction. The mean square for $AB(b)$ for C_1 only is the same as the mean square for between-groups for C_1 only, that is, the mean square for between groups 1, 3, and 5 in the diagram above. Accordingly, when the data are regarded as projected into the AG face of the AGC parallelepiped (with B as the Latin square factor), $ms_{ABC(b)}$ is the mean square for the rows $\times$ columns interaction, which is clearly a "between" effect. The sum of squares for $ABC(w)$ may be computed as a residual by subtracting the sum of squares for $ABC(b)$ from the sum of squares for ABC.

The complete analysis of the total sum of squares for this design is summarized in Table 13. In this table, $ss_{G(AB)}$ is the sum of squares for "between-combined groups," each combination of groups containing all subjects who have received the same treatments so far as factors A and B are concerned, that is, all subjects who have been given the same combinations of A and B, without regard to C. For example, groups 1 and 2 have each had treatments A_1B_1, A_2B_2, A_3B_3, so groups 1 and 2 together therefore constitute one of the "combined groups." If the two $A \times G$ diagrams (upper left) on page 285 are combined, so that Groups 1 and 4 are in the top row, Groups 2 and 5 in the second, and Groups 3 and 6 in the third, then $ss_{G(AB)}$ is the between-rows sum of squares.

In Table 13, ss_G is the sum of squares for between the ac groups into which the subjects were originally divided at random. In the illustration, it is the sum of squares for "between (the six) groups."

TABLE 13

Analysis of Type IV Designs

Source	df		Sums of Squares
Between-Subjects	$acn-1$	59	ss_S
C	$c-1$	1	ss_C
AB (b)	$a-1$	2	$ss_{AB(b)} = ss_{G(AB)}$
ABC (b)	$(a-1)(c-1)$	2	$ss_{ABC(b)} = ss_G - ss_{G(AB)} - ss_C$
error (b)	$ac(n-1)$	54	$ss_{\text{error }(b)} = ss_{\text{res }(b)}$
Within-Subjects	$acn(a-1)$	120	$ss_{wS} = ss_T - ss_S$
A	$a-1$	2	ss_A
B	$a-1$	2	ss_B
$AB(w)$	$(a-1(a-2)$ (3-1)(3-2) 2		$ss_{AB(w)} = ss_{AB} - ss_{AB(b)}$
AC	$(a-1)(c-1)$	2	ss_{AC}
BC	$(a-1)(c-1)$	2	ss_{BC}
ABC (w)	$(a-1)(a-2)(c-1)$	2	$ss_{ABC(w)} = ss_{ABC} - ss_{ABC(b)}$
error (w)	$ac(a-1)(n-1)$	108	$ss_{\text{error }(w)} = ss_{\text{res }(w)}$
Total	a^2cn-1	179	ss_T

It will be noted in Table 13 that when $a = b = 2$, the degrees of freedom for two of the entries reduce to zero, namely $AB(w)$ and $ABC(w)$. In this case, ss_{AB} is identical with $ss_{G(AB)}$. That is, the AB interaction is completely confounded with subject differences (see pages 261 to 264).

Tests of Significance: As in the preceding designs, the significance of any "within" effect is tested against error (w), and of any "between" effect against error (b). Simple effects of A or C at a given level of B, or the simple AC interaction at a given level of B, may be tested as in a simple factorial $(A \times C)$ design, using the data from the given level of B only. Likewise, simple effects of B or C at a given level of A, and the simple BC interaction at a given level of A, may be tested as in a simple factorial $(B \times C)$ design using the data from the given level of A only. For comparisons of individual means (of cells, rows, or columns) within a given level of A or a given level of B, the approximate t-test on page 272 may be applied, using $ms_{w \text{ cells}}$ for the entire table. The validity of any of these tests may be established in ways similar to those employed with previous mixed designs. The student will find it a valuable exercise to demonstrate the validity of each of these tests, and to note specifically the assumptions underlying each.

Uses of the Type IV Design: In general, in this and other mixed designs, mixed interactions cannot be so satisfactorily evaluated as homogeneous interactions, since the evaluation of the between-subjects component of the mixed interaction is usually much less precise than that of the within-subjects component. However, it is expected that these designs will in general be used in situations in which there is relatively little interest in the mixed interactions, and in which these may often not have to be evaluated at all. The Type IV design, for instance, will prove most satisfactory in situations in which the principal interest is in A and B and their interactions with C, and in which C, AB, and ABC are of relatively minor interest.

The Type IV design provides a means of counterbalancing either order effects or criterion effects (see page 277), in an experiment that would otherwise employ a Type I design (with order effects or criterion effects randomized for each subject independently). When either criterion effects or order effects (represented by B) are being counterbalanced, and when none of the interactions [$AB(b)$, $AB(w)$, $ABC(b)$, $ABC(w)$, and BC] with these effects proves significant, the mean squares for these interactions may often safely be pooled in the error terms. In that case, the sums of squares for the pooled error terms are

$$ss_{\text{error }(b)} = ss_S - ss_C, \text{ and } ss_{\text{error }(w)} = ss_{wS} - ss_A - ss_B - ss_{AC},$$

with $c(an - 1)$ and $(a - 1)(acn - c - 1)$ degrees of freedom, respectively.

The Type IV design may also be used to counterbalance both order and criterion effects in what would otherwise be a treatments $\times$ subjects experiment, A representing treatments, B the criterion effect, and C rank order of administration of the A treatments.

Type V Designs

When the number of levels is the same for all three factors ($a = b = c$), it is possible to control subject differences in the evaluation of all of the main effects, leaving all of the interactions as mixed effects. The subjects are divided into a^2 different groups at random, the subjects in each group taking only a of the possible a^3 treatment-combinations, no subject taking any treatment in any classification more than once. For purposes of constituting the groups, the design may be considered as consisting of a blocks, such as those diagrammed below for the case in which $a = 3$. Each block is a Graeco-Latin square, but each block utilizes a different Graeco-Latin square. Note that each block is the same so far as the A–C pattern is concerned, but that the B pattern varies, so that each B treatment is combined only once with each A–C combination.

To diagram the first block of this design, one first prepares an $a \times a$ square, and lets the A-categories correspond to the columns and the groups (G) to the rows. One then selects two orthogonal $a \times a$ Latin squares (see page 265) and lets the numbers in one of these squares represent the B subscripts and those in the other square the C subscripts in the corresponding cells of the diagram. To diagram the next block, one simply transposes the B pattern of Block 1 so that the B's in the first column of Block 1 become those in the last column of Block 2, while the B's in columns 2, 3, etc., of Block 1 become those in columns 1, 2, etc., respectively in Block 2. Each subsequent block is derived from the preceding block in the same fashion. The process might be described as that of "rotating" the columns of the various blocks so far as the B factor is concerned. This has been done for the case in which $a = 3$ in the diagrams below, using the orthogonal Latin squares presented on page 265.

Type V
$a = b = c$

Within Effects: A, B, C

Mixed Effects: All interactions when $a > 2$. (When $a = 2$, all double interactions are "between" effects, and the triple interaction is a "within" effect.)

	Block 1				*Block 2*				*Block 3*		
	A_1	A_2	A_3		A_1	A_2	A_3		A_1	A_2	A_3
G_1	B_1C_1	B_2C_2	B_3C_3	G_4	B_2C_1	B_3C_2	B_1C_3	G_7	B_3C_1	B_1C_2	B_2C_3
G_2	B_3C_2	B_1C_3	B_2C_1	G_5	B_1C_2	B_2C_3	B_3C_1	G_8	B_2C_2	B_3C_3	B_1C_1
G_3	B_2C_3	B_3C_1	B_1C_2	G_6	B_3C_3	B_1C_1	B_2C_2	G_9	B_1C_3	B_2C_1	B_3C_2

This design may also be represented as in the upper left-hand diagram on page 290, each of the layers parallel to the front face being separately shown to the right of the parallelepiped. The numbers in the various cells identify the groups, as in preceding diagrams.

C_1 layer		
B_1	1	6	8
B_2	4	9	2
B_3	7	3	5
	A_1	A_2	A_3

C_2 layer		
5	7	3
8	1	6
2	4	9
A_1	A_2	A_3

C_3 layer		
9	2	4
3	5	7
6	8	1
A_1	A_2	A_3

	C_1	C_2	C_3
B_1	1,6,8	3,5,7	2,4,9
B_2	2,4,9	1,6,8	3,5,7
B_3	3,5,7	2,4,9	1,6,8

Disregarding A

	C_1	C_2	C_3
A_1	1,4,7	2,5,8	3,6,9
A_2	3,6,9	1,4,7	2,5,8
A_3	2,5,8	3,6,9	1,4,7

Disregarding B

	A_1	A_2	A_3
B_1	1,5,9	2,6,7	3,4,8
B_2	3,4,8	1,5,9	2,6,7
B_3	2,6,7	3,4,8	1,5,9

Disregarding C

Analysis of Total Sum of Squares: When the A classification is disregarded the design is clearly a Type II design, in which B and C are "within" effects and BC is a "mixed" effect.

When the B classification is disregarded, the design is again a Type II design, in which A and C are "within" effects and AC is a "mixed" effect.

From the lower right-hand diagram, similarly, it is evident that A and B are "within" effects and that AB is a "mixed" effect.

Now we know that

$$ss_{ABC} = ss_{cells} - ss_A - ss_B - ss_C - ss_{AB} - ss_{AC} - ss_{BC}. \qquad (102)$$

We know also that the sum of squares for cells consists in part of a "between" and in part of a "within" component, as follows:

$$ss_{cells} = ss_G + ss_{CwG} \qquad (103)$$

in which ss_G, the "between" component, is the sum of squares for between the a^2 groups, with $(a^2 - 1)$ degrees of freedom, and ss_{CwG} is the sum of squares for between-cells-within-groups, with $(a - 1)$ degrees of freedom for each of the a^2 groups or a total of $a^2(a - 1)$ degrees of freedom. We know also that

$$ss_{AB} = ss_{AB(b)} + ss_{AB(w)} \qquad (104)$$

$$ss_{AC} = ss_{AC(b)} + ss_{AC(w)} \qquad (105)$$

$$ss_{BC} = ss_{BC(b)} + ss_{BC(w)}. \qquad (106)$$

Substituting from (103), (104), (105), and (106), in (102), and rearranging terms, we may write

$$ss_{ABC} = [ss_G - ss_{AB(b)} - ss_{AC(b)} - ss_{BC(b)}]$$
$$+ [ss_{CwG} - ss_A - ss_B - ss_C - ss_{AB(w)} - ss_{AC(w)} - ss_{BC(w)}] \qquad (107)$$

which makes it clear that ss_{ABC} is partly a "between" and partly a "within" effect. If we let $ss_{ABC(b)}$ equal the first of the expressions in brackets in (107) and let $ss_{ABC(w)}$ represent the second term in brackets, we may summarize the entire analysis as in Table 14. In this table it will be noted that the degrees of freedom for certain components reduces to zero in the case in which $a = 2$, which means that in a $2 \times 2 \times 2$ design there is no within-subjects component of the two-factor interactions and no between-subjects component of the three-factor interaction.

TABLE 14

Analysis in Type V Designs

Source	df	Sums of Squares
Between Subjects	a^2n-1	ss_S
AB (b)	$a-1$	$ss_{AB(b)} = ss_{G(AB)}$
AC (b)	$a-1$	$ss_{AC(b)} = ss_{G(AC)}$
BC (b)	$a-1$	$ss_{BC(b)} = ss_{G(BC)}$
ABC (b)	$(a-1)(a-2)$	$ss_{ABC(b)} = ss_G - ss_{G(AB)} - ss_{G(AC)} - ss_{G(BC)}$
error (b)	$a^2(n-1)$	$ss_{\text{error }(b)} = ss_{\text{res }(b)}$
Within-Subjects	$a^2n(a-1)$	$ss_{wS} = ss_T - ss_S$
A	$a-1$	ss_A
B	$a-1$	ss_B
C	$a-1$	ss_C
AB (w)	$(a-1)(a-2)$	$ss_{AB(w)} = ss_{AB} - ss_{AB(b)}$
AC (w)	$(a-1)(a-2)$	$ss_{AC(w)} = ss_{AC} - ss_{AC(b)}$
BC (w)	$(a-1)(a-2)$	$ss_{BC(w)} = ss_{BC} - ss_{BC(b)}$
ABC (w)	$(a-1)(a^2-3a+3)$	$ss_{ABC(w)} = ss_{ABC} - ss_{ABC(b)}$
error (w)	$a^2(a-1)(n-1)$	$ss_{\text{error }(w)} = ss_{\text{res }(w)}$
Total	a^3n-1	ss_T

Tests of Significance: As in the preceding designs, the significance of any "within" effect is tested against error (w), and of any "between" effect against error (b). Simple effects of either A or B at a given level of C, or the simple AB interaction for a given level of C, may be tested as in a simple factorial design by using the data from the given level of C only. The same applies to simple effects of A or C at a given level of B, or of B or C at a given level of A, since for any single level of any factor the design is a simple factorial design. For comparisons of individual means (of cells, rows or columns) within any single level of any given factor, the approximate t-test of the type given on page 272 may be applied, using $ms_{w \text{ cells}}$ from the entire table. It is left as a possible exercise for the student to demonstrate the validity of each of these tests in ways similar to those employed with previous mixed designs.

Uses of Type V Designs: The Type V design provides another means (in addition to Type IV) of counterbalancing *both* the effects of order and of criterion differences when only one experimental factor is involved. In many such experiments, all interactions with order and with criterion differences may prove nonsignificant, and the assumptions may otherwise be plausible that no such interactions exist. In that case, these interactions may be pooled with the error terms, and the sums of squares for the pooled error terms are

$$ss_{\text{error }(b)} = ss_S, \; df = (a^2 n - 1),$$

and

$$ss_{\text{error }(w)} = ss_{wS} - ss_A - ss_B - ss_C, \; df = (a-1)(a^2 n - 3).$$

Type VI Designs

If it is possible to administer all combinations of two of the factors to the same subjects, an experiment with three factors may be designed so that subject differences are controlled in all effects except the main effect of one factor (C). For the purposes of the experiment, the subjects are divided at random into c groups, each of which takes one level of C in combination with all possible combinations of A and B. This design is diagrammed below for $a = 2$, $b = 3$, and $c = 4$.

Type VI

Within Effects: A, B, AB,
   AC, BC, ABC

Between Effects: C

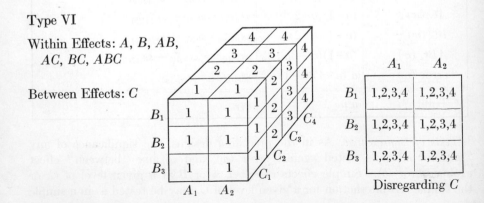

	A_1	A_2
B_1	1,2,3,4	1,2,3,4
B_2	1,2,3,4	1,2,3,4
B_3	1,2,3,4	1,2,3,4

Disregarding C

Analysis of Total Sum of Squares: This design represents a combination of the $A \times B \times S$ design (page 237) and the Type I design (page 267).

When the C classification is disregarded, the design reduces to an $A \times B \times S$ design, in which A, B, and AB are all "within" effects.

When the B classification is disregarded (regarding all data as projected into the top face of the parallelepiped), the design reduces to a Type I design, in which A and AC are "within" effects and C is a "between" effect.

When the A classification is disregarded (regarding all data as projected into the right face of the parallelepiped), the design again reduces to a Type I design, in which B and BC are "within" effects and C is a "between" effect.

In Chapter 9 we noted that in the $A \times B \times S$ design, the appropriate error term for A is AS, for B is BS, and for AB is ABS. That is, we noted that A, B, and AB each required its own error term (except on the assumption that the AS, BS, and ABS interactions are the same). In the Type VI design, which is in part an ABS design, it is again necessary to provide separate error terms for A, B, and AB. For much the same reason, it is necessary to provide separate error terms for AC, BC, and ABC as well.

"Pseudo Replications": To show how the total sum of squares may be analyzed into the components needed for these error terms, we shall resort to a device which we will call that of "pseudo replications." Suppose that *after* the experiment has been conducted, one subject is selected at random from each of the C groups, and that the c subjects thus selected are regarded as constituting a single "replication" of the experiment. A second "replication" is formed by selecting one subject at random from the remaining subjects in each group, and further replications are similarly constituted until n replications have been formed. The diagram for a single replication would look just like the preceding diagrams except that the groups (G) would be replaced by individual subjects (S). Thus, the individual replications could be diagrammed as follows, the numbers on the faces of the parallelepipeds now identifying individual subjects rather than groups of subjects.

Since these replications are not actual replications, in the sense of replications identified in the planning of the experiment and separately admin-

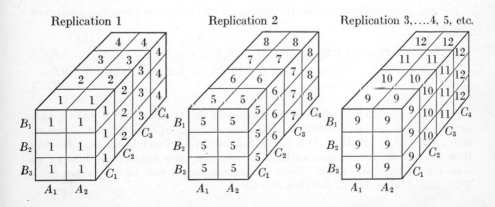

istered during the experiment, we have called them "pseudo" replications. They are, nevertheless, strictly *random* replications, and they are "simple" replications as well. Hence, under the conditions specified on page 191, the significance of any effect not involving R can be tested against its interaction with R, granting that the interaction is not a mixed effect.

We have thus constituted the original three-dimensional design into a four-dimensional design, and the analysis is now into the following components:

A	AB	ABC	$ABCR$
B	AC	ABR	
C	BC	ACR	
R	AR	BCR	
	BR		
	CR		

Now it can be shown [1] that in the population, $AR = ACR$, $BR = BCR$, and

---

[1] To save space, a complete proof of this will be omitted here, but the nature of the proof will be suggested. Consider these effects for only the first two levels of each factor. For any given replication, the A effect then depends upon the comparison

$$\frac{A_1}{(A_1B_1C_1 + A_1B_1C_2 + A_1B_2C_1 + A_1B_2C_2)} \quad - \quad \frac{A_2}{(A_2B_1C_1 + A_2B_1C_2 + A_2B_2C_1 + A_2B_2C_2)}$$
$$= (A_1B_1C_1 + A_1B_2C_1 - A_2B_1C_1 - A_2B_2C_1) + (A_1B_1C_2 + A_1B_2C_2 - A_2B_1C_2 - A_2B_2C_2)$$
$$= \qquad\qquad u \qquad\qquad + \qquad\qquad v,$$

u and v representing the last two terms in parentheses. Now the AR interaction in the population is measured by the variance of the A effects for all possible replications, that is, the AR interaction is measured by $\sigma^2_{(u + v)}$. But in each replication, u and v are based on different randomly selected subjects, so that u and v are independent of one another, or uncorrelated. Accordingly, $\sigma^2_{(u + v)} = \sigma^2_u + \sigma^2_v$ and hence, AR is measured by $\sigma^2_u + \sigma^2_v$.

For any given replication, the AC interaction effect depends upon the comparison

$$A_1C_1 \qquad\qquad A_2C_1 \qquad\qquad A_1C_2 \qquad\qquad A_2C_2$$
$$[(A_1B_1C_1 + A_1B_2C_1) - (A_2B_1C_1 + A_2B_2C_1)] - [(A_1B_1C_2 + A_1B_2C_2) - (A_2B_1C_2 + A_2B_2C_2)]$$
$$= (A_1B_1C_1 + A_1B_2C_1 - A_2B_1C_1 - A_2B_2C_1) - (A_1B_1C_2 + A_1B_2C_2 - A_2B_1C_2 - A_2B_2C_2)$$
$$= \qquad\qquad u \qquad\qquad - \qquad\qquad v.$$

The ACR interaction depends upon the variance of the AC effects for all possible replications, that is, in the population, ACR depends upon $\sigma^2_{(u - v)} = \sigma^2_u + \sigma^2_v$. Accordingly, $AR = ACR$. If $AR = ACR$ for the first two levels of each factor, and if each of these interactions is homogeneous for all levels, then these interactions must be the same for the table as a whole. By a similar reasoning, it may be shown that $BR = BCR$, that $ABR = ABCR$, and that $R = CR$.

$ABR = ABCR$, and that the R effect is equal to CR. This being the case, the corresponding mean squares obtained in the experiment can differ only by chance, and hence can be pooled into more stable error terms. The error sums of squares may be denoted as:

$$SS_{\text{error}_1\ (w)} = SS_{AR} + SS_{ACR}$$

$$SS_{\text{error}_2\ (w)} = SS_{BR} + SS_{BCR}$$

$$SS_{\text{error}_3\ (w)} = SS_{ABR} + SS_{ABCR}$$

It is not necessary actually to constitute the data into "pseudo-random replications" in order to compute these error terms. The device of "pseudo replications" was used primarily as a pedagogical device, to enable the student to understand more readily why these terms are valid as error terms for the indicated effects. It may be shown that the sums of squares for the various error terms may be computed as follows:

$$SS_{\text{error}_1\ (w)} = SS_{\overline{ACS}} - SS_S - SS_A - SS_{AC}$$

$$SS_{\text{error}_2\ (w)} = SS_{\overline{BCS}} - SS_S - SS_B - SS_{BC}$$

$$SS_{\text{error}_3\ (w)} = SS_{wS} - SS_{\overline{ABC}} + SS_C - SS_{\text{error}_1\ (w)} - SS_{\text{error}_2\ (w)}$$

In these expressions $ss_{\overline{ACS}}$, $ss_{\overline{BCS}}$, and $ss_{\overline{ABC}}$ have the same significance as in previous designs. That is, $ss_{\overline{ACS}}$ is the sum of squares for "between A–C–S combinations." Each subject takes all A treatments in combination with only one C treatment, hence there are a such combinations for each subject. We will let $A_1B_1C_1S_1$ represent the criterion measure for Subject 1 in Group 1 for the $A_1B_1C_1$ treatment combination, etc. The total for a single A–C–S combination for Subject 1 in Group 1 would then be

$$T_{A_1S_1} = X_{A_1B_1C_1S_1} + X_{A_1B_2C_1S_1} + \ldots + X_{A_1B_bC_1S_1}.$$

For this subject we may then compute

$$\frac{T^2_{A_1S_1} + T^2_{A_2S_1} + \ldots + T^2_{A_aS_1}}{b}.$$

If we add these sums for all subjects in all groups, and subtract T^2/N, we have $ss_{\overline{ACS}}$.

A similar procedure may be followed to compute $ss_{\overline{BCS}}$. The sums of squares for error$_1$ (w) and error$_2$ (w) may then be readily computed, and the sum of squares for error$_3$ (w) may be obtained as a residual.

The various components of the total sum of squares are classed as "between" and "within" effects in Table 15 on the following page, in which the degrees of freedom and the computational procedures are also indicated.

TABLE 15

Analysis in Type VI Designs

Source	df	Sums of Squares
Between- Subjects	$cn - 1$	ss_S
C	$c - 1$	$ss_C = ss_G$
error (b)	$c(n - 1)$	$ss_{\text{error }(b)} = ss_S - ss_C$
Within- Subjects	$cn(ab - 1)$	$ss_{wS} = ss_T - ss_S$
A	$a - 1$	ss_A
B	$b - 1$	ss_B
AB	$(a-1)(b-1)$	ss_{AB}
AC	$(a-1)(c-1)$	ss_{AC}
BC	$(b-1)(c-1)$	ss_{BC}
ABC	$(a-1)(b-1)\times$ $(c-1)$	ss_{ABC}
error (w)	$c(ab-1)\times$ $(n-1)$	$ss_{\text{error }(w)} = ss_{wS} - ss_A - ss_B - ss_{AB} - ss_{AC}$ $\qquad\qquad\qquad\qquad\quad - ss_{BC} - ss_{ABC}$ $\qquad\qquad = ss_{wS} - ss_{\overline{ABC}} + ss_C$
error$_1$ (w)	$(a-1)\times$ $(n-1)c$	$ss_{\text{error}_1 (w)} = ss_{\overline{ACS}} - ss_S - ss_A - ss_{AC}$
error$_2$ (w)	$(b-1)(n-1)c$	$ss_{\text{error}_2 (w)} = ss_{\overline{BCS}} - ss_S - ss_B - ss_{BC}$
error$_3$ (w)	$(a-1)(b-1)\times$ $(n-1)c$	$ss_{\text{error}_3 (w)} = ss_{\text{error }(w)} - ss_{\text{error}_1 (w)} - ss_{\text{error}_2 (w)}$
Total	$abcn - 1$	ss_T

Tests of Significance: In general, as in any random replications design, any homogeneous effect may be tested against its own interaction with R (on the assumption that the interaction effects with R are normally and independently distributed with the same variance for each treatment or treatment-combination). However, since more stable error terms may be obtained by pooling the interaction with R in the manner indicated, the various tests of significance are made as follows: A and AC against error$_1$ (w), B and BC against error$_2$ (w), AB and ABC against error$_3$ (w), and C against error(b).

If one is willing to assume on *a priori* grounds that for each level of C the AS, BS, and ABS interactions are the same except for chance, in which case it would follow [1] that except for chance $ms_{AR} = ms_{BR} = ms_{ABR}$, one can

---

[1] If, in each replication, $ms_{AS} = ms_{BS} = ms_{ABS}$, then, for all replications it must follow that $ms_{AR} = ms_{BR} = ms_{ABR}$, since each replication is an independent random sample of subjects.

employ a single pooled error term for all "within" effects. In general, however, it is better not to pool the error (w) terms until it has first been demonstrated by means of the Bartlett test that there are no statistically significant differences among them. The only safe procedure in general is the relatively laborious one of analyzing the total sum of squares into all the terms shown in Table 15.

Type VII Designs

If it is possible but not desirable in a three-factor experiment, to administer *all* treatment combinations to each subject, and if $a = b$, it is possible to control subject differences in the evaluation of all effects except the AB interaction effect. The subjects are divided at random into a groups of the same size, each of which takes ac of the possible a^2c treatment-combinations. The design is illustrated below for $a = b = 3$ and $c = 2$. In this case, the subjects are divided into three groups. The design for any single level of C is a Type II design, but the same groups are involved at each level of C (as contrasted with the Type IV design in which different sets of groups were employed for each level of C). The upper left-hand figure below represents the design for level 1 of C alone. The design for level 2 of C is exactly the same. The parallelepiped to the right constitutes an alternative way of representing exactly the same design. It will be seen from the diagram that Group 1 takes $A_1B_1C_1$, $A_1B_1C_2$, $A_2B_2C_1$, $A_2B_2C_2$, $A_3B_3C_1$, and $A_3B_3C_2$, etc. The numbers on the faces of the parallelepiped identify the groups taking the corresponding treatment-combinations.

Type VII		C_1		
		A_1	A_2	A_3
$a = b$	G_1	B_1	B_2	B_3
Mixed Effects: AB	G_2	B_3	B_1	B_2
Within Effects: All except AB	G_3	B_2	B_3	B_1

	C_1	C_2
B_1	1,2,3	1,2,3
B_2	1,2,3	1,2,3
B_3	1,2,3	1,2,3

Disregarding A

	C_1	C_2
A_1	1,2,3	1,2,3
A_2	1,2,3	1,2,3
A_3	1,2,3	1,2,3

Disregarding B

Analysis of Total Sums of Squares: It is evident from this diagram that the design is a combination of the $A \times B \times S$ design on page 237 and the Type II design. Disregarding the C classification (viewing the front face of the parallelepiped only), it is clear that the design reduces to a Type II design, in which the main effects of A and B are "within" effects and AB is "mixed."

Disregarding the A classification, it is evident that all subjects take each of the B–C combinations, or that the design reduces to a $B \times C \times S$ design, in which all treatment effects (including interactions) are "within" effects. Similarly, disregarding the B classification, it is evident that the design reduces to an $A \times C \times S$ design, in which all treatment effects are "within" effects.

The "between" components of AB is the same as the between-groups component, that is, $ms_{AB(b)} = ms_G$. The interaction of $AB(b)$ with C, that is, the interaction of G with C, is clearly a "within" effect. The interaction of $AB(w)$ and C is also a "within" effect, and hence, ABC is a "within" effect. Thus all of the effects are "within" effects except for a part of the AB effect.

Since so far as B and C alone or A and C alone are concerned, the Type VII design is a treatments $\times$ treatments $\times$ subjects design ($B \times C \times S$ or $A \times C \times S$), it is evident that several error terms may be required for A, B, C, $AB(w)$, BC, AC, and ABC. It is possible, but not necessary, to compute these by again constituting the subjects into pseudo random replications, with a subjects in each replication. The diagram for the first replication would then be the same as the parallelepiped on the preceding page, except that the numbers on the faces of the parallelepiped would identify individual subjects rather than groups. The diagram for the second replication would be similar, except that 4, 5, and 6 would replace 1, 2, and 3, respectively, etc. An interaction with R could then be computed for each of the treatment effects and treatment interactions. Now it may be shown [1] that in the population the mean squares for AR, BR, and $AB(w)R$ are the same — the term $AB(w)R$ representing the interaction with R of the "within" component

---

[1] Again, complete proof of these equalities will be omitted here, but the nature of the proofs will be suggested.

Consider the design diagrammed on page 297. A single replication in this design is diagrammed in a different fashion below, x_1 representing the criterion measure for $A_1B_1C_1$, x_2 that for $A_2B_2C_1$, etc. There are three subjects involved in each replication, the x's representing the criterion measures for one subject, the y's those for another, and the z's those for the other.

	A_1	A_2	A_3
B_1	x_1	y_1	z_1
B_2	z_2	x_2	y_2
B_3	y_3	z_3	x_3

C_1

	A_1	A_2	A_3
B_1	x_4	y_4	z_4
B_2	z_5	x_5	y_5
B_3	y_6	z_6	x_6

C_2

So far as A_1 and A_2 alone are concerned, the A effect for a single replication is measured by

of AB. It may also be shown that the population mean squares of ACR, BCR, and $AB(w)CR$ are the same, as are those of CR and $AB(b)CR$.

Accordingly, the sums of squares for each of these sets of interactions with R may be pooled to form more stable error terms, as follows:

$$SS_{\text{error}_1 (w)} = SS_{AR} + SS_{BR} + SS_{AB(w)R}$$

$$SS_{\text{error}_2 (w)} = SS_{CR} + SS_{AB(b)CR}$$

$$SS_{\text{error}_3 (w)} = SS_{ACR} + SS_{BCR} + SS_{AB(w)CR}$$

A_1	A_2
$(x_1 + z_2 + y_3 + x_4 + z_5 + y_6) - (y_1 + x_2 + z_3 + y_4 + x_5 + z_6)$	
$= (x_1 - x_2 + x_4 - x_5) - (y_1 - y_3 + y_4 - y_6) + (z_2 - z_3 + z_5 - z_6).$	

So far as A_1 and A_2 are concerned, the AR interaction in the population is measured by the variance of the A effects for all possible replications in the population. That is,

$$AR = k\sigma^2_{[(x_1 - x_2 + x_4 - x_5) - (y_1 - y_3 + y_4 - y_6) + (z_2 - z_3 + z_5 - z_6)]}$$
$$= k\sigma^2_{(x_1 - x_2 + x_4 - x_5)} + k\sigma^2_{(y_1 - y_3 + y_4 - y_6)} + k\sigma^2_{(z_2 - z_3 + z_5 - z_6)} \quad \text{(a)}$$
$$= k(\sigma^2_1 + \sigma^2_2 + \sigma^2_3)$$

in which $\sigma^2_1 = \sigma^2_{(x_1 - x_2 + x_4 - x_5)}$ etc., and k is a constant, dependent upon a and c, which we need not identify now.

In a similar fashion, it may be shown that so far as A_1 and A_3 alone are concerned

$$AR = k\sigma^2_{(x_1 - x_3 + x_4 - x_6)} + k\sigma^2_{(y_3 - y_2 + y_6 - y_5)} + k\sigma^2_{(z_2 - z_1 + z_3 - z_4)} \quad \text{(b)}$$

$$= k(\sigma^2_1 + o^2_5 + \sigma^2_6)$$

and that, so far as A_2 and A_3 alone are concerned,

$$AR = k\sigma^2_{(x_2 - x_3 + x_5 - x_6)} + k\sigma^2_{(y_1 - y_2 + y_4 - y_5)} + k\sigma^2_{z_1 - z_3 + z_4 - z_6)} \quad \text{(c)}$$

$$= k(\sigma^2_7 + \sigma^2_8 + \sigma^2_9).$$

If AR in the population is homogeneous, so that the values of AR in (a), (b), and (c) are the same, then it follows that

$$AR = \frac{k}{3}\left[\sigma^2_1 + \sigma^2_2 + \sigma^2_3 + \sigma^2_4 + \sigma^2_5 + \sigma^2_6 + \sigma^2_7 + \sigma^2_8 + \sigma^2_9\right].$$

In an exactly similar fashion it may be shown that BR for all levels of A is given by

$$BR = \frac{k}{3}\left[\sigma^2_1 + \sigma^2_4 + \sigma^2_7 + \sigma^2_2 + \sigma^2_5 + \sigma^2_8 + \sigma^2_3 + \sigma^2_6 + \sigma^2_9\right]$$

and that hence, $AR = RB$.

The nature of the proofs that $AR(= BR) = [AB(w)]R$, that $ACR = BCR = [AB(w)]CR$ and that $CR = [AB(b)]CR$ are similar to the preceding.

As with the Type VI design, it is not necessary actually to constitute the data into pseudo random replications to compute these error terms. Rather, they may be computed in the manner indicated in Table 16. To compute $ss_{\text{error}_1 \,(w)}$, one must first compute $ss_{\overline{ABS}}$, which is the sum of square for between A–B–S combinations. In the design diagrammed on page 297, there are three such combinations for each subject in Group 1, and the total for each combination is the sum of the two criterion measures for the two levels of C within this combination. For example, the total for the combination $A_1B_1S_1$ is the sum of the criterion measures for $A_1B_1C_1S_1$ and $A_1B_1C_2S_1$.

The analysis of the total sum of squares is given in Table 16 below. It will be noted that when $a = 2$, the degrees of freedom and sums of squares involving $AB(w)$ vanish, and that AB becomes entirely a "between" effect.

Tests of Significance: As in any random replications design, the appropriate

TABLE 16

Analysis in Type VII Designs

Source	df	Sums of Squares
Between-Subjects	$an - 1$	ss_S
$\quad AB(b)$	$a - 1$	$ss_{AB(b)} = ss_G$
$\quad$ error (b)	$a(n - 1)$	$ss_{\text{error} \,(b)} = ss_S - ss_{AB(b)}$
Within-Subjects	$an(ac - 1)$	ss_{wS}
$\quad A$	$a - 1$	ss_A
$\quad B$	$a - 1$	ss_B
$\quad C$	$c - 1$	ss_C
$\quad AB(w)$	$(a - 1)(a - 2)$	$ss_{AB(w)} = ss_{AB} - ss_{AB(b)}$
$\quad AC$	$(a - 1)(c - 1)$	ss_{AC}
$\quad BC$	$(a - 1)(c - 1)$	ss_{BC}
$\quad AB(b)C$	$(a - 1)(c - 1)$	$ss_{AB(b)C} = ss_{GC}$
$\quad AB(w)C$	$(a - 1)(a - 2) \times (c - 1)$	$ss_{AB(w)C} = ss_{ABC} - ss_{AB(b)C}$
$\quad$ error (w)	$a(ac - 1)(n - 1)$	$ss_{\text{error} \,(w)} = ss_{wS} - ss_{\overline{ABC}} + ss_{AB(b)}$
$\quad \text{error}_1 \,(w)$	$a(a - 1)(n - 1)$	$ss_{\text{error}_1 \,(w)} = ss_{\overline{ABS}} - ss_S - ss_A - ss_B$ $- ss_{AB(w)}$
$\quad \text{error}_2 \,(w)$	$a(c - 1)(n - 1)$	$ss_{\text{error}_2 \,(w)} = ss_{\overline{CS}} - ss_S - ss_C - ss_{AB(b)C}$ $= ss_{\overline{CS}} - ss_S - ss_{\overline{CG}} + ss_G$
$\quad \text{error}_3 \,(w)$	$a(a - 1) \times (c - 1)(n - 1)$	$ss_{\text{error}_3 \,(w)} = ss_{\text{error} \,(w)} - ss_{\text{error}_1 \,(w)} - ss_{\text{error}_2 \,(w)}$
Total	$a^2 cn - 1$	ss_T

error term for any homogeneous effect is its interaction with R, but because of the pooling of equal interactions, the various tests of significance are as follows: A, B, and $AB(w)$ against error$_1$ (w); AC, BC, and $AB(w)C$ against error$_2$ (w); C and $AB(b)C$ against error$_3$ (w); $AB(b)$ against error (b).

If a Bartlett test fails to reveal that the three "within" error terms are heterogeneous, the pooled error term, $ms_{\text{error }(w)}$ may be used as a common error term for all of the "within" effects. The error term for $AB(b)$, which is $ms_{\text{error }(b)}$, consists of the R and the $ABR(b)$ effects, but these are properly pooled into a single error term since it may be shown that their mean squares cannot differ except by chance.

Simple effects of either A or B at a given level of C, or the simple AB interaction at a given level of C, are tested against error$_1$ (w).

Simple effects of C for a given level of A or B or for a given AB combination are tested against error$_2$ (w).

The simple effects of A for a given level of B are tested against error (b) computed in the Type I design for that level of B only. The simple AC interaction for a given level of B is tested against error (w) computed in this Type I design. Simple effects of B and the simple BC interaction at a given level of A are similarly treated.

The simple effects of A for a given BC combination are tested against ms_{wA} for the given BC combination only. Simple effects of B are similarly treated.

Summary of Two-and Three-Factor Designs

It may be well at this point to summarize in table form the characterizing features of the mixed designs that have thus far been considered. This has been done in Table 17, page 302 From this table the experimenter can more readily select the design appropriate to his peculiar experimental conditions.

Additional Designs

Table 17 by no means presents all of the mixed designs that may be devised for two-and three-factor experiments. For instance, in a three factor experiment in which $a = b = c$, it is possible to divide the subjects at random into a groups, each group being given a^2 of the possible a^3 treatments. This design is diagrammed at the bottom of page 302 for the cases in which $a = 2$ and $a = 3$. In this design, when any one factor is disregarded, the design reduces to a treatments $\times$ treatments $\times$ subjects design, so far as the other two factors are concerned. Hence, all effects except ABC are "within" effects, while ABC is mixed.

TABLE 17
Summary of Two- and Three-Factor Mixed Designs

Type	Numbers of Factors	Special Condition	"Within" Effects	"Mixed" Effects	"Between" Effects
I (page 267)	2		A AB		B
II (page 273)	2	a = b	A B	AB*	
III (page 281)	3		A AB, AC, ABC		B, C, BC
IV (page 285)	3	a = b	A, B, AC, BC	AB* ABC*	C
V (page 288)	3	a = b = c	A, B, C	AB*, AC* BC*, ABC**	
VI (page 292)	3		A, B AB, AC, BC ABC		C
VII (page 297)	3	a = b	A, B, C, AC, BC ABC	AB*	

* A "between" effect when $a = 2$.
** A "within" effect when $a = 2$.

The pseudo replications device must be employed to provide separate error terms for the various treatments effects.

	A_1		A_2	
	C_1	C_2	C_1	C_2
B_1	1	2	2	1
B_2	2	1	1	2

$a = 2$

	A_1			A_2			A_3		
	C_1	C_2	C_3	C_1	C_2	C_3	C_1	C_2	C_3
B_1	3	1	2	2	3	1	1	2	3
B_2	2	3	1	1	2	3	3	1	2
B_3	1	2	3	3	1	2	2	3	1

$a = 3$

It may be noted also that Table 17 is concerned only with designs in which either all treatments in the same classification are given to the same subjects, or each is given to different subjects. For example, either all A comparisons are "within" comparisons or all are "between" comparisons. There are other designs in which each subject may take some but not all of the treatments in any given classification. Suppose, for example, that in a simple-randomized design involving three treatments, it is *possible* to administer all of the treatments to the same subjects, but it is not *desirable* to do so, because doing so would place undue demands upon the subjects, or would be impracticable for other reasons. Suppose that, for some reason, it is practicable to administer no more than two treatments to each subject. A design like that diagrammed below might then be employed. The subjects are divided at random into three groups of the same size, and each group is given two of the three treatments. Group 1 takes Treatments A_1 and A_2, Group 2 takes Treatments A_3 and A_1, and Group 3 Treatments A_2 and A_3.

$$A_1 \quad A_2 \quad A_3$$

1	1	2
2	3	3

The treatments effect in either row of this design is obviously mixed and hence heterogeneous. In the upper row, two of the treatment-comparisons are between-subjects comparisons and one is a within-subjects comparison. For the table as a whole, however, the treatment-comparisons are homogeneous, even though each is a mixed comparison, since each is half a within-subjects and half a between-subjects comparison. Accordingly, by means of the device of "pseudo" random replications, a valid error term can be found for testing the treatments effect. The test would be given by $F = ms_A/ms_{AR}$, in which R represents the pseudo random replications. Whether or not this design is more efficient than a simple-randomized design depends on the correlation between the different criterion measures obtained for the same subjects. If this correlation were quite low, the design could be less efficient than a simple-randomized design, due to the loss of the degrees of freedom which are associated with "between (pseudo) replications" and the "residual" components which are not included in the error term. For example, if 9 subjects were used, there would be only 4 degrees of freedom available for error out of the total of $17 - 5 = 12$ degrees of freedom not associated with the treatment effects.

This idea is carried further in the $3 \times 2 \times 2$ design diagrammed on page 304, in which the subjects are divided at random into 6 groups of the same size and each group takes 6 of the 12 treatment-combinations. It is evident from this table that all main effects are "within" effects, as are the AB and AC interactions. It is evident also that the comparison of any two $B–C$ combinations consists in part of "between" and in part of "within" comparisons, but that these are in the same proportion for each comparison of $B–C$ combinations. To secure valid error terms for the various effects, it is necessary to employ the pseudo replications device. It should be evident from what has just been said that each of the various interactions with R is a "mixed" effect. In this design, as in the preceding, there is a considerable loss of degrees of freedom from the error term.

		A_1			A_2			A_3		
3×2^2	B_1C_1	2	3	5	1	4	5	1	3	6
BC and ABC	B_1C_2	1	4	6	2	3	6	2	4	5
Confounded	B_2C_1	1	4	6	2	3	6	2	4	5
	B_2C_2	2	3	5	1	4	5	1	3	6

The designs that have here been presented as examples have not, to the writer's knowledge, ever been employed in educational and psychological research, but they suggest still further designs that might have interesting possibilities in these fields.

Partial Confounding

We have noted that in two- and three-factor experiments it is possible to leave subject differences uncontrolled in evaluating a selected effect. That is, we may let any selected single effect (except the triple interaction in three-factor experiments) be a "between" or a "mixed" effect, all of the remaining effects being "within" effects. This is true, of course, granting that any possible combination of treatments is administrable to a single subject. This suggests that instead of leaving the same effect uncontrolled with all subjects, we might let one effect be uncontrolled with some subjects, another effect with others, and still another effect with still other subjects, etc. For example, in a $2 \times 2 \times 2$ factorial experiment, one might divide the subjects at random into three sets of the same size, letting AB be a mixed or between effect in the first set, AC in the second, and BC in the third. The (within) mean square for each interaction would then be computed only for the data from those sets in which this interaction is a within-effect, the mean squares for main effects being computed from the data for all sets. Thus, in this particular example, no information about main effects would be sacrificed, while two-thirds of the information available on main effects would be available on each interaction. This is an example of what is known as *partial confounding*.

The technique of partial confounding has been widely used in agriculture, but thus far the writer has found no reported instance of its use in the research literature of education and psychology.

Mixed Higher-Order Experiments

It should now be apparent that there is a very large number of possible combinations of the basic two- and three-factor designs in factorial experiments involving four or more factors. Any three-factor design, for example, can be replicated independently for each level of a fourth factor, or for each combination of a fourth and fifth factor. One of the many possible designs for four-factor experiments is diagrammed below. The supplementary diagrams suggest how that design might be viewed as a combination of more basic designs. Another design is diagrammed on page 306. This design is of particular interest as an example of an "incomplete" factorial design — not all of the possible treatment-combinations being represented in the design. This design may be regarded as a combination of the Type I and Type V designs, each level of B being imposed on a different one of the "blocks" represented on page 306. This design is useful on the assumption that the factor D does not interact with any of the other factors or their interactions. Because of the incomplete character of the design, the four-factor interaction cannot be computed. However, the main effects and the two- and three-factor interactions can be computed and tested. Several of the interactions are mixed and must be analyzed into their homogeneous components. All "between" effects involving D, including the main effect of D, can be pooled into a single "between" error term, and all "within" interactions involving D may be pooled into a single "within" error term. In experiments of this type, this design can be used to control *order* and *criterion* effects, since if D does not interact with A it may be safely assumed not to interact with any of the other effects.

2^4 Design: Four Factors: AB and CD Confounded

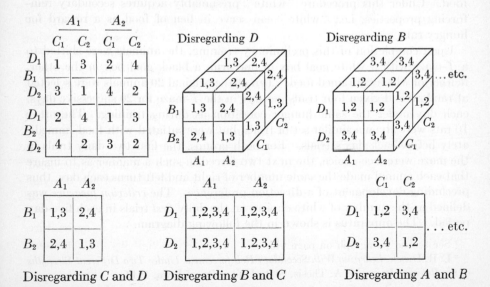

Disregarding C and D Disregarding B and C Disregarding A and B

			A_1			A_2			A_3		
			C_1	C_2	C_3	C_1	C_2	C_3	C_1	C_2	C_3
		D_1	1				2		3		
3^4 Design	B_1	D_2		5		6					4
Four Factors		D_3		9			7		8		
Assumes no		D_1		3		1			2		
Interactions											
with D	B_2	D_2	4				5			6	
AB, AC, CB		D_3	8			9					7
and ABC											
Confounded		D_1		2		3					1
	B_3	D_2		6			4		5		
		D_3	7					8		9	

STUDY EXERCISES [1]

1. An experiment [2] was carried out to investigate the learning of a T-maze by white rats under conditions of secondary reinforcement. Twenty female hooded rats, under 22 hours of hunger, were given 10 trials per day in a straight runway for seven successive days. Seven of the trials each day were to a white goal box containing food, the other three to a black goal box without food. Under this procedure "white" presumably acquires secondary reinforcing properties, i.e., "white" can serve in lieu of food as a reward for hungry rats.

Upon completion of this preliminary training, the animals were shifted to a T-maze with a white goal box in one arm, a black goal box in the other, neither of which contained food. Ten of the original 20 animals were selected at random and given four trials per day in the T-maze for 20 successive days, each day under the same hunger condition as during training. The other 10 rats were given a similar set of trials, but were satiated with food immediately before each day's trials. For both groups, the first two daily trials in the maze were free-choice, the next two forced in such a manner as to insure that each animal made the same number of right and left turns each day, thus precluding development of a direction preference. The *criterion measure* was defined as the number of white choices on the daily *first* trials in each five-day period. The apparatus is shown in the following diagram.

---

[1] See second paragraph on page viii.

[2] E. R. Dusek, *Learning With Secondary Reinforcement Under Two Different Strengths of the Relevant Drive*, M. A. Thesis, State University of Iowa, 1949.

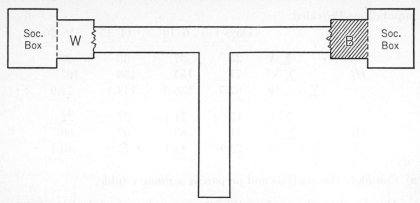

The social boxes each contained another rat and served to motivate the animals to move through the maze. These boxes were interchanged each day. To preclude the influence of inherent turning preferences, the white goal box was always in the left arm of the maze for a random half of each group of 10 rats, in the right arm for the other half.

The data are as follows;

Trial Categories

		T_1	T_2	T_3	T_4	
	Animal	Days 1–5	6–10	11–15	16–20	Total
	1	3	3	3	3	12
	2	2	2	4	4	12
	3	4	2	5	5	16
	4	3	5	5	5	18
	5	2	5	5	4	16
Hungry (H_1)	6	3	5	4	0	12
	7	1	3	4	1	9
	8	4	5	3	3	15
	9	3	5	4	2	14
	10	0	2	1	0	3
	Total	25	37	38	27	127
	11	0	1	2	2	5
	12	3	0	2	2	7
	13	2	3	4	4	13
	14	0	1	2	1	4
	15	1	3	5	4	13
Satiated (H_2)	16	1	2	3	2	8
	17	2	5	1	1	9
	18	2	3	4	2	11
	19	3	1	2	1	7
	20	3	2	2	3	10
	Total	17	21	27	22	87

Computations Provided:

		Days 1–5	6–10	11–15	16–20
	$\sum X$	25	37	38	27
H_1	$\sum X^2$	77	155	158	105
	$(\sum X)^2/10$	62.5	136.9	144.4	72.9
	$\sum X$	17	21	27	22
H_2	$\sum X^2$	41	63	87	60
	$(\sum X)^2/10$	28.9	44.1	72.9	48.4

a) Complete the analysis and prepare a summary table.

b) May the hypothesis of no HT interaction be rejected at the 5% level? Calculate the TS interaction effects for the first three observations in the H_1T_3 cell of the table. The test of the HT interaction involves what assumption concerning such interaction effects?

c) What are the numerical values of the over-all T_1, T_2, etc., means? Test (at the 5% level) the hypothesis of no differences among the corresponding population means.

d) Define the T_2 treatment population. Need one specify anything about the proportion of animals in this population subject to the H_1 and H_2 conditions? Explain.

e) Explain why one may *not* conclude from the test of (c) that the animals had "learned" to choose the white arm of the maze. Carry out a test that will permit a tentative conclusion about this matter.

f) Test the simple trial effects for each hunger condition (recognizing that this test would ordinarily not be made when the interaction is non-significant). May one infer from these results that "learning" took place in one group and not in the other, or that there is a real T-effect at one level of H, but not at the other? Explain why there is no real inconsistency between these results and the results obtained in (b).

g) Test (at the 5% level) the hypothesis of equal over-all population means for the H_1 and H_2 conditions. Define the populations involved and specify the distributions to which the assumptions of homogeneity and normality apply.

h) Test the simple effect of H at the T_2 level, using the data for this level only. Explain why the same error term is not valid for testing both the simple and the main effects of H.

i) Compute the TS mean square for H_1 alone. For H_2 alone. What is the relation of these two mean squares to $ms_{\text{error }(w)}$ computed for the entire experiment?

j) Which of the main effects in this experiment is more precisely evaluated? Explain.

k) What principle of experimental design was violated in this experiment in connection with counterbalancing the social boxes and position of goal box?

2. One purpose of a study carried out by Heyman [1] was to investigate transposition behavior in white rats trained to discriminate between visual stimuli differing in "brightness." Rats were trained in a T-maze to choose the arm associated with the brighter of a stimulus pair, and were then tested on other stimulus pairs whose brightness *ratio* remained constant but whose absolute brightness values were in all cases higher than those used in training. The apparatus was a simple elevated T-maze with a glass surface over the stimulus area as shown in the following sketch.

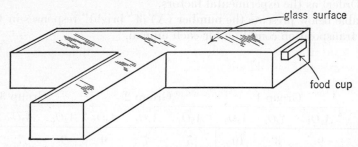

The stimulus conditions consisted of different brightness levels produced by the reflection of the overhead light from paper strips of various shades of grey placed on the alley floor. The rat was required to choose the brighter arm in order to obtain food. The stimulus conditions used were as follows:

Conditions	Brightness of Arms in Apparent Foot-Candles
Training	.33 and .98
Transposition (A_1)	.69 and 2.05
Transposition (A_2)	.98 and 3.11
Transposition (A_3)	2.05 and 6.11

Fifteen female hooded rats were selected, all of which had previously been used in a bar-pressing experiment. Preliminary procedure consisted of exploration, adjustment to a feeding schedule, and four reinforced trials to each arm of the maze with no stimuli in place. The *training procedure* consisted of 20 trials per day with the training stimuli in place. Responses

[1] M. N. Heyman, *An Investigation of Hypothetical Generalization Gradients in a Visual Transposition Situation*, M. A. Thesis, State University of Iowa, 1951.

to the brighter side (correct response) were rewarded with a pellet of food at the end of the arm. The brighter stimulus appeared equally often in each arm of the maze. The training was continued until an animal made 18 correct choices out of 20 trials with the last 10 correct.

Upon reaching the training criterion, the animal was given 10 rewarded trials on one of the three transposition conditions (A_1, A_2, and A_3). After this series of trials was completed, the animal was returned to the original training condition until it ran 10 consecutive correct trials. The animal was then given 10 trials on the second transposition condition, then more training, followed by 10 trials on the third condition. The order (but not sequence) of the administration of the transposition conditions was counter-balanced by dividing the animals at random into three equal groups, and assigning one to each of the orders $A_1A_2A_3$, $A_3A_1A_2$, and $A_2A_3A_1$. In other words, a Type II design was employed, with A (Transposition conditions) and O (Order) as the experimental factors.

The table below presents the number (X) of "bright" responses in 10 trials on each transposition condition for each animal.

| | Group 1 | | | Group 2 | | | Group 3 | | |
	A_1O_1	A_2O_2	A_3O_3	A_3O_1	A_1O_2	A_2O_3	A_2O_1	A_3O_2	A_1O_3
X_1	9	8	10	5	7	9	9	7	10
X_2	10	9	7	4	10	6	9	5	10
X_3	10	8	6	5	8	9	9	7	10
X_4	7	10	6	7	10	9	8	6	9
X_5	10	8	5	8	10	5	5	5	6
$\sum X$	46	43	34	29	45	38	40	30	45
$\sum X/5$	9.2	8.6	6.8	5.8	9.0	7.6	8.0	6.0	9.0
$\sum X^2$	430	373	246	179	413	304	332	184	417
$(\sum X)^2/5$	423.2	369.8	231.2	288.8	168.2	405	180	405	320

a) Analyze the results and prepare a summary table.

b) Test (at the 1% level) the hypothesis of no AO interaction. Define the population involved in this test.

c) In Type II experiments in general, if one component of the interaction is found significant and the other is not, what are the two possible interpretations of this finding? Which interpretation would you *usually* favor in experiments of this kind? Explain.

d) Suppose that the five animals in each group had been kept in the same living cage during the course of this experiment, and that extraneous factors affecting the cages systematically had produced differences in their criterion means. To what "effect" in the analysis would these cage differences contribute? Is it possible, then, that the "within" component of AO is zero in the population, while the "between" component is real (other than zero)? Explain.

e) Had the "within," rather than the "between," component of AO been found significant, could one likewise *plausibly* contend that the "within" component is real while the "between" component is zero in the population? Explain. (See page 274.)

f) How do the assumptions underlying the test of one component of the AO interaction differ from those for the other component? If there were an extreme violation of the assumption of homogeneity of variance underlying $AO(b)$, how would it show up in the preceding table?

g) What "corrections" must be applied to the data (see page 280) in order that the corrected data may be regarded as corresponding to a simple-randomized design involving only the *order* effect? How do you know that the ratio of the mean squares for between-orders and for within-orders computed for the corrected data must be equal to the mean square ratio used in the preceding test?

h) Test (at the 1% level) the main effect of the transposition conditions (A). Do the assumptions underlying this test differ from those underlying the test of the "within" component of AO? Explain.

i) What advantage is gained in this experiment by counterbalancing the order effects as opposed to randomizing them? Justify your answer.

j) What error term would you use to test the simple effect of A for O_2? Why not pool such error terms for the three levels of O to obtain a more stable term?

k) If you had occasion to test the significance of the difference between the means for A_1O_1 and A_2O_2, what error term would you employ? Explain.

l) The mean square for O in this experiment is "significantly" *smaller* than that for error (w), and at a very high level of significance. In general, granting that the experiment was well designed and properly administered, how does one account for a finding of this kind?

3. An experiment was concerned with the effects of massed and distributed practice on the learning of successive lists of adjectives. Each subject learned a different list of 14 two-syllable adjectives each day for four successive days. The words were presented by memory drum at a two-second exposure rate. Practice was continued each day until the subject correctly anticipated all words in the list on a single trial. The learning score for each subject each day was the number of trials needed to reach this criterion,

The purpose of the experiment was to determine if the time required to learn a list decreased more rapidly under one distribution of practice than under the other.

Forty-eight college students were assigned at random to one of two groups of 24 each. The subjects of one group learned a list each day under conditions of massed practice (P_1), with a two-second interval between trials. The other group learned each list under distributed practice (P_2), with a 30-second interval between trials. Each of these groups was randomly subdivided into four subgroups of six subjects each, and one sub-group was assigned to each of four orders in which the lists were learned. In other words, "lists" were counterbalanced with respect to "days" in each group.[1]

The sum and the mean of the criterion scores for each LDP combination are given in the following table. The total sum of squares is 15,788 and that for between-subjects is 6,884.

Massed Practice (P_1)					Distributed Practice (P_2)				
	List	*Day*	*Sum*	*Mean*		*List*	*Day*	*Sum*	*Mean*
	I	1	198	33		I	1	150	25
Subgrp	II	4	120	20	Subgrp	II	4	84	14
1	III	2	156	26	5	III	2	108	18
	IV	3	150	25		IV	3	126	21
	I	2	144	24		I	2	120	20
Subgrp	II	3	144	24	Subgrp	II	3	156	26
2	III	1	186	31	6	III	1	138	23
	IV	4	114	19		IV	4	150	25
	I	3	120	20		I	3	96	16
Subgrp	II	2	120	20	Subgrp	II	2	84	14
3	III	4	126	21	7	III	4	90	15
	IV	1	186	31		IV	1	150	25
	I	4	90	15		I	4	114	19
Subgrp	II	1	126	21	Subgrp	II	1	90	15
4	III	3	114	19	8	III	3	66	11
	IV	2	126	21		IV	2	90	15

a) Complete the analysis and prepare a summary table.

b) May the hypothesis of no LD interaction be rejected at the 5% level?

[1] The data in this exercise are hypothetical, but the situation is much like that reported by Benton J. Underwood in *Journal of Experimental Psychology*, vol. 42; (November, 1951), pp. 291–295.

c) What characteristic of the lists might cause List I to be more difficult to learn on the first day (when preceded by no other lists) than on a later day (when immediately preceded by List III)? Would this difference affect one or both components of the LD interaction? Explain in terms of the analysis of the 4×4 square on page 274.

d) Suppose that there is an intrinsic interaction (of the type just suggested) in this experiment, but no extrinsic interaction. How, in that case, could you explain why one component of the LD interaction is significant, while the other is not?

e) Can you suggest any specific extraneous factors or circumstances that would increase (or decrease) $ms_{LD(b)}$ without affecting $ms_{LD(w)}$?

f) Can you find any plausible way of explaining an *intrinsic* $LD(b)$ interaction and a zero $LD(w)$ interaction in an experiment of this kind?

g) Which of the preceding interpretations (d, e, and f) of the results of (b) do you prefer? Why?

h) Test (at the 5% level) the null hypotheses regarding the main effects of P, D, and L. Does it appear important to have "taken out" List differences? Could this have been known in advance of the experiment?

i) Specify the assumptions underlying each of the tests in (h).

j) Is there any fundamental interest in this experiment in the mixed interactions for their own sake? In any of the List effects?

k) If all effects involving Lists were ignored, to what type of design would this reduce? What would be the numerical values of $ms_{\text{error }(b)}$ and $ms_{\text{error }(w)}$, if the data were so analyzed? Would the *interpretation* of the P, D, and PD effects have differed?

l) What is the "order" effect in this experiment? Why is it not isolated as a factor apart from treatments?

4. An experiment carried out by Kalish [1] was designed to investigate the effects of varying numbers of acquisition and extinction trials on the strength of anxiety in white rats. The apparatus used for the acquisition and extinction trials is shown in the sketch on page 314. Four identical boxes were

---

[1] H. I. Kalish, *Strength of Fear as a Function of the Numbers of Acquisition and Extinction Trials*. Ph.D. Thesis, State University of Iowa, 1952.

used, all operated by the same controls so that four animals could be run simultaneously.

In each acquisition trial the animal was placed in the box and the buzzer

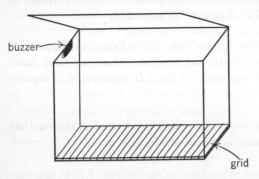

was sounded for a five-second interval, during the last second of which the animal was given an electric shock through the grid in the floor of the box. Each extinction trial was identical with the acquisition trial, except that the electric shock was omitted.

A random fourth of the experimental animals were given 1 acquisition trial, another fourth 3, another fourth 9, and the last fourth 27 acquisition trials. Within each acquisition category a random fourth of the animals received 0 extinction trials, another fourth 3, another fourth 9, and the last fourth 27 extinction trials. There were thus 16 different treatment-combinations, each administered to a different random group of animals.

The entire experiment consisted of eight random replications. In each replication 16 animals selected at random from the available colony were identified by tail markings and placed two in each of eight living cages. The animals were then randomly assigned one to each of 16 treatment-combinations. On the first day of each replication, four animals assigned to the same acquisition category were taken from the living cages and placed one in each of the four boxes for a period of 81 minutes. The four animals then received the specified number of acquisition trials. The trials were spaced at three-minute intervals and were so arranged that the last trial (or the only trial in the case of one-trial acquisition) started at the end of the 78th minute in the box. Immediately following the 81-minute period, the four animals were returned to the living cages and the process repeated successively with the three remaining groups of four rats (or for the three remaining levels of acquisition). Six hours were required to complete the running of the acquisition trials for the 16 animals in one replication.

On the following day, the four groups of rats assigned to the four extinction categories were successively placed in the boxes for 81 minutes and given the appropriate number of extinction trials. Immediately following the extinction trials, each animal was placed in a box identical to the conditioning boxes, except for a $\frac{2}{3}$ guillotine door at the end opposite the buzzer. After 15 seconds the buzzer was sounded and the door raised, presenting a two-inch hurdle over which the rat could escape to an empty box. Each animal was given 12 such hurdle-jumping trials at five-minute intervals, and a latency measure was recorded for each trial. For purposes of analysis, the 12 trials were treated as four blocks of three trials each. The *criterion measure* for each animal for each block was 2 plus the logarithm of the mean latency for the three trials in the block.

This basic experiment was repeated eight times over a period of six weeks, each time with a separate independent random sample of 16 rats from the same colony. Food and water were available at all times in the living cages during the course of each replication. In each replication the order in which the acquisition and extinction groups were run was randomly determined. All replications were handled by the same experimenter, and care was taken to see that identical procedures were followed in each replication. Each of the replications thus employed a Type III design with T (trials) and all interactions with T as the "within" effects, and with the remaining effects — A (acquisition conditions), E (extinction conditions) and AE — as the "between" effects. The entire design is thus a mixed $A \times E \times T \times R$ design.

The means (over-all replications) of the criterion measures for the four blocks of trials are given for each treatment-combination in the table to the left below. The upper right-hand table presents the mean of the criterion measures (over-all replications and extinction conditions) for each acquisition condition, and the lower right-hand table presents the mean of the criterion measures (over-all replications and acquisition conditions) for each extinction condition.

Mean Criterion Scores

	Trials						Trials			
	1–3	4–6	7–9	10–12			1–3	4–6	7–9	10–12
A_1E_1	2.90	2.73	2.59	2.51		A_1	3.02	2.95	2.85	2.76
A_1E_2	3.21	3.19	2.97	2.86		A_2	2.97	2.80	2.76	2.75
A_1E_3	2.92	2.84	2.78	2.75		A_3	2.98	2.77	2.68	2.71
A_1E_4	3.03	3.05	3.06	2.83		A_4	2.82	2.45	2.32	2.26
A_2E_1	2.82	2.52	2.45	2.32						
A_2E_2	3.02	2.82	2.81	2.86			Trials			
A_2E_3	2.98	2.84	2.80	2.74			1–3	4–6	7–9	10–12
A_2E_4	3.05	3.03	3.00	3.10		E_1	2.82	2.52	2.38	2.29
						E_2	2.97	2.72	2.59	2.53
A_3E_1	2.76	2.47	2.36	2.24		E_3	2.98	2.78	2.72	2.70
A_3E_2	2.92	2.62	2.40	2.40		E_4	3.01	2.95	2.92	2.91
A_3E_3	3.11	2.96	2.94	3.04						
A_3E_4	3.10	3.02	2.99	3.14						
A_4E_1	2.82	2.36	2.09	2.07						
A_4E_2	2.71	2.27	2.16	2.12						
A_4E_3	2.91	2.47	2.38	2.30						
A_4E_4	2.84	2.72	2.65	2.57						

The following sums of squares are provided:

$$ss_A = 13.8518 \qquad ss_{\overline{AE}} = 33.1120 \qquad ss_{\overline{AER}} = 73.8277$$
$$ss_E = 13.3390 \qquad ss_{\overline{AT}} = 23.7999 \qquad ss_{\overline{AET}} = 46.0231$$
$$ss_T = 8.2200 \qquad ss_{\overline{AR}} = 23.1194 \qquad ss_{\overline{ATR}} = 36.7313$$
$$ss_R = 3.8645 \qquad ss_{\overline{ET}} = 23.5763 \qquad ss_{\overline{ETR}} = 43.3426$$
$$\qquad\qquad\qquad ss_{\overline{ER}} = 29.2573 \qquad ss_{\overline{AETR}} = 101.8745$$
$$\qquad\qquad\qquad ss_{\overline{TR}} = 12.8225$$

a) Prepare a summary table of the complete analysis, classifying the various main effects and interactions as "between" and "within" effects, as has been done for each design in this chapter.

b) Identify one of the totals involved in computing $ss_{\overline{AETR}}$.

c) Apply tests of homogeneity to the "between" interactions with R, ... to the "within" interactions with R. How do you account for the difference in the outcomes of these tests?

d) In which case may the interaction with R be pooled to provide a more stable error term? On what assumption? Is any important advantage gained by such pooling in this case? Explain.

e) Estimate the error variance of the difference between the means (over-all other factors) of two "acquisition" categories. Estimate the error variance of the difference between the (over-all) means of two "trial" categories. How many times as many cases would be needed to make the first of these error variances in an augmented experiment as small as the second is in this experiment?

f) Test (at the 1% level) the hypothesis of no AT interaction in the population. Specify the assumptions underlying this test.

g) May one infer from the test of (f) that there is an *intrinsic* AT interaction? Explain.

h) It appears that there is probably an AE interaction in the population, since the observed AE interaction is significant at the 5% level. What inferences may one draw concerning the rank order of the acquisition categories from one extinction level to another? ... about the rank order of the extinction categories from one acquisition level to another?

i) Test the simple effect of A for E_1. For E_4.

j) Suggest some extraneous factors that might differ systematically from replication to replication. Under what circumstances, in general, can such factors affect the treatment comparisons? Why do these systematic factors seem of little consequence in this experiment?

k) How are factors affecting cages systematically in each replication handled in this experiment? Do such factors give rise to extraneous interaction in this experiment? Could they "account for" a significant interaction? Explain.

14

Analysis of Covariance

Nature and Purposes of Analysis of Covariance

Many of the designs thus far considered have involved the *experimental* control of a concomitant variable or variables while observations are being made of the effect of a given experimental variable. In the treatments × levels design, for example, the effect of a concomitant variable is controlled experimentally by so selecting the treatment groups that each shows the same distribution by levels of that variable. In the simple factorial $(A \times B)$ design, the effect of the B factor is similarly controlled in comparisons of the A categories, since within each A category the distribution by B categories is the same. There are some experimental situations, however, in which it is either impossible or impracticable thus to control a concomitant variable by direct selection of the subjects. Sometimes administrative conditions make direct control impracticable. For example, a school principal may permit an educational experimenter to administer different experimental methods of instruction to different school classes, but may require that he use the classes as they are already organized. That is, he may not allow the experimenter to reorganize the classes into "matched" classes for the purposes of the experiment, since such reassignments would introduce conflicts in other aspects of the students' class schedule. Sometimes, too, the variations in the concomitant variable do not arise or are not observable until after the experiment has begun. For example, in a methods of instruction experiment the concomitant variable may be the number of hours spent in study by individual students — a variable which it may be practicable to observe and measure but not to control experimentally.

In situations in which *experimental* control of a concomitant variable may be either impossible or impracticable, it is sometimes possible to resort to *statistical* control of that variable. That is, observations may be made of the uncontrolled concomitant variations and appropriate *adjustments* may be made in the criterion means for the various treatment groups, as well as in the error term used in the test of significance. This method of statistical control is that known as the method of *analysis of covariance.*

317

Suppose that in a simple randomized experiment with just two treatments, measures are available not only for the criterion variable (Y) but also for a concomitant (and uncontrolled) variable (X). For each treatment group, one could then compute the correlation (r_{xy}) between these variables, and the coefficient of regression of Y on X (b_{yx}). If the treatments are alike in their effects on the criterion variable (which is the hypothesis to be tested) then, except for chance, these coefficients are the same for both treatment groups. We will call the estimate of the common true regression coefficient the within-groups regression coefficient (b), and of the common true correlation coefficient the within-groups correlation. By means of the regression equation we can then compute for each subject the "expected deviation" of his Y-measure from the general Y-mean — that is, the deviation expected in consideration of the deviation (x) of his X-measure from the X-mean.

Suppose that we then subtract from each subject's actual Y-measure the expected deviation (bx) of that measure from the general Y-mean, and that we call the result $(Y$-$bx)$ his *adjusted* criterion measure. The adjusted criterion measure for any individual subject would then be independent of his X-measure. A given subject may have a high X-measure, and his "expected" Y-measure may therefore also be high, but his actual Y-measure may be either above or below expectation. Similarly, the mean X-score, and hence the expected mean Y-score, may be higher for Group 1 than for Group 2, but yet the mean of the *adjusted* scores for Group 1 may be either higher or lower than that for Group 2. If we then find that the mean of the adjusted criterion scores is higher for the group that received Treatment 1 than for the group that received Treatment 2, we would know that the difference is not due to any difference in the X-factor for the two groups, but must be due either to chance fluctuations in random sampling or to the effect of the treatments (or possibly to the effect of some uncontrolled extraneous variable).

Suppose we thus compute the adjusted criterion score for each subject in both treatment groups, and that we then apply the usual methods of analysis of variance, not to the actual criterion measures, but to the *adjusted* criterion measures, and that we finally apply an F-test to test the significance of the treatment difference. If the difference in adjusted criterion means is found to be significant, we can then be reasonably certain that it is due, not to sampling fluctuations, but to a real treatment effect (or, if the experiment has not been closely controlled, possibly to the effect of some uncontrolled extraneous variable). Thus, through a purely *statistical* control we can secure the same precision in the evaluation of the treatment effect as if we had *experimentally* controlled the X-factor by actually matching the groups with reference to X, or by constituting the subjects into levels on the basis of X and using the appropriate test in a treatments $\times$ levels design.

The procedure just described is essentially that of the method of analysis of covariance. The method is simply an extension of the method of analysis of variance, applied to the adjusted rather than to the actual criterion measures. Why it is called the method of analysis of covariance will be made clear in the following section, concerned with the basic formulas and computational procedures needed in the application of the method.

Basic Formulas

The *covariance* of two variables for a given population is defined as the mean of the products of the deviations of the paired variables from their respective population means. The covariance for a sample is the mean product of the deviations from the sample means. The covariance of X and Y for a given sample is thus $\sum xy/N$, in which $x = X - M_X$ and $y = Y - M_Y$ are the deviations of X and Y from their respective sample means.

The best [1] estimate of the covariance of the *population* that may be obtained from a random sample of N cases is $\dfrac{N}{N-1}$ times the covariance of the sample, just as the best estimate of the population variance is $\dfrac{N}{N-1}$ times the sample variance. That is, the best estimate of the covariance of the population is $\sum xy/(N-1)$. (The proof of this, which is closely similar to the proof that the best estimate of the population variance is $\sum x^2/(N-1)$, is left as an exercise for the student.) Thus the degrees of freedom for the variance of X or Y and for their covariance are the same.

We shall let sp represent the "sum of products" ($sp = \sum xy$), just as we have previously let ss represent the sum of squares. In this case, $ss_X = \sum x^2$ and $ss_Y = \sum y^2$.

If the total sample consists of a groups, the "total" sum of products may be analyzed into its between-groups and within-groups components, just as may the sum of squares of either X or Y. The proof is as follows:

Let $\bar{x}_i$ represent the means of the x's for group i, and let $\bar{y}_i$ represent the mean of the y's. Then, for any subject in group i,

$$(x - \bar{x}_i)(y - \bar{y}_i) = xy - x\bar{y}_i - y\bar{x}_i + \bar{x}_i\bar{y}_i.$$

Summing such expressions for all n_i subjects in group i, we get

$$\sum (x - \bar{x}_i)(y - \bar{y}_i) = \sum xy - \bar{y}_i\sum x - \bar{x}_i\sum y + n_i\bar{x}_i\bar{y}_i.$$

Summing these expressions for all a groups, and simplifying, we get

$$\sum_{i=1}^{a}\sum (x - \bar{x}_i)(y - \bar{y}_i) = \sum_{i=1}^{a}\sum xy - \sum_{i=1}^{a} n_i\bar{x}_i\bar{y}_i,$$

from which

$$\sum_{i=1}^{a}\sum xy = \sum_{i=1}^{a}\sum (x - \bar{x}_i)(y - \bar{y}_i) + \sum_{i=1}^{a} n_i\bar{x}_i\bar{y}_i. \tag{108}$$

Thus, we see that the "total" *sum of products* $\left(sp_T = \sum_{i=1}^{a}\sum xy\right)$ of the

---

[1] According to the least squares criterion.

deviations of the X and Y measures from their respective general means is composed of two components. One of these (the first right-hand term) is the sum of the sums of the products for the individual groups of the deviations of the measures from their respective group means. This we will refer to as the within-groups sum of products (sp_w). The other $\left(\sum\limits_{i=1}^{a} n_i \bar{x}_i \bar{y}_i \right)$ is the sum of the weighted products of the deviations of the group means from their respective general means. This is the sum of products for between-groups (sp_A).

Formula (108) may then be rewritten

$$sp_T = sp_w + sp_A.$$

The formulas for computing the sums of products from the original measures (X and Y) are closely similar to the formulas for computing the corresponding sums of squares. The "total" sum of products is

$$sp_T = \sum_{i=1}^{a} \sum xy = \sum_{i=1}^{a} \sum XY - \frac{T_X T_Y}{N} \tag{109}$$

in which the summation of the XY products is over all groups, and in which $T_X = \sum\limits_{i=1}^{a} \sum X$, $T_Y = \sum\limits_{i=1}^{a} \sum Y$, and N represents the total number of subjects in all groups.

Similarly, the sum of products for between-groups (A) is

$$sp_A = \sum_{i=1}^{a} n_i \bar{x}_i \bar{y}_i = \sum_{i=1}^{a} \frac{T_{Xi} T_{Yi}}{n_i} - \frac{T_X T_Y}{N} \tag{110}$$

in which T_{X_i} represents the sum of the X's for group i, and n_i represents the number in the group, etc. [The derivation of formulas (109) and (110) from the basic expressions in formula (108) is left as an exercise for the student.]

The sum of products for within-groups is then obtained as a residual by

$$sp_w = sp_T - sp_A. \tag{111}$$

It will be recalled that in the more complex experimental designs the analysis of the total sum of squares into a number of components consists essentially of successive applications of the method of analysis into two components. The same is true with reference to the analysis of the total sum of products. In any experimental design for which measures of two variables are available for each subject, the analysis of the total sum of products follows exactly the analysis of the total sum of squares for either variable. Thus, in the simple ($A \times B$) factorial design, the sum of products for interaction (AB) is equal to the sum of products for between-combinations (between cells) less the sums of products for A and B, just as the sum of squares for interaction is equal to the sum of squares for between-combinations minus the sums of squares for the main effects.

We may next recall, from simple correlation theory, that the coefficient of correlation between X and Y for a sample may be written

$$r_{xy} = \frac{\sum xy}{\sqrt{\sum x^2 \cdot \sum y^2}} = \frac{sp_T}{\sqrt{ss_{T_X} \cdot ss_{T_Y}}}$$

in which ss_{T_X} and ss_{T_Y} are the "total" sums of squares for the X and Y distributions. Since, when a sample consists of a number of groups, $\sum xy$, $\sum x^2$, $\sum y^2$ may each be analyzed into its between-groups and within-groups components, we may obtain *three different correlation coefficients* from the sample — one for total, based on the "total" sums of squares and products, one for between-groups, and one for within-groups, as follows;

$$r_{xy(T)} = \frac{sp_T}{\sqrt{ss_{T_X} \cdot ss_{T_Y}}} \tag{112}$$

$$r_{xy(A)} = \frac{sp_A}{\sqrt{ss_{A_X} \cdot ss_{A_Y}}} \tag{113}$$

and

$$r_{xy(w)} = \frac{sp_w}{\sqrt{ss_{wX} \cdot ss_{wY}}} \tag{114}$$

in which ss_{A_X} is the between-groups sum of squares for the X measures, etc.

When all groups are of the same size, $r_{xy(A)}$ is simply the correlation between the group means for X and Y, $r_{xy(w)}$ is the "average" of the correlations between X and Y for the individual groups, and $r_{xy(T)}$ is the correlation computed for all the measures.

We know from simple correlation theory that the coefficient of regression of Y on X is equal to $\sum xy / \sum x^2$. Accordingly, the regression coefficient for the total sample is

$$b_T = \frac{\sum\limits_{i=1}^{a}\sum xy}{\sum\limits_{i=1}^{a}\sum x^2} = \frac{sp_T}{ss_{T_X}}. \tag{115}$$

(In this discussion, since we are not interested in the regression of X on Y, it will be understood that any regression coefficient referred to is a regression of Y on X.)

Similarly, the regression coefficient for within-groups is

$$b_w = \frac{sp_w}{ss_{wX}}. \tag{116}$$

If we now let $Y' = Y - b_w x$ represent what we have called an adjusted criterion score, we may note that the mean of those adjusted scores for the total sample will be

$$M_Y' = \frac{\sum\limits_{i=1}^{a}\sum(Y - b_w x)}{N} = M_Y$$

and that the deviation of a single adjusted criterion score from the general mean of adjusted criterion scores is

$$y' = (Y - b_w x) - M_Y = y - b_w x.$$

The deviation of a group mean of adjusted scores, or the adjusted mean of the group, from the general mean, is given (for group i) by

$$\bar{y}_i' = \frac{\sum(y_i - b_w x_i)}{n_i} = \bar{y}_i - b_w \bar{x}_i,$$

in which x_i is the deviation of a measure in group i from the general X-mean and similarly for y_i.

The deviation of a single adjusted score in group i from the adjusted mean of the group is given by

$$y_i' - \bar{y}_i' = (y_i - b_w x_i) - (\bar{y}_i - b_w \bar{x}_i)$$
$$= (y_i - \bar{y}_i) - b_w(x_i - \bar{x}_i).$$

For any one group, the sum of the squared deviations of the adjusted scores from the adjusted mean for the group would be

$$\sum[(y_i - \bar{y}_i) - b_w(x_i - \bar{x}_i)]^2.$$

By summing these expressions over all a groups, we get the sum of the squared deviations of all of the adjusted measures from their respective group means, which we will call the "adjusted" within-groups sums of squares, (ss_{wy}') as follows:

$$ss_{wY}' = \sum_{i=1}^{a}\sum[(y_i - \bar{y}_i) - b_w(x_i - \bar{x}_i)]^2$$

$$= \sum_{i=1}^{a}\sum(y_i - \bar{y}_i)^2 - \frac{\left[\sum_{i=1}^{a}\sum(x_i - \bar{x}_i)(y_i - \bar{y}_i)\right]^2}{\sum_{i=1}^{a}\sum(x_i - \bar{x}_i)^2}$$

$$= ss_{wY} - \frac{(sp_w)^2}{ss_{wX}}. \tag{117}$$

The degrees of freedom for this "adjusted" sum of squares for within-groups is not the same as that for the sum of squares for within-groups for the unadjusted Y measures, since one degree of freedom has been lost by imposing the linear restriction that the deviations be computed from the within-groups regression line. Accordingly, the degrees of freedom for the adjusted within-groups sum of squares is $N - a - 1$, and the adjusted mean square for within-groups is

$$ms_w' = ss_{wY}'/N - a - 1.$$

The next step is to compute an adjusted sum of squares for total. This is the sum of the squared deviations of all of the measures from the regression line fitted to the total sample and is computed as follows:

$$ss_{T_Y}' = ss_{T_Y}^* - \frac{(sp_T)^2}{ss_{T_X}}. \tag{118}$$

The derivation of (118) is similar to that for (117).

An adjusted sum of squares for between-groups is next found by subtracting the adjusted sum of squares for within-groups from that for total as follows:

$$ss'_A = ss'_{T_Y} - s\dot{s}_{wY}. \qquad (119)$$

This is contrary to the usual practice of securing the sum of squares for within-groups as a residual. A different adjusted sum of squares for between-groups could be directly computed as $\sum_i^a (\bar{y}_i - b_w\bar{x}_i)^2$, using the within-groups regression coefficient. However, an adjusted sum of squares for between-groups thus computed would be inflated by sampling error in the estimate (b_w) of the regression coefficient employed, and would make the between-groups effect appear more significant than it really is. What we have called the adjusted sum of squares for between-groups is sometimes called the "reduced" sum of squares for between-groups, since it is not thus inflated. Furthermore, if the same regression coefficient were used to compute the adjusted sums of squares for between-groups and within-groups, the corresponding mean squares would not be independent, and their ratio would not be distributed as F.

We may now compute an adjusted mean square for between-groups and form an F-ratio between the adjusted mean squares for between-groups and within-groups,

$$F = ms'_A/ms'_w, \quad df = (a - 1)/(N - a - 1). \qquad (120)$$

Proof that this ratio is distributed as F will not be given here. The conditions under which it is distributed as F are those numbered 3 to 8 in the list below. The additional conditions (1 and 2) are necessary if, in a controlled experiment, one is safely to conclude from a significant F that the experimental *treatments* have different effects.

1) The subjects in each treatment group were originally drawn either (a) at random from the same parent population, or (b) selected from the same parent population on the basis of their X-measures only — the selection being random with reference to all other factors for any given value of X.

2) The X-measures are unaffected by the treatments.

3) The criterion measures for each treatment group are a random sample from those for a corresponding treatment population.

4) The regression of Y on X is the same for all treatment populations.

5) This regression is linear.

6) The distribution of adjusted scores for each treatment population is normal.

7) These distributions have the same variance.

8) The mean of the adjusted scores is the same for all treatment populations.

Condition 3 is contained in Condition 1, and is that part of Condition 1 which is necessary to an F-distribution of ms'_A/ms'_w.

Since, under Conditions 3 to 8, the population means of the adjusted scores would be identical only if the line of regression of Y on X is the same for all populations, Condition 8 could also be stated: "The regression lines of Y on X for the various populations coincide." When all of Conditions 3 to 8 are satisfied, the relation among the X–Y scatterplots for the populations may be roughly pictured as in Figure 6.

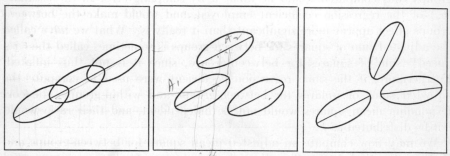

FIGURE 6. *Relation among XY scatterplots of populations under Conditions 3 to 8*   FIGURE 7. *Relation of scatterplots when only Condition 8 is not satisfied*   FIGURE 8. *Relation among scatterplots when only Conditions 4 and 8 are not satisfied*

The straight line in Figure 6 represents the common line of regression of Y on X for all treatment populations. A significant F in an experiment, granting Conditions 3 to 7, would suggest that the relationship among the population scatterplots is as pictured in Figure 7. If neither Condition 4 nor Condition 8 is satisfied, but Conditions 3, 5, 6, and 7 are met, the relationship might be as pictured in Figure 8.

If we regard Conditions 3 to 7 as the assumptions underlying the test, the F-ratio of (120) provides a test of the hypothesis that the population means of the adjusted scores are identical, or that the lines of regression of Y on X coincide. Whether or not the equality (or inequality) of the adjusted means implies equality (or inequality) of treatment effects, however, depends upon how the treatment groups were selected. They might have been so selected that, due to differences existing before administration of the treatments, the adjusted criterion means would differ at the close of the experiment even though all groups had received the *same* experimental treatment. Again, there might have been initial differences among the groups that just counter-balanced the differences among the experimental treatments, so that at the close of the experiment, but not before, the adjusted criterion means are equal. Before we may infer from a significant F that the *treatments* differ, then, we must be able to say that had all groups received the same treatment (or equally effective treatments) the adjusted criterion means would have been the same (except for chance), or the lines of regression of Y on X would have coincided.

We can say this with complete confidence, of course, if all treatment groups have been originally drawn at random from the same population, granting that all extraneous factors have been experimentally controlled or equalized during the course of the experiment. We can also say it with confidence if we know that all treatment groups were originally *selected* from the *same* population on the basis of their X-measures only, but essentially at random with reference to any other factors. For instance, one treatment group might have been selected from the upper end of the X-distribution for the parent population, but so that for any selected value of X all individuals with that value of X in the population have an equal chance of being drawn. The other treatment group might be similarly drawn from the lower end of the X-distribution, etc. We could, then be sure that if all treatment groups are given the same treatments, the line of regression of Y on X would be the same for all treatment groups. If, however, the treatment groups are selected on any other basis, so that they exhibit systematic differences other than those resulting from the X-selection, then these differences, rather than differences in the experimental treatments, could account for the final equality (or inequality) of the adjusted criterion means. It is possible that with groups otherwise selected the lines of regression of Y on X will coincide if all groups are treated alike, but the methods of selection suggested in Condition 1 seem to be the only *operational* procedures for *insuring* that the lines would coincide for the same treatment. The practical significance of Condition 1 will be more fully considered later.

If Condition 1 is satisfied, then, of course, Condition 3 is satisfied also. Obviously, however, Condition 3 could be satisfied even though Condition 1 were not.

It should be emphasized that these conditions apply to a *controlled* experiment. Presumably there are no *systematic* differences among the treatment groups in the effects of any extraneous factor.

It should be noted that the method of analysis of covariance is worth while (assuming a correlation between X and Y) even though the X means are identical for all treatment groups, in which case no adjustments would need to be made in the Y means. Nevertheless, assuming some correlation between X and Y, the within-groups variance of the adjusted measures would be less than that of the unadjusted measures, so that the precision of the experiment would be increased.

An Illustrative Example

Suppose that a learning experiment involving three treatments has been performed with 12 subjects, four for each treatment, the subjects having been assigned at random to the treatments. Let Y represent the criterion score, and let X represent a measure of aptitude for learning, to be used as the control variable. Let A_1, A_2, and A_3 represent the treatments. The scores for the 12 subjects are given below.

Control and Criterion Scores in a Hypothetical Experiment

	A_1		A_2		A_3		
	X	Y	X	Y	X	Y	$M_X = 30.0$
	33	18	34	31	34	15	
	42	34	55	45	4	8	$M_Y = 22.0$
	40	22	9	1	12	18	
	31	24	50	33	16	15	
Means	36.5	24.5	37.0	27.5	16.5	14.0	

The steps in the computation are as follows:

1) Compute the sum of squares for treatments (A), within-groups (w) and total (T), for X and Y separately, and then compute the corresponding sum of products.

2) Compute the adjusted sums of squares for within-groups and total by means of (117) and (118), respectively. Then secure the adjusted sum of squares for treatments (A) as a residual, by means of (119).

3) Compute the adjusted mean squares for treatments and within-groups and form the F-ratio between them to test the significance of the differences among the treatment means.

The results of these computations are summarized in the table below. The student is advised to check all computations as an exercise in order to familiarize himself with the procedures.

Sources	df	ss_X	sp	ss_Y	ss'_Y	df	ms'_Y
A	2	1094.0	651.0	402.0	19.6	2	9.8
w	9	1854.0	1261.0	1244.0	386.3	8	48.29
Total	11	2948.0	1912.0	1646.0	405.9	10	

$$F = 9.8/48.29 = .2+$$

Since the F is less than 1, it is obvious that the treatment differences are not significant.

It will be noted that the error variance for the unadjusted criterion scores is $1244/9 = 138.2$. Accordingly, through an analysis of covariance, the error variance has been reduced from 138.2 to 48.29, or the precision of the experiment has been almost tripled.[1]

---

[1] The ratio 138.2 to 48.29 overestimates slightly the gain in precision since it ignores the sampling error in b. A method of making allowance for this sampling error is given in Cochran and Cox, *Experimental Designs*, pages 81–82.

The extent to which the use of the methods of analysis of covariance increases the precision of an experiment of this type depends upon the within-groups correlation between the criterion and control variables. The ratio between the adjusted error variance and the unadjusted error variance is very nearly equal to $(1 - r_w^2)$. In the illustration here used, the within-groups correlation is .83, and the ratio between the adjusted and unadjusted error variances is .35, which is very nearly equal to $(1 - .83^2)$. The correlation of .83 found in this example is, of course, higher than would be found in most actual experiments, but very often the correlation is high enough to increase the precision of the experiment very substantially.

If the overall F proves significant, one will wish to compute the adjusted treatment means in order to be able to test differences for individual pairs of treatments. To do this, in this example, we must first find the value of the within-groups regression coefficient, which according to (116) is .6801. Accordingly, the adjusted criterion mean for A_1 is $24.5 - .6801(36.5 - 30.0) = 20.08$, for A_2 is 22.74, and for A_3 is 23.17. The corresponding unadjusted criterion means are 24.5, 27.5, and 14.0, respectively. Thus we see that the differences among the treatment means for adjusted scores are very much less than for the unadjusted scores. We know then that the differences among the treatment means of unadjusted criterion scores is very largely accounted for by chance differences in the learning ability of the subjects. We note particularly how much the unadjusted mean for A_3 was lowered by the low aptitude of the subjects in the A_3 group. After adjustment, the A_3 mean is higher than the others, where before it had been much lower. If the differences among the treatment means had proven significant, we might have wished to test the significance of the difference in a particular pair of adjusted treatment means. The error variance of the difference between two adjusted criterion means $(\overline{Y}_i' - \overline{Y}_j')$ is given by

$$\sigma^2_{\overline{Y}_i' - \overline{Y}_j'} = \left[\frac{1}{n_i} + \frac{1}{n_j} + \frac{(\overline{X}_i - \overline{X}_j)^2}{ss_{wX}} \right] ms_{wY}',$$

in which the adjusted sums of squares may be computed either from the entire experiment or only from the data for A_i and A_j alone. (Proof of this formula will not be given here.)

In the example, the error variance of the difference in the adjusted means for A_1 and A_2 is

$$\sigma^2_{M'_{A_1} - M'_{A_2}} = \left[\frac{1}{4} + \frac{1}{4} + \frac{(36.5 - 37.0)^2}{1854.0} \right] 48.29 = 24.14$$

and hence, this difference is tested by

$$t = \frac{20.8 - 22.74}{\sqrt{24.14}} = \frac{1.66}{4.91}$$

which, in this case, of course is not significant.

Importance of the Assumptions Underlying the Test of Significance
of the Treatments Effect

Judging by past applications of the method of analysis of covariance in educational and psychological research, the assumptions underlying the test of the hypothesis of equal treatment effects are, in general, in greater need of critical attention than is true with most, if not all, of the designs previously considered. Generally the method has been employed with little regard to the conditions under which the test is valid, and instances are numerous in which one or more of the conditions have clearly not been satisfied.

The first condition, concerning the manner of selection of the treatment groups, has perhaps most often been violated with serious consequences. In a few applications of the method, the treatment groups have been originally drawn at random from the same parent population. In these applications the method has been used to make adjustments only for *chance* differences in the control variable, and the chief advantage gained through the use of the method has been that of increased precision in the treatment comparisons. However, in most applications of analysis of covariance in educational and psychological research — particularly in the former field — the method has apparently been used in an effort to correct or to make adjustments for *systematic* differences existing among the treatment groups before administration of the treatments, and only rarely have the treatment groups been selected with reference only to the control variable used in the analysis. Many experimenters seem to have assumed that in a single-classification experiment the method of analysis of covariance with a control variable X is always the equivalent of a treatments $\times$ levels experiment with the same control variable, regardless of the manner in which the treatment groups may have been selected. That is, they seem to have assumed that the method eliminates the effects of *any* systematic differences that may have existed originally among the treatment groups, even though some of these differences may be quite independent of the X variable employed. It should be noted that the treatments $\times$ levels design does eliminate not only chance differences in the control variable, but also initial systematic differences in *any* other factor, due to the random assignment of subjects to treatments within levels. This is true of the method of analysis of covariance, however, only if Condition 1 is satisfied.

Consider, for example, the use of the method in an experimental comparison of three ways of teaching fourth grade arithmetic. Suppose that the experiment is performed in a school in which there are available three fourth-grade classes which were organized in the usual way at the beginning of the school year, with no knowledge that an experiment was later to be performed. The experiment is performed during the first six weeks of the second semester, each experimental instructional method being used with a different class. A test of general intelligence is administered to all students at the beginning of the experiment and the score on this test constitutes the control variable (X) used in an application of the method of analysis of covariance. A significant difference is found in the F of (120), and the conclusion is drawn that the instructional methods differ in effectiveness. Many applications of this general type have been reported in the literature of educational research.

How valid this procedure is depends on the history of the classes up to the time of the beginning of the experiment, as well as upon the adequacy of control of extraneous factors during the course of the experiment. Suppose, on the one hand, that all classes had originally been organized on essentially a random basis, so that at the beginning of the school year there were no differences among the classes larger than could readily be attributed to random sampling. Suppose also that throughout the first semester all classes had essentially the same educational experiences — all classes had been taught by the same teacher and received the same assignments, etc. — so that there was no apparent reason to believe that systematic differences among the classes had been created since the beginning of the first semester. In that case, at the time of the beginning of the experiment the classes might still be reasonably regarded as randomly selected from a single population, and the use of the method of analysis of covariance is valid (granting Conditions 4 to 8).

Suppose, on the other hand, that throughout the first semester the classes had had different arithmetic teachers, who had not only differed in personal effectiveness but also had used somewhat different methods of teaching arithmetic. Suppose the teacher of the class that was later to use experimental Method A used a method much like Method A, so that when the experiment began the pupils were able at once to use the experimental method with near maximum effectiveness. Suppose, however, that the teacher of the class that was later to use Method B had used a method which conflicted with Method B, so that considerable time was required early in the experiment before the pupils were able to use this method effectively. In this case, no "adjustments" based on initial intelligence test scores, or even on initial arithmetic achievement test scores, could possibly account for the effects of these differences upon the final adjusted means of the treatment groups. In any such application it would be dangerous, to say the least, to infer from a significant F [of (120)] that the differences among the adjusted treatment means are due to the treatments themselves.

The situation is much worse, of course, if the classes were originally selected not at random but so as to differ markedly with reference to some trait or characteristic related to the criterion variable in the experiment. Suppose, for example, that the classes had been selected according to ability and interest, that the abler and more industrious students had been assigned to one class and the least able to another, and that appropriate modifications in instruction had been used with these classes during the first semester. Suppose then that an initial achievement test administered at the beginning of the experiment provided the X-measures used in the analysis of covariance. In this case, not only would Assumption 1 be invalid, but differences in regression

(Assumption 4) and in variability of adjusted scores (Assumption 7) or even differences in the nature of the regression (Assumption 5) might well be expected. Nevertheless, many applications of this type also may be found reported in the research literature.

Whenever the X-measures are obtained during the course of or after the close of an experiment, careful consideration should be given to Condition 2. If the X-measures are taken at the beginning of the experiment or before, they could obviously not be affected by the treatments no matter what X may represent. If they are taken during the course of or after the conclusion of the experiment, they may or may not be affected by the treatments. For example, if X is a measure of chronological age, it clearly cannot be affected by the treatments no matter when the X observations are made. However, if the experiment is a learning experiment and X is the score on an intelligence test administered at the close of the experiment, it is readily conceivable that the X means could be affected by the treatments. If the latter is the case, then in "taking out" the effects of X, we would be taking out part of the treatments effect itself. It is sometimes useful to make such an analysis, but we must be careful in this case not to regard the differences among the adjusted criterion means as measures of "the" treatment effect.

Condition 2 has caused little trouble in past applications of the method of analysis of covariance in education and psychology, since in nearly all applications the X measures have been obtained before administration of the treatments. The consequences of a failure to satisfy Condition 2 will be further considered later in the section on "Analysis of Covariance as a Means of Introducing an Additional Factor into a Factorial Experiment."

Of the remaining assumptions, perhaps the most critical in practice is the assumption (Condition 4) that the regression of Y on X is the same for all treatment populations. Decisions concerning the validity of the other assumptions — linearity of regression, normality of distribution, and homogeneity of variance — must generally represent judgments based on *a priori* considerations like those discussed in earlier chapters, since available statistical tests of the validity of these assumptions are both low in power and difficult to apply. A statistical test of homogeneity of regression, however, is readily available and is described in the following section.

Test of Homogeneity of Regression

The adjusted sum of squares *for any one group* is the sum of the squared deviations from the regression line for that group based on the common within-groups regression coefficient. The sum of these sums of squares for all groups is the adjusted sum of squares (ss'_{wY}). This adjusted sum of squares may be analyzed into two components, one of which is the sum of the squared deviations of the measures each from the regression line for its own group (based on the regression coefficient for that group only), the other of which is due to differences among these group regression lines. If it can be shown that the latter component is significantly larger than the first, we must conclude that there are real differences among the group regressions.

For *Group i* alone, the sum of the squared deviations from the regression line for that group only is

$$\sum y_i^2 - \frac{(\sum x_i y_i)^2}{\sum x_i^2}$$

with $(n_i - 2)$ degrees of freedom. For the illustrative exercise, for example, this sum of squares for Group A_1 is equal to 82.99.

Summing these expressions for all a groups, we get

$$ss_{\text{dev. fr. grp. regr.}} = \sum_{i=1}^{a}\sum y_i^2 - \sum_{i=1}^{a}\frac{(\sum x_i y_i)^2}{\sum x_i^2}$$

with $\sum_{i=1}^{a}(n_i - 2) = (N - 2a)$ degrees of freedom. Since the first right-hand term is already known (ss_{wY}), we need only compute $\sum_{i=1}^{a}\frac{(\sum x_i y_i)^2}{\sum x_i^2}$. For the illustrative example, the sum of squares for deviation from group regression is 204.7. The sum of squares for differences among group regression lines is obtained by

$$ss_{\text{among grp. regr.}} = ss'_{wY} - ss_{\text{dev. fr. grp. regr.}}$$

with $(N - a - 1) - (N - 2a) = a - 1$ degrees of freedom. For the illustrative example, this result is $386.3 - 204.7 = 181.6$.

It may be shown that on Conditions 3, 5, 6, and 7 the ratio $ms_{\text{among grp. regr.}}/ms_{\text{dev. fr. grp. regr.}}$ is distributed as F, with $(a - 1)$ and $(N - 2a)$ degrees of freedom. Accordingly, this F may be used to test the hypothesis that there are no differences among group regressions. For the example, this F is 2.66 whereas the 10% point in the F-distribution for 2 and 6 degrees of freedom is 3.46. Hence, the assumption of homogeneous regression is clearly tenable.

Granting that Conditions 1 and 2 have been met in a controlled experiment, to say that the regression of Y on X is heterogeneous (but linear) is to say that there *is* a "treatments effect" but that the relative effectiveness of the treatments differs for different values of X. There may be some value of X for which the treatments are equally effective. If so, for higher values of X a certain treatment may be superior to a certain other treatment, but below this value the reverse would be true. There is a way of testing the hypothesis, for any given value of X, that the Y means in the populations are identical. However, we are rarely interested, in educational and psychological experiments, in the relative effectiveness of the treatments for any *particular* single value of X; rather we are interested in the relative effectiveness of the treatments for populations that are variable with respect to X. Accordingly, it hardly seems worth while to describe this procedure here.[1]

---

[1] See Alexander Mood, *Introduction to the Theory of Statistics* (New York: McGraw-Hill Book Company, 1950), pp. 350–357, and M. G. Kendall, *The Advanced Theory of Statistics*, Volume II, Third Edition (London: Charles Griffin and Company, Ltd., 1951), pp. 237–245, for more advanced discussions of analysis of covariance.

Generalized Procedure

We are now ready to generalize the method of analysis of covariance for application in any of the experimental designs that have heretofore been considered, granting that for each subject there are available measures of two related variables, one of which is to be used as a *control* and the other as a *criterion* variable.

As has already been noted, it is always possible to analyze the total sum of products into components corresponding exactly to those into which the total sum of squares for either the criterion or the control variable may be analyzed. This aspect of the analysis, then, should present no problem.

We have seen also that in some of the more complex designs it may be desirable to test the significance of each of a number of different effects, each of which may involve the employment of a different error term. (For an example, refer to the discussion of the $A \times B \times R$ design, pages 230–237.) For any of these several separate tests of significance, the procedure involved in the application of the method of analysis of covariance may be described in the same general terms.

Let U represent the "effect" the significance of which is to be tested. The "effect" may be the main effect of a treatment, the simple effect of a treatment, a first or higher order interaction, or an interaction of two factors for a given level of a third, and so forth. Let E represent the appropriate error term for U. The error term may be the within-cells component or it may be an interaction of any order, or it may be derived by pooling the sums of squares for a number of interactions. For example, in a four-factor $(A \times B \times C \times D)$ design, U may represent AB and E may represent a pooling of all the higher order interactions. In these terms, the generalized procedure for testing the significance of U is as follows:

1) Compute the sums of squares for U and E for both X and Y (the control and criterion variables) separately, and then compute the corresponding sums of products.

2) Add the sums of squares for U and E for the X-measures to compute the sum of squares for $U + E$. Similarly, compute the sum of products for $U + E$ and the sum of squares for $U + E$ for the criterion variable.

3) Compute the *adjusted* sum of squares for E and $U + E$ respectively, substituting in (117) and (118) the corresponding sums of squares for the control or criterion variables, and the corresponding sums of products.

4) Subtract the adjusted sum of squares for E from that for $U + E$ to secure the adjusted sum of squares for U.

5) Divide the adjusted sums of squares for U and E each by their respective degrees of freedom to secure the corresponding adjusted mean squares,

noting that the degrees of freedom for the adjusted mean square for E is one less than for the corresponding mean square for the unadjusted criterion scores, due to the use of the regression coefficient.

6) Form the F-ratio between the adjusted mean squares for U and E to test the significance of the U effect.

It will be observed that where a number of different tests of significance must be made in the same design, the computation in an analysis of covariance may become rather tedious,[1] but if the correlation between the control and the criterion variables is substantial, the increased precision may be enough to justify the additional computational labor involved.

Analysis of Covariance vs. the Treatments × Levels Design as a Means of Increasing the Precision of an Experiment

The relative importance of the assumptions underlying the test of significance may be further clarified by directly contrasting the method of analysis of covariance with the use of the treatments × levels design. These may be regarded as alternative ways of increasing the precision of the experiment through the control of a concomitant variable — the one employing a statistical and the other an experimental control. When both methods are available, the use of the treatments × levels design is generally to be recommended. In this situation, the method of analysis of covariance offers certain administrative advantages or conveniences, but these are generally of relatively minor importance. For example, the use of the method of analysis of covariance may simplify the administration of the experiment by avoiding the necessity, before the experiment may begin, of constituting the subjects into levels with proportional frequencies at each level. It does this at the cost of some additional computational labor, but this may be negligible in relation to the administrative conveniences gained. Furthermore, when the method of analysis of covariance is used, the control measures may be secured at a more convenient time, either during the course of the experiment, or even after its conclusion, depending upon the nature of the control variable. The treatments × levels design, however, has the very important general advantage that it requires much less restrictive assumptions than the method of analysis of covariance. The method of analysis of covariance assumes *linear* regression: the test of the treatments effects in the treatments × levels design is valid no matter what the nature of the regression, so long as the assumptions of within-cells homogeneity and normality are satisfied. The test of the treatments effect in the method of analysis of covariance assumes *homogeneous* regression for all treatment groups, which is equivalent in a treat-

---

[1] See Cochran and Cox, *Experimental Designs*, page 81, for approximate shortcut procedures.

ments × levels design to assuming that there is *no interaction* of treatments
and levels. The test of the main effect of treatments in the treatments × levels
design is valid whether or not an interaction exists.

There are differences, too, in the kind of information that may be derived
from the experimental data. A test of interaction may be made in either case
— as previously noted, with the method of analysis of covariance the test of
homogeneity of regression is equivalent to the test of interaction in the
treatments × levels design — but the computational procedures are considerably simpler with the treatments × levels design. The use of the treatments × levels design permits a study of the "simple" effects of the treatments at any given level. (See the reference of the footnote on page 331 for a
less convenient way of studying simple effects with analysis of covariance.)

In general, then, it would appear that the method of analysis of covariance
should be employed only when the use of the treatments × levels design is
not a practicable alternative, and only when careful consideration indicates
that the underlying assumptions are at least approximately satisfied.

It may be worth noting that it is possible to apply both techniques simultaneously — using the method of analysis of covariance for statistical control
of one concomitant variable in an experiment in which another concomitant
variable is experimentally controlled through the use of the treatments × levels
design.

Analysis of Covariance as a Means of Introducing an Additional Factor
into a Factorial Experiment

In most of the preceding discussions, it was implied that the method of
analysis of covariance was being employed primarily in order to increase the
precision of the experiment and to adjust for initial differences in X, and
not because the relationship of the control and criterion measures was of any
interest in itself. In many instances, however, the X-factor may be introduced for exactly the same reasons that any other "factor" is introduced in
a factorial experiment — that is, in order to study its relationship to the
other factors or the manner in which it may affect the comparisons within
any of the other classifications.

For example, in an experiment concerned with methods of instruction of a
school subject, it may be suspected that certain of the methods may motivate
the pupils to spend more time in study out of class than others. The experimenter may accordingly wish to know which method would have resulted in
highest achievement had the pupils spent the same total time in study under
each method or what part of the effect of each method is a direct and what
part is an indirect effect brought about through the increase in study time.
Suppose that a record was kept during the experiment of the amount of
study time for each pupil, and that from this record the total time for each
pupil was determined. By the method of analysis of covariance, the mean

scores on the criterion achievement tests could then be adjusted so as to eliminate the effect of the time differences.

Statistical Control of More than One Concomitant Variable

If it is desired to control statistically the effect of more than one concomitant variable, the adjustments must be made by means of the *multiple regression equation* between the criterion and the concomitant variables. The regression coefficient can be computed as before from the error terms secured through analyses of the variances and covariances of the variables involved.

In the case where allowances are to be made for two initial measures (X and Z), the multiple regression equation will be

$$y' = b_1x + b_2z.$$

To compute these regression coefficients, an analysis of variance must be carried through for each of the three variables and for the three possible covariances. Having found the error term (sum of squares or products) in each of these analyses, the results may be substituted in the following simultaneous equations, which may be then solved for b_1 and b_2.

$$\sum xy = b_1\sum x^2 + b_2\sum xz$$
$$\sum zy = b_1\sum xz + b_2\sum z^2.$$

The formula for computing any adjusted score (Y') will then be

$$Y' = Y - b_1x - b_2z.$$

The total sum of squares for the adjusted scores will be

$$\sum y'^2_{(tot)} = \sum(y - b_1x - b_2z)^2$$
$$= \sum y^2 - 2b_1\sum xy - 2b_2\sum zy + b_1^2\sum x^2 + 2b_1b_2\sum zx + b_2^2\sum z^2.$$

Each of the components of the adjusted total sum of squares may be computed by the same formula from the corresponding components of the sums of squares and products for the three variables involved. The error variance for adjusted scores will then be computed as before, after having allowed for the *two* degrees of freedom utilized in computing regression coefficients. The variance for treatments would then be computed as a residual in a manner similar to that already described.

Similar methods could be employed to allow for still other concomitant measures, but obviously with a tremendous increase in the amount of labor involved. The computational task for two control measures is not at all unmanageable, and may sometimes be worth while, considering the ease with which additional measures may sometimes be secured. The advantage gained depends upon the magnitude of multiple correlation coefficient for the contemplated number of variables as compared with that for the best combination of any smaller number. Experience with educational tests has shown that in situations of this kind the multiple correlation of two measures with the criterion will seldom be very much higher than the higher of the two zero order correlations, and that usually only a negligible increase in the multiple correlation is secured by adding a third dependent variable (assuming, of course, that the two already selected are the best two for the purpose). It is hardly worth while, therefore, to attempt here a description of the more complex procedures required for three or more concomitant measures.

For the case of the two concomitant measures already considered, it may be worth pointing out that the multiple correlation $R_{y.xz}$ between the initial concomitant measures and the criterion may be computed from the formula

$$R_{y.xz}^2 = \frac{b_1 \sum xy + b_2 \sum zy}{\sum y^2}.$$

How much the labor of allowing for both variables is worth while is then dependent upon how much

$$\sqrt{1 - R_{y.xz}^2}$$

is less than either

$$\sqrt{1 - r_{xy}^2} \text{ or } \sqrt{1 - r_{zy}^2}.$$

STUDY EXERCISES [1]

1. In a simple-randomized experiment, measures of a related variable (X), as well as of the criterion variable (Y), were obtained for all subjects. These measures are given in the table below:

A_1		A_2		A_3		A_4	
X	Y	X	Y	X	Y	X	Y
97	23	93	21	96	20	89	9
106	19	85	15	127	36	95	15
105	23	86	25	107	24	91	9
76	23	107	30	105	23	110	22
128	33	115	22	106	28	96	20
107	24	83	15	106	22	107	21
103	10	120	30	98	14	109	21
95	23	112	23	106	4	117	20
104	27	104	24	107	12	79	8
109	28	109	18	126	20	86	21
101	27			77	7		
109	18			103	23		
129	33						
94	18						

[1] See second paragraph on page viii.

a) Prepare a table (similar to that on page 326) summarizing the results of an analysis of variance and covariance of these data and giving the F needed to test the treatments effect. Give the degrees of freedom for this F.

b) Compute the error mean square obtained in an analysis of the variance of the Y measures only. Express the error mean square of (a) as a percent of this mean square. What is the meaning of this ratio?

c) Compute the estimated $r_{xy(w)}$. Compute $[1-r^2_{xy(w)}]$. Compare with the result of (b).

d) What is the estimated coefficient of regression of Y on X for the A_1 group alone?

e) Test the hypothesis that the within-group regressions are homogeneous.

f) Compute the t needed to test the hypothesis that the mean of the A_1 and A_2 treatment populations are identical. What is the number of degrees of freedom for this t?

2. An experiment was performed by Kruglak [1] to determine the relative effectiveness of two laboratory procedures in teaching elementary college physics: the "conventional" (or control) method, in which the students worked in pairs and performed each experiment by following a manual, and the experimental method, in which the instructor performed the experiment while the students observed and recorded results.

Subjects for the experiment were selected from 194 college students registered for physics "lab" at the University of Minnesota. Subjects included in the sample were male, Minnesota high school graduates who could take lab on Tuesdays. Four laboratory periods were held on Tuesday, two morning (8–10 and 10–12) and two afternoon (1–3 and 3–5) periods. Two sections were scheduled during each period. Subjects who could take lab in a particular period were assigned at random to one of the two sections for that period. Different numbers of students were available at each time period. In order to facilitate statistical analysis, cases were rejected at random until each subgroup was equal in size to the smallest one. This resulted in 56 students for the analysis, 7 in each section.

Four instructors were scheduled to teach lab sections on Tuesdays. Each instructor had a morning and an afternoon section. The two instructors scheduled at each period were assigned at random to either the control or experimental section — each taught the opposite section (method) at the other time of day. Thus each instructor taught a control section and an experimental section.

---

[1] Hayn Kruglak, "A Comparison of the Conventional and Demonstration Methods in the Elementary College Physics Laboratory," *Journal of Experimental Education*, vol. 20 (March, 1952), pp. 293–300.

A 30-item *pre-test* of laboratory practice was administered to all subjects at the beginning of the quarter. The scores on this test were used as *control* measures. The *criterion* measure for each subject was his score on the same test administered at the close of the quarter during which the experiment was in progress. A summary of sums of squares and products is presented below.

	df	Control ss_X	Criterion sp_{XY}	ss_Y
Methods (A)	1	23.14	371.57	5,965.79
Instructors (I)	3	154.07	123.43	1,140.00
Interaction (AI)	3	274.14	121.57	2,332.21
Within	48	7,836.00	7,554.86	24,685.71
Total	55	8,287.35	8,171.43	34,123.71

a) Using the "within" term as "error," compute the adjusted (reduced) sums of squares and mean squares for A, I, and AI, as well as the adjusted sum of squares and mean square for "within," and present these in a summary table.

b) The sum of $(\sum xy)^2 / \sum x^2$ for the eight groups is 8185.0,[1] x and y representing deviations from the group means. Test (at the 5% level) the hypothesis that the regression is homogeneous for the eight AI populations.

c) What is your estimate of the (presumably common) correlation between initial and final measures within individual sections? Is this correlation high enough to make the use of the method of analysis of covariance worth while? Justify your answer by a comparison of the unadjusted and the adjusted mean squares for "within."

d) Test, at the 1% level, the hypothesis that there is no AI interaction in the population. Specify the population.

e) Represent the design as a 2×4 diagram, in which columns correspond to treatments and rows to instructors, with "a.m." or "p.m." in each cell to indicate the time of day involved. Suppose that there is a general tendency for the morning sections to do better than the afternoon sections, either because of a selection of students or because the morning is more favorable to high achievement. How does this "time-of-day" factor affect the A-effect in this design? ... the I-effect? ... the AI-effect? In other words, with what is the time-of-day factor confounded? Since the "within" term is being used as "error," is this confounding desirable or undesirable? Explain.

---

[1] This figure is a guess; Kruglak did not report the data needed to compute this term.

f) Considering your reasoning in (e), is it plausible that the AI interaction is partly extrinsic? Is it possible that a substantial intrinsic interaction was accidentally cancelled by the extrinsic interaction in this experiment? Explain. Do you feel safe in concluding from the test of (c) that there is no intrinsic interaction in the population?

g) Test, at the 1% level, the hypothesis that the treatment means in the population are identical. Specify the population, on the assumptions (1) that there is no AI interaction and (2) that there is an AI interaction.

h) Suppose that the four instructors involved in this experiment may be regarded as a simple random sample from a meaningful population of instructors. Suppose also that there is an intrinsic AI interaction but no extrinsic interaction. How then would you test the A-effect in this experiment? Why? For the data here reported, compute and report the necessary adjusted mean squares and their degrees of freedom, and report also the F-ratio on which the test is based. On the basis of this test, is the observed A-effect significant at the 1% level?

i) Why was the supposition necessary in (h) preceding that there is no extrinsic interaction? Had the sections been assigned to instructors wholly at random within each treatment, without regard to time of day, would this supposition be necessary and would the test of (h) be valid? Explain.

j) Was there any real need to make the number of subjects the same in each cell (AI combination)? How could the experiment have been improved in this respect?

k) What are the obstacles to the use of the treatments × levels design in this experiment?

l) In his report of this study, Kruglak did not report any means, nor any sums of squares or products for individual groups. Comment on this omission from the point of view of good practice in general in research reporting.

① A   SS x   P   Y   Y' ✓ corrected A
     23.14   371.57   5965.79   out
  W 7836.00   7554.86   24685.71
    TX   TP   TY

I   SS x   SS r   SS Y   Y' ✓ corrected I
   154.07   123.43   1140   out
  7836.00   7554.86   24865.71

                     2332.21 — corrected
A×I   274.14   121.57   24685.71   ent   A×I
   7836.00   7554.86

Corrected total =
Corrected w/in =   34,123.71 $\dfrac{-(8171.43)^2}{8287.35}$
            24685.71 − 7554.86
                  7836.00

15

Tests Concerned With Trends

Introduction

Treatment-classifications in experimental designs are of two major types. One is the type in which the various treatments represent different amounts, or durations, or intensities, etc., of a single common experimental factor, and in which the treatments therefore are clearly ordered. For example, the treatments in a certain classification may represent different amounts of practice in the same task, or different degrees of intensity of the same visual stimulus, or different lengths of time in which forgetting may take place, or increasing numbers of trials or attempts to perform a certain task, etc. The other type of treatment-classification is that in which the various treatments are essentially unordered, and in which their distinguishing characteristics or differences are described in categorical and usually in qualitative rather than in quantitative terms. For example, the treatments may represent complex methods of teaching a school subject, or different kinds of interpolated activity in a learning series, or different kinds of situations in which stuttering may take place, or different ways of distributing practice in the same task, etc.

In experiments concerned with the latter of these two types, the interest is usually in *null* hypotheses, that is, in hypotheses that the treatments or treatment-combinations have the *same* effect on the means of the populations involved. In experiments concerned with ordered treatments, however, the interest may be primarily in *how* the population means of the criterion variable *change* with changes in the experimental factor, rather than in whether or not the criterion means do change at all. The hypothesis to be tested in such experiments, stated in general terms, may be any of the following:

H_1: The treatment means are unaffected by changes in the experimental variable, that is, the experimental data reveal *no trend* at all.

H_2: The changes in the treatment means are directly proportional to the changes in the experimental variable, that is, the trend is *linear*.

H_3: The population means follow a trend (fall along a curve) established on an *a priori* basis without reference to the experimental results.

H_4: The population means follow a trend derived from the experimental data, that is, they fall on a curve that has been "fitted" to the observed means.

Experiments may also be concerned with differences among the trends in the treatment means observed under different experimental conditions. Stated in general terms of factors A and B, the hypothesis to be tested is

H_5: The trend in the A means (treatments) is the *same* for all levels of B (conditions).

Experiments concerned with a single trend may employ the simple-randomized, the treatments $\times$ subjects, or almost any of the more complex designs. Experiments concerned with differences among trends are, of course, always factorial in character.

Experiments thus concerned with the successive changes in the criterion variable accompanying experimental variations in a given treatment, and experimental comparisons of such trends for different populations or under different conditions, constitute a large and important class of psychological experiments. The purpose of this chapter is to describe, for various basic types of experimental designs, how exact statistical tests may be applied to hypotheses of the general types just suggested.

Tests of Trend in the Simple-Randomized Design

The simplest design that may be employed in a study of trend is the simple-randomized design. For example, suppose that several groups of subjects were originally selected at random from the same population, and that one group was subjected to a certain treatment for one hour, another group was given the same treatment for two hours, another for three, etc. For each group, measures of a certain trait (Y) were obtained immediately following administration of the treatment. Figure 9 represents the possible outcome of an experiment of this type, the open dots representing the means of the criterion variable for the various groups arranged in order of *duration* (X) of treatments. The problem would, of course, be the same if X represented amount, or intensity, or number of repetitions, etc., of the treatment. The X-increment or interval need not be uniform.

Test for Presence of Trend: Usually the first question to be answered in an experiment of this kind is — do the data reveal any trend at all? That is, are the means consistent with the hypothesis (H_1) that the treatment means are unaffected by differences in X? This of course is simply the null hypothesis considered in Chapter 3, which is tested by

$$F = ms_A/ms_w, \ df = (a - 1)/(N - a), \tag{121}$$

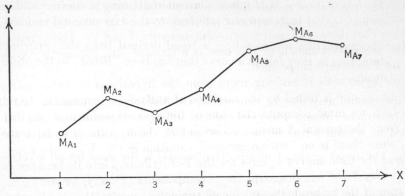

FIGURE 9. *Treatment means for various values of X*

in which ms_A is the mean square for *treatments* and ms_w is the mean square for *within-treatments*, in which a represents the number of treatments (or number of values of X at which observations are made) and N the total number of subjects.

Especially careful consideration should be given in such experiments to the underlying assumption that the population variance (of Y) is the same for all values of X. This is sure to be an unsound assumption if the line of means begins at, or at any point closely approaches, the base line ($Y = 0$) and if negative values of Y are impossible. In such cases, however, it may sometimes be possible to test the hypothesis along only that part of the X-scale for which the Y-variance may be considered fairly constant, disregarding the rest of the data. Sometimes, also, transformations (see pages 88 to 90) may be employed that will render the criterion measures more nearly homogeneous in variability.

In some situations, there may be strong *a priori* reason for believing that if Y depends at all upon X the relationship is monotonic (see page 99), although the relationship need not be linear. If this is the case, a more sensitive test for the presence of trend is usually a test of the significance of the difference in the Y-means for the first and last groups only. That is, a t-test of the significance of the difference $(M_{A_1} - M_{A_a})$ is much more likely to be significant than the F-test suggested above. If the assumption of homogeneity of variance is questionable, the difference in these two means may be tested by the Behrens-Fisher test (see pages 96–98) or a modification of it.

It should be clear from what has just been said that if the only purpose of the experiment is to test for *presence* of trend, and if it is fairly certain that the relationship between X and Y, if any, is monotonic, there is no point in making observations for more than two values of X. If it is possible, however, that Y may increase (or decrease) with increases of X up to a certain point, and that beyond that point Y may decrease (or increase) with further increases in X, observations must be made for a number of values of X in order to secure a dependable test for presence of trend.

Test for Linear Trend: If H_1 proves untenable, it may be desired to test the hypothesis (H_2) that increases in X are accompanied by proportional changes in Y, or that there is a *linear* relationship between X and Y. The hypothetical line of population means in this case is a straight line, but neither its slope nor its Y-intercept is specified.

This hypothesis is nothing more than the hypothesis of *linear regression* of Y on X, and is tested by the methods of analysis of covariance. To make this test, we must compute the sum of the squared deviations (ss_X) of the X's from the general X-mean. (This is the "total" sum of squares for the X's, since there is no "within groups" variation in the X's.) We must also analyze the total sum of squares for the Y-distribution into its between-treatments (ss_{A_Y}) and within-groups (ss_{wY}) components. Finally, we must compute the sum of the xy products (sp) for all subjects.

We have seen (page 322) that the sum of the squared deviations of the Y-measures in the entire sample from the line of regression of Y on X is given by

$$\sum (y - bx)^2 = \sum y^2 - \frac{\left(\sum xy \right)^2}{\sum x^2} = ss_{T_Y} - \frac{(sp)^2}{ss_X}$$

in which b is the regression coefficient.

If the observed means had all fallen exactly on the regression line, then the sum of the squared deviations of the individual Y-measures from the regression line would be the same as the sum of squares for within-groups (ss_{wY}), that is, ss_{wY} would equal $\sum (y - bx)^2$. We know that $ss_{wY} = ss_{T_Y} - ss_{A_Y}$. Accordingly, if $ss_{wY} = \sum (y - bx)^2$, it follows that $ss_{A_Y} = (sp)^2 / ss_X$. However, since all the A-means do not fall on the regression line, ss_{A_Y} will be larger than $(sp)^2 / ss_X$, and the difference between these terms will be indicative of the amount of departure from linearity.

We may think, then, of ss_{A_Y} as consisting of two components, one of which, $(sp)^2 / ss_X$, is due to linear regression, and the other of which, $ss_{A_Y} - (sp)^2 / ss_X$ is due to departure from linearity. The component due to linear regression has one degree of freedom; that due to departure from linearity, therefore, has one less degree of freedom than ss_{A_Y}, or $(a - 2)$ degrees of freedom. The mean square for departure from linearity is then

$$ms_{\text{dep from lin}} = \left[ss_{A_Y} - \frac{(sp)^2}{ss_X} \right] \Big/ (a - 2).$$

If the departure from linearity is due only to chance, then the mean square derived from the sum of squares due to departure from linearity should be the same, except for chance, as the mean square derived from ss_{wY}.

It may be shown that under certain conditions the ratio between these mean squares is distributed as F, that is, we may employ the test

$$F = ms_{\text{dep from lin}} / ms_{wY}, \; df = (a - 2)/(N - a), \tag{122}$$

to test H_2.

The conditions under which this mean square ratio is distributed as F are

1) Each treatment group is a random sample from a corresponding population (for which X is constant at the given value).

2) The criterion measures are normally distributed for each population.

3) The criterion measures have the same variance for each population.

4) The population means are a linear function of X, that is, the regression of Y on X for the combined populations is linear.

The last of these conditions constitutes the hypothesis (H_2) to be tested, the other three are the assumptions underlying the test.

It should be noted that the test of linearity is not very powerful, and can be expected to reveal only quite marked curvilinearity unless the sample is very large. Even with a large sample, it may fail to identify situations in which the regression is linear throughout most of the range of the X and Y distributions, but is sharply curvilinear at either end where the frequencies are small.

Goodness of Fit to A Priori Trends: It may sometimes be desired to test a completely _a priori_ hypothesis, that is, one which has been specified in advance of the experiment without any reference to the experimental data. Such an hypothesis would specify the exact values $(\mu'_1, \ldots, \mu'_i, \ldots, \mu'_a)$ of the population means corresponding to the various values of X, or would completely define the curve of population means. Figure 10 illustrates such a situation — the heavy dots representing the _observed_ treatment means (M_1, M_2, M_3, and M_4) in a particular experiment, and the line H representing the hypothetical curve of population means. (It does not matter how one arrives at the hypothetical values, so long as they have not been selected on the basis of an inspection of the experimental data. Presumably the hypothesis is based on theory only. Actually, there are very few situations in which theory can completely describe the line of population means. The testing of goodness of fit to _a priori_ trends is therefore of relatively little practical importance in itself, but it requires consideration here as a step in the development of a test of goodness of fit to _fitted_ trends, which is discussed in the following section.)

We will let $\mu_1, \mu_2, \ldots, \mu_a$ represent the actual treatment population means. The hypothesis (H_3) to be tested is then that the successive population means have the values $\mu'_1, \ldots, \mu'_i, \ldots$ and μ'_a, respectively, or that $\mu_1 = \mu'_1$, $\mu_2 = \mu'_2$, etc.

It is at once apparent that the hypothetical means might differ from the corresponding actual population means by a constant amount, or that the line H may be parallel to the line describing the actual population means. This possibility has been graphically represented in Figure 10. Thus the hypothesis (H_3) might correctly describe the _pattern_ of the actual population means, but may be incorrect so far as their _vertical placement_ is concerned. We can thus regard the hypothesis (H_3) as consisting of two separate hypotheses, one (H_{3a}) describing the _pattern_ of the population means, the other (H_{3b}) describing their _vertical placement_. We will frequently be more interested in the pattern of the hypothetical means than in their absolute values,

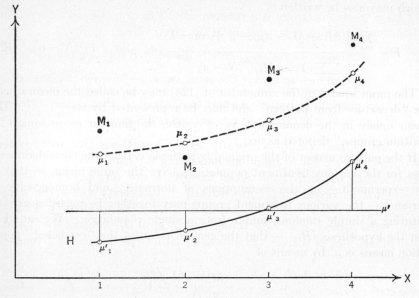

FIGURE 10. *Observed and hypothesized means*

and hence will wish to be able to make separate tests of these two aspects of the original hypothesis.

We may first note that if H_{3a} is true, then by subtracting appropriate constants from the measures in the various treatment populations, we can make the actual population means of the "corrected" measures identical for all treatment populations. Let

$$\mu' = \sum_{i=1}^{a} \mu'_i/a$$

represent the general mean of the hypothetical treatment population means. If we could then "correct" each measure in the ith treatment population by subtracting $(\mu'_i - \mu')$ from it, and could similarly correct the measures in each of the other treatment populations, the population means of the corrected measures would all have the same value (although this value would not necessarily equal μ', since H_{3b} may be false). We will let $Y'_i = Y_i - (\mu'_i - \mu')$ represent a single corrected measure in Group i, and will let the mean of these corrected measures be represented by $M'_i = M_i - (\mu'_i - \mu')$. The general mean of the corrected measures would then be the same as the general mean of the uncorrected measures $(M' = M)$. Now, to test H_{3a}, we have only to test the null hypothesis as applied to the corrected measures. That is, we may test H_{3a} by

$$F = \frac{\sum_{i=1}^{a} n_i(M'_i - M')^2/(a-1)}{\sum_{i=1}^{a} \sum (Y'_i - M'_i)^2/N - a} \tag{123}$$

which may also be written

$$F = \frac{\sum_{i=1}^{a} n_i[(M_i - M) - (\mu_i - \mu')]^2/(a - 1)}{\sum_{i=1}^{a}\sum(Y_i - M_i)^2/(N - a)}, df = (a - 1)/(N - a). \quad (124)$$

The mean square in the numerator of (124) may be called the mean square for "departure from pattern" and may be represented by $ms_{\text{dep fr patt}}$. The mean square in the denominator is, of course, the familiar mean square for "within groups," denoted as ms_{wg}.

If the pattern aspect of the original hypothesis is true, the corrected measures for the various treatment populations have the same mean, so that in the experiment — on the assumptions of normality and homogeneity of variance — the various treatment groups may together be regarded as constituting a simple random sample from a single population. We can then test the hypothesis (H_{3b}) — that the general mean of the "corrected" population means is μ' by means of

$$F = \frac{\dfrac{(M' - \mu')^2}{\sigma^2/N} \Big/ 1}{\dfrac{\sum_{i=1}^{a}\sum(Y_i' - M_i')^2}{\sigma^2} \Big/ (N - a)}$$

which may also be written

$$F = \frac{N(M - \mu')^2}{\sum_{i=1}^{a}\sum(Y_i - M_i)^2/(N - a)}. \quad (125)$$

We may call the mean square in the numerator of (125) the mean square for "vertical placement," and denote it by ms_{vp}.[1]

Since H_{3b} is of little interest when H_{3a} is false, one would ordinarily test H_{3a} first and then test H_{3b} only if H_{3a} is tenable. If either H_{3a} or H_{3b} is untenable, of course, H_3 is untenable also.

Goodness of Fit to Curves Fitted to the Experimental Means: It may sometimes be desired to test an hypothesis (H_4) represented by a curved line which has been "fitted" to the experimental means. If the hypothetical

---

[1] It is easy to show that

$$ss_{\text{dep fr }H} = ss_{wg} + ss_{\text{dep fr patt}} + ss_{vp}$$

in which $ss_{\text{dep fr }H}$ is the sum of the squared deviations of the individual measures from their respective hypothetical means. That is,

$$ss_{\text{dep fr }H} = \sum_{i=1}^{a} \sum (y_i - \mu_i')^2.$$

It may also be shown that the F-tests of (124) and (125) are independent of one another, so that either H_{3a} or H_{3b} may be tested without regard to the truth or falsity of the other.

curve has been fitted [1] by the method of least squares, the procedure would be exactly like that in the test of H_{3a} in the preceding section, except that the degrees of freedom for the numerator of F would be a minus the number of constants in the regression formula that were derived from the experimental means. For example, if $Y = AX + B$ had been fitted to the means, the degrees of freedom for the numerator of F would be $(a-2)$; if $Y = AX^3 + BX^2 + CX + D$ had been fitted, the degrees of freedom would be $(a - 4)$, etc. (In the preceding expression, the A representing one of the coefficients in the regression equation should not be confused with the A representing the treatment classification.)

In the case of a curve fitted to the experimental data, there would be no question of vertical displacement, and hence no need for a test like that for H_{3b}.

We may now note that if H_3 is of the type $Y = AX^2 + BX + C$, we may use the F of (124) to test the hypothesis that A and B are correct. Then, on the assumption that A and B are correct, the F of (125) may be used to test the hypothesis that C is correct also. If one wishes to test the hypothesis that the trend is of the form $Y = AX^2 + BX + C$, without specifying A, B, or C, the test of H_4 would be used. The procedure would be similar if H_3 is type $Y = AB^x + C$, $Y = A \log X + C$, etc.

Tests for Trend in Treatments × Levels Designs

To secure higher precision per subject in a study of trends than is possible with a simple-randomized design, the various treatment groups may be matched on the basis of a control variable, using the treatments × levels design described in Chapter 5. With this design, the tests of trend are very much the same as in a simple-randomized design except for the use of a different error term, as is shown in the following paragraphs.

Tests for Presence of Trend: To test the hypothesis that the criterion means are unaffected by differences in X, the data are analyzed in the manner described in Chapter 5, and the hypothesis is tested by

$$F = ms_A/ms_w, \quad df = (a - 1)/(N - al) \tag{126}$$

in which ms_w is the within-cells mean square, l is the number of levels, and N is the total number of subjects.

The assumptions underlying this test are that each treatment group is a sample _representative_ (with reference to levels) of the population to which inferences are to be drawn, and that within each level the criterion measures are normally distributed with the same variance for each value of X.

The preceding test is concerned with the hypothesis that the "main" trend

---

[1] For methods of fitting curved regression lines by the method of least squares, see George W. Snedecor, _Statistical Methods_, Chapter 14 (Curvilinear Regression). The methods there described are methods for fitting curved regression lines to individual observations, but, of course, are applicable to means as well.

is a horizontal straight line (the null hypothesis) — the "main" trend being the average of the "simple" trends for the various levels. It is possible that the main trend is a horizontal straight line, even though the simple trends are not. If desired, one may test the hypothesis that the simple trends differ from one another. The procedure for testing this hypothesis will be suggested later (page 350).

Test for Linear Trend: To test the hypothesis that the trend is linear in a treatment × levels design, a test similar to that used in the simple-randomized design (page 343) involving analysis of covariance must be employed. In addition to the terms needed to test the null hypothesis, the sum of products (sp) and the sum of squares for the X-variable (ss_X) must be computed. The linear hypothesis may then be tested by

$$F = \frac{ss_{A_Y} - \frac{(sp)^2}{ss_X}}{a - 2} \Big/ ms_{wY}, \quad df = (a - 2)/(N - al). \tag{127}$$

To understand the preceding test, suppose that arithmetic corrections have been applied to the original Y-measures so as to eliminate the sums of squares for levels and treatments × levels. So far as the corrected measures are concerned, the design would then reduce to a simple-randomized design, in which the linear hypothesis could be tested by means of (122). The test given by (127) is essentially that of (122) applied to the corrected data, ss_L and ss_{AL} having been eliminated.

To test the linear hypothesis for any single level considered alone, the test of (122) would be applied to the data for that level only, since so far as any one level is concerned, the design is a simple-randomized design.

Tests for A Priori and Fitted Trends: With the treatments × levels design, the tests for *a priori* and for fitted trends are the same as those employed with the simple-randomized design, except that the error mean square is that for within-cells rather than for within-treatments.

Tests for Trend in Treatments × Subjects Designs

Studies of trends will frequently be concerned with the effect of varying amounts, or of varying durations, etc., of a treatment upon the *same* subjects. The treatments × subjects design, therefore, is a particularly important design for purposes of trend analysis.

The tests of H_1, H_3, and H_4 are, except for the error term employed, exactly the same as in the simple-randomized and treatments × levels design. The error mean square in the treatments × subjects design is, of course, the interaction mean square (treatments × subjects).

With the treatments × subjects design, the linear hypothesis is tested by

$$F = \frac{ss_{A_Y} - \frac{(sp)^2}{ss_X}}{a - 2} \Big/ ms_{(AS)_Y}, \tag{128}$$

for which the degrees of freedom are $(a - 2)$ and $(a - 1)(n - 1)$, in which n is the total number of subjects per group.

Tests of Trend in Type II (Confounded) Designs

In studies of trend concerned with the effects of increasing amounts, intensities, etc., of the experimental factor upon the same subjects, it may be necessary to use a different *form* of the criterion test for each value of X. If *equivalent* forms of the test are not available, it is possible to counterbalance the effects of varying difficulties of the forms by using a Type II mixed design (see page 273). Suppose, for example, that the study is concerned with the effect of increasing amounts of fatigue upon the time (or number of repetitions) required to learn a list of 20 words. Suppose that observations are to be made for five degrees of fatigue and that therefore five different lists are employed. The subjects may then be divided at random into five equal groups and the lists may be administered according to the following diagram:

	A_1 $(X = 1)$	A_2 $(X = 2)$	A_3 $(X = 3)$	A_4 $(X = 4)$	A_5 $(X = 5)$
Gr 1	L_1	L_2	L_3	L_4	L_5
Gr 2	L_5	L_1	L_2	L_3	L_4
Gr 3	L_4	L_5	L_1	L_2	L_3
Gr 4	L_3	L_4	L_5	L_1	L_2
Gr 5	L_2	L_3	L_4	L_5	L_1

The tests of H_1, H_3, and H_4 would, except for the error term employed, be the same as in the simple-randomized design. With the Type II design, of course, the *error* mean square for testing the main effect of A would be $ms_{\text{error }(w)}$ computed in the manner indicated in Table 11, page 278. This error term would also be employed in testing H_3 and H_4.

To test the linear hypothesis, one would use

$$F = \frac{ss_{A_Y} - \dfrac{(sp)^2}{ss_X}}{a - 2} \Bigg/ ms_{\text{error }(w)} \qquad (129)$$

in which the degrees of freedom are $(a - 2)$ and $a(a - 1)(n - 1)$, and n is the number of subjects in each group.

Comparisons of Trends

Trend Comparisons in Simple Factorial and Treatments × Levels Designs:
Some experiments are designed, not to test for a single trend, but to determine
whether or not two or more trends *differ* from one another. In a simple factorial experiment, for example, one may wish to test the hypothesis (H_5) that the
trend in the A-means is the same for all levels of B, or, in a treatments × levels
($A \times L$) design, one may wish to determine whether or not the A-trend is the
same at all levels of the control variable. Suppose, for instance, that the
experiment described on page 341 is replicated at each of three levels of a
concomitant experimental factor (B), or at each of three levels of a control
variable (the procedure would be the same in either case). The results might
be represented as in Figure 11. We may regard these three curves as representing different populations, all "generated" from the same parent population — that from which the three samples were originally drawn. One
population is like the parent population except that all members have received
Treatment B_1 in combination with the A treatments. In another, all members

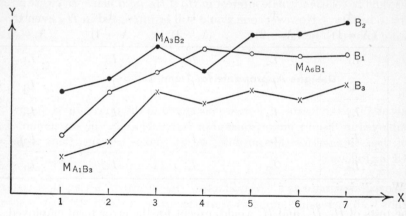

FIGURE 11. *Treatment means for three levels of B*

have received Treatment B_2 in combination with the A treatments, etc. The
hypothesis to be tested is that the various population means coincide for each
of the given values of X.

As in testing an *a priori* hypothesis concerning a single trend, two separate
tests are required.

We are first concerned with the more specific hypothesis, H_{5a}, that the
various sets of A means follow the same "pattern," in the sense that the curves
describing the population means are all "parallel" to one another, or that for
any two populations the *difference* in the criterion means is the *same* for each
value of X. This, of course, is equivalent to the hypothesis that there is no
interaction between A and B. This hypothesis is tested by

$$F = ms_{AB}/ms_w, \; df = (a - 1)(b - 1)/ab(n - 1) \qquad (130)$$

in which a represents the number of A treatments (number of values of X), b represents the number of levels of the B factor, and n represents the number of subjects in each treatment-combination group.

To test the significance of the difference for any particular *pair* of trends, a similar test is employed, except that ms_{AB} is computed only for the data for the two levels of B involved.

The preceding test is concerned with the hypothesis (H_{5a}) that the true (population) trends are "parallel" to one another, or that they follow the same *pattern*, but it does not test the hypothesis that the trends coincide. If H_{5a} proves tenable, another aspect of H_5 may be tested by

$$F = ms_B/ms_w, \quad df = (b-1)/ab(n-1). \tag{131}$$

This tests the hypothesis (H_{5b}) that the main effect of B is zero, or that for any two levels of B the mean of the successive *differences* in population means is equal to zero. However, H_{5b} could be true even though H_{5a} were false. If either of these hypotheses must be rejected, the over-all hypotheses (H_5) must be rejected also. The test of H_{5a} would usually be applied first, since ordinarily there would be relatively little interest in H_{5b} if H_{5a} (and hence H_5) were already known to be false. However, one would still be interested in H_{5a} even though H_{5b} were known to be false.

Designs Appropriate for Trend Comparisons

Almost all of the factorial designs considered in the preceding chapters may be employed in trend comparisons. For convenience in the discussion of the use of these designs for this purpose, we will define certain terms to be employed, as follows:

We will designate as a "trend factor" one in which the trend of criterion means with increasing amounts or at successive levels of the factor is to be observed.

We will designate as a "control factor" one whose effect upon the specified trend is either to be observed or controlled. If, in an $A \times B$ design the trends in the A-means at the various levels of B are to be compared, A is the trend factor and B the control factor. If, in an $A \times B \times L$ design, the A trends are to be compared at the various levels of B, and if L is introduced in order that its effect upon the trends may be equalized and the comparisons made more precise, L also will be called a control factor. It does not seem worth while to employ different terms to distinguish between these two possible purposes of the control factor, since the distinction has no bearing upon the selection of the design or upon the statistical analysis and tests of significance employed. We noted previously that it is sometimes difficult to decide whether a particular design is to be called a treatments $\times$ levels or a factorial design, and the difficulty in distinction here is of exactly the same character. A control factor may be introduced into a design both because it is desired to compare trends in some other factor at different levels of the given factor and in order to increase the precision of other comparisons, and neither purpose may predominate sharply over the other.

We will designate as a "repeatable" factor one all levels of which may be administered to the same subject with results meaningful for the purposes of the experiment, and for which comparable criterion measures may be obtained for the subjects at all levels of that factor. The mixed designs of Chapter 14 may be used, of course, only if one or more of the factors involved is repeatable.

We will designate as a "counterbalanced" factor one whose effect on one or more of the other factors is to be counterbalanced in the experiment. "Order" of administration and "form" of the criterion tests are prominent examples of "counterbalanced" factors. A counterbalanced factor is nearly always non-repeatable; otherwise it would be regarded as a control factor in a simpler design.

Most trend studies involve only a single trend factor, but experiments may be designed in which trends in more than one factor are to be observed simultaneously. With reference to a given trend factor, there may be one or several control factors, one or more of which may be introduced to observe its effect on the specified trend, and one or more of which may be introduced simply to increase the precision of the other comparisons. The design may also involve more than one counterbalanced factor, each of which may be counterbalanced with reference to one or more of the other factors.

The selection of the design most appropriate for a given trend study depends obviously upon the numbers of trend, control, and counterbalanced factors involved, and upon which of these factors are repeatable; and subsequent suggestions for the selection of designs will be organized along these lines. In any particular situation, however, the selection of a design may be dictated also by factors of administrative convenience or expediency, but because of the great variety of possibilities of this type, no systematic provision can be made for them here.

The following suggestions will be limited to the case in which there is only one trend factor, and the selection of designs will be considered for various combinations of control and counterbalanced factors.

Only one control factor; both trend and control factors non-repeatable: In this case only one design is possible — the $A \times B$ design. The tests of H_{5a} and H_{5b} for this design have already been considered. It is possible, of course, to compare both the A trends for the various levels of B and the B trends for the various levels of A, so that both factors may at the same time be trend factors and control factors. Similar possibilities exist in all of the subsequent designs, but, for the sake of simplicity of discussion, this possibility will not be specifically considered again.

Only one control factor; trend factor repeatable, but control factor non-repeatable: In this situation one might employ the Type I design, A representing the trend factor and B the control factor. (However, administrative considerations may dictate the use of the less precise $A \times B$ design.) The test of H_{5a} is made by $F = ms_{AB}/ms_{\text{error }(w)}$, and of H_{5b} by $F = ms_B/ms_{\text{error }(b)}$. If tests of simple trends are desired, the error term is $ms_{\text{error }(w)}$.

Only one control factor; trend factor non-repeatable, but control factor repeatable: Again the Type I design may be employed, in this case with B as the trend factor and A as the control factor. In this case, both aspects of H_5 may be tested by precise tests, but if an F-test of a simple B-trend is desired, the error term must be the "within-treatments" mean square computed for the data from the given level of A only, for reasons given in the discussion of the Type I design on page 271.

Only one control factor; both trend and control factor repeatable: In this situation, the use of the $A \times B \times S$ design will result in the maximum precision in all comparisons, but if the interest is only in the tests of H_5, the design offers little advantage over the Type I design. In any event, administrative considerations may dictate the use of the less precise Type I or $A \times B$ designs, even though both factors are repeatable.

Two control factors; all factors non-repeatable: In this case, the only possible design is the $A \times B \times C$ (or $A \times B \times L$) design. Comparisons of A-trends may be made, of course, both for the various levels of B and for the various levels of C, and also for the various BC combinations. If one wishes to test the hypothesis that the A-trends are parallel for all BC combinations, one would test the ABC interaction. The test of the ABC interaction provides an answer to the question "Does the effect of B on the A-trends differ for different levels of C, or, does the effect of C upon the A-trends differ for the various levels of B?" If, on the further assumption that the A-trends are parallel for all BC combinations, one wished to test the hypothesis that the A-trends coincide (for these combinations) one would test H_{5a} by testing the BC interaction.

Two control factors, both non-repeatable; trend factor repeatable: In this case, the Type III design may be used, with A as the trend factor.

Two control factors, one non-repeatable; trend factor non-repeatable: Again the Type III design may be used, but with A as the repeatable control factor.

Two control factors; trend factor and one control factor repeatable: The Type VI may be used, with C as the repeatable control factor.

Two repeatable control factors; trend factor non-repeatable: The Type VI design may be used, with C as the trend factor.

Two control factors; all factors repeatable: In this case the $A \times B \times C \times S$ design will provide the maximum precision in all comparisons, but any of the preceding three-dimensional designs may be employed, depending on considerations of administrative expediency and the relative emphasis placed on the various specific purposes of the experiment.

One repeatable control factor; trend factor non-repeatable; a third factor to be counterbalanced with reference to the control factor: The Type IV design may be used, with *C* as the non-repeatable (or repeatable) trend factor.

Trend factor repeatable; one non-repeatable control factor, with a third factor to be counterbalanced with reference to the trend factor: The Type IV design may be used, with *C* as the non-repeatable (or repeatable) control factor.

Trend factor and (one) control factor repeatable, with a third factor to be counter-balanced with reference to both the trend and control factors: A Latin-square design similar to the Type II design may be employed. If we let *A* and *B* represent the trend and control factors, the square will have *ab* columns corresponding to the various *A–B* combinations, with *ab* rows corresponding to the different equal groups of subjects needed, and with *C* as the Latin-square factor. This design again will be practicable only when *ab* is quite small.

The preceding outline should provide for most of the trend studies that might be made in educational and psychological research, although, of course, this outline could be extended indefinitely for still larger numbers of control and counterbalanced factors, using higher-dimensional and more complex designs, obtained by combining designs already considered.

STUDY EXERCISES [1]

1. Reconsider Exercise 1 of Chapter 3 (page 101).

    a) Plot the means of the treatment groups in the fashion of Figure 9 on page 342, letting *X* equal the area of the test circle.

    b) What did your computations in the original exercise reveal about the presence of trend?

    c) Let us suppose that you have no theoretical or *a priori* reason to expect any particular type of trend, and that your purpose in the experiment is primarily to secure an *estimate* of the true trend, rather than to test any particular *a priori* hypothesis. Obviously, however, you prefer a simple type of estimate to a complex one, so you begin by fitting a straight line to the data. What is the *slope* of the straight line of "best fit" to the observed treatment means? (See page 321.) On the chart constructed in (a), plot the point ($X = 48.8$, $Y = 9.39$) representing the general means of *X* and *Y*, then draw a line with the specified slope through this point.

    d) You may wish to determine if this straight line constitutes a tenable hypothesis concerning the trend of the population means. In applying the test of this hypothesis, what risk are you willing to take of making a Type I error? Justify your choice of a level of significance for this test, pointing out the consequences of setting a very high or a very low level of significance. Is the linear hypothesis tenable?

---

[1] See second paragraph on page viii.

e) In the test of (d), may either the F itself, or the probability with which it would be exceeded if the hypothesis were true, be regarded as a measure of "goodness (or badness) of fit," in any absolute sense, of the line to the observed means? . . . to the treatment population means? Explain, pointing out upon what the F depends, in addition to the absolute goodness of fit of the line to the observed means.

f) On the suppositions of (c), and considering the outcome of the test of (d), is there any point in testing any more complex hypotheses? Explain.

g) On the chart of (a), draw the lines $Y = .14X + 3.2$ and $Y = .087X + 4.4$. Do these lines constitute tenable hypotheses (at the 5% level) concerning the trend of the treatment population means? Explain. What does this imply about the power of the test of (d)?

h) Suppose that before this experiment was performed, someone had suggested that the line of population means is described by $Y = 2 + .001X^2$. On the chart of (a), plot the points on this line for the values of X corresponding to the various "treatments," and then draw a smooth freehand curve through these points. In light of the results of this experiment, does this line constitute a tenable hypothesis concerning the population means? Explain. Is the hypothesis tenable so far as *form* of the line alone is concerned? Explain.

i) Suppose that the only purpose of this experiment was to test the hypothesis that the trend of population means is linear. Would the experiment then have been more efficient if observations had been made only for $X = 20$, 50, and 79, rather than for five values of X? Explain.

j) What is the advantage of making observations at five values of X, rather than at only three? (Consider the possible forms that the trend of treatment population means may take if the linear hypothesis is false.)

2. Reconsider Exercise 2 of Chapter 6 (page 169).

a) Plot the means of the treatment (I) groups.

b) Compute the F needed to test the linear hypothesis as applied to the corresponding population means. Is this hypothesis tenable (use the 5% level)?

c) Is higher precision needed to reveal that the preceding hypothesis is false than was needed to reject the simple null hypothesis concerning the treatment population means? [See question (i) on page 171.]

d) Describe how, given the necessary data, you would test the hypothesis that the population means for I_I and I_{II} are equal. Does this test involve any assumption of homogeneity? If the outcome of this test were significant, could one retain the hypothesis that the relation between intensity of a stimulus and intensity of response is monotonic? Explain.

3. Reconsider Exercise 3 of Chapter 13 (page 311).

a) Plot the over-all D means in the manner of Figure 9 on page 342. Plot the straight line of best fit to these means. (See Exercise 1c preceding.)

b) Test (at the 5% level) the hypothesis that in the population the D means (over-all lists) fall on a single straight line. What conclusion do you draw from the results of this test?

c) When a line of the type $Y = A + BX + CX^2$ is fitted to these means, the values of the coefficients are found to be $A = 31.125$, $B = -7.05$, and $C = 1.00$. Plot the points on this line for $X = 1, 2, 3,$ and 4 days, and draw a smooth freehand curve through these points.

d) Compute the F needed to test the hypothesis that the population means fall on the curve just plotted.

e) On a separate chart, plot the D means for each of the four lists, in the manner of Figure 11 on page 350. Is the hypothesis tenable that the corresponding lines based on population means are "parallel" to one another?

f) Compute the F needed to test the linear hypothesis as applied to the D means for List 1 alone. Do you accept this hypothesis? Explain.

g) What is the value of Y on the line of (c) when $X = 10$? The line fits the observed means fairly closely between the values of $X = 1$ and $X = 4$, but is it a plausible description of the functional relationship between Y and X? Explain. What should be the characteristics of the line if it is to represent a plausible description of the functional relationship?

4. Reconsider the experiment by Kalish described in Exercise 4 on page 313.

a) Plot the T-trends for the four levels of A (see upper right-hand table on page 315) and compute the F needed to test the hypothesis that these trends are parallel for the population.

b) The data in the left-hand table on page 315 describe the T-trends for the 16 treatment-combinations. Compute the F needed to test the hypothesis that these trends are parallel.

c) Compute the F needed to test the hypothesis that the 16 trends of (b) coincide (on the assumption that they are parallel).

d) Compute the F needed to test the hypotheses that the T-trends for A_1E_1, A_1E_2, A_1E_3, and A_1E_4 are parallel ... that they coincide (on the assumption they are parallel).

16

Estimation of Variance Components in
Reliability Studies

Introduction

In the preceding chapters, we have been concerned primarily with the use of the methods of analysis of variance with particular experimental designs in the *testing of hypotheses* concerning the treatment effects. There is, however, another important application of these designs and analytical procedures, in which the interest is in the *estimation* of population parameters rather than in tests of significance. Among the most important applications of this type in psychological and educational research are those concerned with the *reliability* of the measures obtained.

The usual procedure in reliability studies in psychology and education has been to describe the reliability of the obtained measures in terms of "reliability coefficients." This procedure is fairly adequate when there is only one distinguishable source of random errors, as in computing the reliability coefficient of a pencil-and-paper objective test by the "odds-evens items" method, although even in this case it is usually desirable to know the standard error of measurement as well as the reliability coefficient. The procedure is decidedly inadequate, however, when several sources of random error may be distinguished, as is often the case in performance testing. Suppose, for example, that in a study of the reliability of measures of the ability to perform a certain task, each of a number of subjects is required to perform the task twice independently for each of three different observers — each observer recording an independent "proficiency rating" for each performance. The three observers may be regarded as a random sample from a population of observers, the six trials as a random sample from a population of trials, while the n subjects are a random sample from a population of subjects.

In this situation, it is possible to compute a number of correlation coefficients which may be described as "reliability coefficients." For instance, one could determine, for all subjects in the sample, the correlation between the two observations of a single observer, or one could correlate an observation for one observer with an observation by another observer. These reliability coefficients would have some descriptive value, but they would not lead directly to a quantitative estimate of the relative importance of the various sources of variation, nor would they contain in themselves any specific suggestions for the construction of a measurement schedule. A much more useful and constructive approach would involve regarding a single obtained score as consisting of several independent components, and of securing estimates of the population variance of each component. In this case, for example, an obtained score (X) may be regarded as consisting in part of a true score (t) which is the average of an infinite number of observations of this subject by an infinite number of observers, in part of a systematic bias (o) on the part of the particular observer involved (a bias which is constant for all subjects), in part of a variable bias (i) associated with that observer (variable from subject to subject), due to the fact that he may define the task somewhat differently than other observers, and in part to variations in the subject's performance from trial to trial plus a variable error of observation on the part of the observer. We will let v represent the sum of these last two variations. Thus,

$$X = t + o + i + v.$$

Presumably these components are independent of one another, so that the variance of X for all subjects in the population is equal to the sum of the population variances of the components.

$$\sigma_X^2 = \sigma_t^2 + \sigma_o^2 + \sigma_i^2 + \sigma_v^2.$$

The "error variance" would then be the sum of the last three components. That is,

$$\sigma_{\text{error}}^2 = \sigma_o^2 + \sigma_i^2 + \sigma_v^2.$$

If we could secure unbiased estimates of these variance components, we would of course know directly what is the relative potency of the different sources of variation, and could utilize this information constructively in a number of different ways. For example, if we knew the "overhead" cost for a single observer, as well as the additional per-observation cost for each observer, we could determine what number of observations per observer would result in the most efficient measurement at a given cost, or in the most reliable mean score per subject for a given expenditure. Again, we could determine what number of observers combined with what number of observations per observer would be required to secure a mean score whose standard error of measurement does not exceed a specified value.

We shall see in this chapter how the methods of analysis of variance may be applied to secure unbiased estimates of variance components of this kind, and how this information may be employed to secure estimates of various reliability coefficients, as well as how it may be used constructively in further planning of measurement schedules. We shall see that in these applications the usual F-tests of significance are of little or no interest, that the reliability coefficients obtained are of secondary interest only, and that the basic desired information consists of the estimated components of the total error variance.

In this chapter it will not always be possible to provide derivations in terms that the student untrained in mathematics can understand, and hence some propositions will be presented without proof.

The One-Dimensional Design

Suppose that for a random sample of subjects from a specified population a number of measures (scores) of a certain trait have been obtained for each subject, and that a description is desired of the reliability of these measures. Where only two measures have been obtained for each subject, the usual procedure is to compute the correlation between the two scores for each subject and to regard this coefficient as the "coefficient of reliability" of the obtained scores. When several observations have been made of each subject, or several scores obtained, the procedure could be followed of computing the correlation for each of the possible pairs of scores and of using the average of these coefficients to describe the reliability of the scores. A more convenient and satisfactory procedure, however, is provided by the methods of analysis of variance.

Suppose we have n scores for each of s subjects, or a total of ns observations. Using the methods of Chapter 3, we can then analyze the total sum of squares for these ns observations into its "between-subjects" and "within-subjects" components, and compute a mean square for each component. We shall let M_i represent the mean of the n scores for the ith subject and μ_i the mean of an infinite number of such scores for the subject. In the language of the theory of mental measurement, μ_i is the "true score" for the subject. We shall let σ_ϵ^2 represent the variance of an infinite number of obtained scores for the subject. In the language of measurement theory, the square root (σ_ϵ) of this variance is the "standard error of measurement." We shall assume that σ_ϵ^2 is the same for all subjects in the population. We shall let $\sigma_{M_i}^2$ represent the variance of the M_i's for all subjects in the population and $\sigma_\gamma^2 = \sigma_{\mu_i}^2$ represent the variance of the true scores for the entire population. We may then note that a single obtained score may be written

$$X = \mu_i + (X - \mu_i)$$

or

obt'd score = true score + error in obt'd score.

The variance of a distribution consisting of one obtained score for each subject in the population would then be

$$\sigma_X^2 = \sigma_{\mu_i}^2 + \sigma_{(X-\mu_i)}^2 = \sigma_\gamma^2 + \sigma_\epsilon^2.$$

Similarly, the mean of n obtained scores for a single subject is

$$M_i = \mu_i + (M_i - \mu_i)$$

and

$$\sigma_{M_i}^2 = \sigma_{\mu_i}^2 + \sigma_{(M_i - \mu_i)}^2$$

$$= \sigma_\gamma^2 + \frac{\sigma_\epsilon^2}{n}.$$

From this it follows that

$$\sigma_\gamma^2 = \sigma_{M_i}^2 - \frac{\sigma_\epsilon^2}{n}. \tag{145}$$

Now we know (page 60) that the expected value of ms_w is σ_ϵ^2, or that ms_w is an unbiased estimate of σ_ϵ^2. We also know that an unbiased estimate of $\sigma_{M_i}^2$ is given by

$$\text{est'd } \sigma_{M_i}^2 = \frac{\sum_{i=1}^{s}(M_i - M)^2}{s - 1}.$$

By substituting these unbiased estimates for the variances in the right of (145), we can then secure an unbiased estimate of σ_γ^2, as follows:

$$\text{est'd } \sigma_\gamma^2 = \frac{\sum_{i=1}^{s}(M_i - M)^2}{s - 1} - \frac{ms_w}{n}$$

$$= \frac{\frac{n\sum_{i=1}^{s}(M_i - M)^2}{s - 1} - ms_w}{n}.$$

But the first term of the numerator is ms_s. Hence,

$$\text{est'd } \sigma_\gamma^2 = \frac{ms_s - ms_w}{n}. \tag{146}$$

This is consistent with our previous reasoning concerning the expected mean squares in a simple analysis of variance. On page 62 we noted that the expected value of ms_s is

$$E(ms_s) = \sigma_\epsilon^2 + \frac{n\sum_{i=1}^{s}(\mu_i - \mu)^2}{s - 1}.$$

If we regard the μ_i's in our sample as a random sample from a population of μ_i's, then $\dfrac{\sum_{i=1}^{s}(\mu_i - \mu)^2}{s - 1}$ is an unbiased estimate of $\sigma_{\mu_i}^2 = \sigma_\gamma^2$, so that we may write

$$E(ms_s) = \sigma_\epsilon^2 + n\sigma_\gamma^2. \tag{147}$$

We noted earlier that

$$E(ms_w) = \sigma_\epsilon^2. \tag{148}$$

From the two preceding expressions, we then get

$$\sigma_\gamma^2 = \frac{E(ms_s) - E(ms_w)}{n}.$$

Substituting ms_s and ms_w for their expected values, we again get

$$\text{est'd } \sigma_\gamma^2 = \frac{ms_s - ms_w}{n}. \tag{149}$$

Now the "coefficient of reliability" of an obtained score for a specified population may be defined as the ratio of the variance of the true scores to the variance of the obtained scores for this population. That is, if we let r_{11} represent the reliability coefficient,

$$r_{11} = \frac{\sigma_\gamma^2}{\sigma_X^2} = \frac{\sigma_\gamma^2}{\sigma_\gamma^2 + \sigma_\epsilon^2}. \tag{150}$$

We can then obtain an estimate of r_{11} by substituting for the variances in (150) their estimated values, as follows:

$$\text{est'd } r_{11} = \frac{ms_s - ms_w}{ms_s + (n-1)ms_w}. \tag{151}$$

Thus, from the results of a simple analysis of variance of the ns obtained scores for our sample, we can secure an estimate of the reliability coefficient of the obtained scores for the specified population. This is what R. A. Fisher describes as an "intraclass" correlation, the n "classes" in this case corresponding to the various sets of scores. We note from (145) that the population variance of the mean of k scores for each individual is given by $\sigma_\gamma^2 + \dfrac{\sigma_\epsilon^2}{k}$. Accordingly, the reliability of the mean (or sum) of k scores for each individual is given by

$$r_{kk} = \frac{\sigma_\gamma^2}{\sigma_\gamma^2 + \dfrac{\sigma_\epsilon^2}{k}}$$

from which we derive

$$\text{est'd } r_{kk} = \frac{ms_s - ms_w}{ms_s + \left(\dfrac{n}{k} - 1\right)(ms_w)}. \tag{152}$$

From (151) and (152) it is easy to derive the Spearman-Brown formula for estimating the reliability of a lengthened test.

The reliability coefficient r_{11} may also be estimated in terms of $F = ms_s/ms_w$. Dividing the numerator and denominator of (151) by ms_w, we get

$$\text{est'd } r_{11} = \frac{F-1}{F + (n-1)}. \tag{153}$$

It is possible to establish a confidence interval for r using the table for F, granting that a confidence interval consistent with the tabled values of F is selected. We do this by first establishing the confidence limits for F, and then substituting these in (153). To obtain the upper limit (F_u) of the $(100 - 2X)\%$ confidence interval for the true F, we simply multiply the obtained value (F_o) by the value of F at the $X\%$ point in the F-distribution, as read from Table 3, page 41. That is, $F_u = F_o \cdot F_{X\%}$. The lower limit (F_l) of the confidence interval is given by $F_l = F_o/F_{X\%}$. For example, if the obtained F, for 5 and 14 degrees of freedom, is 11.7, the upper limit of the 90% confidence interval is $11.7 \times 2.96 = 34.63$, while the lower limit is $11.7/2.96 = 3.95$.

Having thus established the limits of the confidence interval for F, these may be substituted in (153) to obtain the corresponding upper and lower limits for r. For the preceding example, these are .85 and .33, n being equal to 6.

Since the tabled values of F are restricted to $X = 20, 10, 5, 2.5, 1.0, 0.5$ and .1, confidence limits for r can be conveniently established in this fashion only for the 60, 80, 90, 95, 98, 99 and 99.8% confidence intervals without resorting to interpolations between the table values of F, but these should suffice for nearly all practical purposes.

For large values of s, the sampling distribution of est'd σ_γ^2 is approximately normal, and its estimated variance is

$$\text{est'd } \sigma_{\text{est'd } \sigma_\gamma^2}^2 = \frac{2}{n^2}\left(\frac{ms_s^2}{df_s} + \frac{ms_w^2}{df_w}\right).$$

Similarly, est'd σ_ϵ^2 is normally distributed for large values of df_w, and its estimated sampling variance is

$$\text{est'd } \sigma_{\text{est'd } \sigma_\epsilon^2}^2 = \frac{2ms_w^2}{df_w}.$$

Confidence limits for σ_γ^2 and σ_ϵ^2 can therefore be readily established if s is large.

The Two-Dimensional Design

The application of the two-dimensional design in reliability studies may best be explained in terms of a specific illustration. Suppose that a random sample of s subjects is drawn from a certain population, and that for each subject n independent observations or measurements of a certain trait are made by each of a observers. These a observers are regarded as a random sample from a population of observers. The ans observations or scores may then be entered in a double-entry table, in which columns correspond to observers $(A_1, A_2, \ldots A_a)$, rows to subjects $(S_1, S_2, \ldots S_s)$, with n observations or obtained scores in each cell. For each mean in this table there is a corresponding "true" mean. The true mean μ_{ij} (corresponding to M_{ij}, a cell mean) is the mean of an infinite number of observations of subject i by observer j. This, in the language of mental measurement theory, is the "true score" for subject i so far as observer j is concerned. We will call it an "observer true score," or an A true score. The true mean $\mu_{i.}$ (corresponding to $M_{i.}$, a row mean) is the mean of the observer true scores for subject i for an infinite number of observers. This is the "true" true score for subject i. We will call it simply his true score. The true mean $\mu_{.j}$ (corresponding to $M_{.j}$, a column mean) is the mean of the observer true scores for observer j for all subjects in the population. It is also the mean of the distribution consisting of a single obtained score from observer j for each subject in the population. The true score mean μ (corresponding to M, the general mean) is the mean of the true scores for all subjects in the population.

We may now write the identity

$$X - \mu = (X - \mu_{ij}) + (\mu_{.j} - \mu) + (\mu_{i.} - \mu) + (\mu_{ij} - \mu_{i.} - \mu_{.j} + \mu)$$

$$= \epsilon + \alpha + \gamma + \alpha\gamma. \tag{154}$$

In this expression, $\epsilon = (X - \mu_{ij})$ represents the error of observation or of measurement which is specific to observer j and subject i. Its variance is σ_ϵ^2, which we will assume is the same for all subjects and all observers. The term $\gamma = (\mu_{i.} - \mu)$ represents the deviation of the subject's true score from the population mean. Its variance, which we will represent by σ_γ^2, is the population variance of the true scores, and may be called the "trait" variance for the population. The term $\alpha = (\mu_{.j} - \mu)$ represents the "general bias" of observer j. We will let its variance be represented by σ_α^2. The term $\alpha\gamma = (\mu_{ij} - \mu_{i.} - \mu_{.j} + \mu)$ is the true interaction effect for subject i and observer j. It may be written $[(\mu_{ij} - \mu_{i.}) - (\mu_{.j} - \mu)]$. The term $(\mu_{ij} - \mu_{i.})$ represents the total bias in observer j's observations of subject i. The difference between $(\mu_{ij} - \mu_i)$ and $(\mu_{.j} - \mu)$ represents the difference between observer j's total bias for subject i and his general bias, and may be called his specific bias with reference to subject i. The population variance of these specific biases, that is, the population variance of the true interaction effects, we will represent by $\sigma_{\alpha\gamma}^2$. We will assume that it is the same for all observers. Thus, (154) indicates that the deviation of an individual's obtained score from the population mean consists in part of a deviation of his true score from the population mean, in part of a specific observer bias, in part of a general observer bias, and in part of an error of measurement or of observation.

Following the methods of Chapter 6, we may analyze the total sum of squares among the ans observations in the sample into its between-subjects (S), between-observers (A), subjects $\times$ observers (AS), and within (w) components, and may compute a mean square for each component. The expected values [1] of these mean squares are as follows:

---

[1] Suppose that corrections are applied in the double-entry table so as to eliminate ms_S and ms_A. This twice-corrected table may then be regarded as representing a simple-randomized design, in which, according to the reasoning underlying (147),

$$E(ms_{AS}) = \sigma_\epsilon^2 + n\sigma_{\alpha\gamma}^2.$$

Proofs of (155) and (156) will be supplied later (footnote on page 367).

$$E(ms_A) = \sigma_\epsilon^2 + n\sigma_{\alpha\gamma}^2 + sn\sigma_\alpha^2 \tag{155}$$

$$E(ms_S) = \sigma_\epsilon^2 + n\sigma_{\alpha\gamma}^2 + an\sigma_\gamma^2 \tag{156}$$

$$E(ms_{AS}) = \sigma_\epsilon^2 + n\sigma_{\alpha\gamma}^2 \tag{157}$$

$$E(ms_w) = \sigma_\epsilon^2. \tag{158}$$

Hence, we can secure estimates of each of the variance components as follows:

$$\text{est'd } \sigma_\alpha^2 = \frac{ms_A - ms_{AS}}{sn}$$

$$\text{est'd } \sigma_\gamma^2 = \frac{ms_S - ms_{AS}}{an} \tag{159}$$

$$\text{est'd } \sigma_{\alpha\gamma}^2 = \frac{ms_{AS} - ms_w}{n}$$

$$\text{est'd } \sigma_\epsilon^2 = ms_w.$$

Estimates of the sampling variances of these variance estimates are given by

$$\text{est'd } \sigma_{\sigma_\alpha^2}^2 = \frac{2}{n^2 s^2}\left(\frac{ms_A^2}{df_A} + \frac{ms_{AS}^2}{df_{AS}}\right)$$

$$\text{est'd } \sigma_{\sigma_\gamma^2}^2 = \frac{2}{n^2 a^2}\left(\frac{ms_S^2}{df_S} + \frac{ms_{AS}^2}{df_{AS}}\right) \tag{160}$$

$$\text{est'd } \sigma_{\sigma_{\alpha\gamma}^2}^2 = \frac{2}{n^2}\left(\frac{ms_{AS}^2}{df_{AS}} + \frac{ms_w^2}{df_w}\right)$$

$$\text{est'd } \sigma_{\sigma_\epsilon^2}^2 = \frac{2ms_w^2}{df_w}.$$

When the degrees of freedom involved are large, the variance estimates are approximately normally distributed, and approximate confidence limits can be established in the ordinary way. The use of these estimation techniques in reliability analysis is definitely *not* recommended when s is small.

From these variance estimates (160), we may infer a number of "reliability coefficients" for the entire population of subjects. One of the most significant of these is the correlation between the mean of n' measures in each of a' categories of A, and the mean of n' *independent* measures in each of these *same* A-categories. One of these means (for subject i) may be represented by $M_{iI} = \frac{1}{a'}\sum_{j=1}^{a'} M_{ij}$ and the correlation by $r_{M_{iI}M_{iI}}$. In general, in the notation of this chapter, a Roman numeral in the subscript will indicate that a specified number of categories of the corresponding factors have been averaged. In this case, the I in M_{iI} means that for subject (i) the mean of a' categories of the A classification has been obtained, whereas the 1 in M_{i1} would refer to a single A-category (A_1).

The reliability coefficient for any "obtained" score for a specified population is defined as the ratio of the population variance of the corresponding true scores to the population variance of the obtained scores. In the case of $r_{M_{iI}M_{iI}}$, the obtained score is M_{iI}. The corresponding population mean is $\mu_{iI} = \dfrac{1}{a'}\sum\limits_{j=1}^{a'}\mu_{.j}$. To obtain an expression for the population variance of M_{iI} or of

$$(M_{iI} - \mu_{.I}) = \frac{1}{a'}\sum_{j=1}^{a'}(M_{ij} - \mu_{.j}),$$

we write the identity

$$\frac{1}{a'}\sum_{j=1}^{a'}(M_{ij} - \mu_{.j}) = \frac{1}{a'}\sum_{j=1}^{a'}(M_{ij} - \mu_{ij})$$

$$+ \frac{1}{a'}\sum_{j=1}^{a'}(\mu_{ij} - \mu_{i.} - \mu_{.j} + \mu) \qquad (161)$$

$$+ \frac{1}{a'}\sum_{j=1}^{a'}(\mu_{i.} - \mu).$$

Since the right-hand terms of (161) are independent, the variance of the left-hand term, or of M_{iI}, is equal to the sum of the variances of the right-hand terms. The variance of $(M_{ij} - \mu_{ij})$ is $\dfrac{\sigma_\epsilon^2}{n}$. Hence, the variance of the first right-hand term is

$$\frac{1}{a'^2}\sum_{j=1}^{a'}\frac{\sigma_\epsilon^2}{n'} = \frac{\sigma_\epsilon^2}{a'n'}.$$

The variance of $(\mu_{ij} - \mu_{i.} - \mu_{.j} + \mu)$ is $\sigma_{\alpha\gamma}^2$; hence, the variance of the second right-hand term is $\dfrac{\sigma_{\alpha\gamma}^2}{a'}$. We next note that

$$\frac{1}{a'}\sum_{j=1}^{a'}(\mu_{.j} - \mu) = (\mu_{.j} - \mu),$$

since $(\mu_{.j} - \mu)$ is the same for all values of j. The variance of $(\mu_{.j} - \mu)$, or of the third right-hand term of (161), is σ_γ^2. Hence, the variance of M_{iI} is

$$\sigma_{(M_{iI} - \mu_{.j})}^2 = \frac{\sigma_\epsilon^2}{a'n'} + \frac{\sigma_{\alpha\gamma}^2}{a'} + \sigma_\gamma^2. \qquad (162)$$

The variance of the corresponding true scores is found by letting $n' = \infty$ in (162). Hence, the variance of the true scores is $\dfrac{\sigma_{\alpha\gamma}^2}{a'} + \sigma_\gamma^2$. Accordingly,

$$r_{M_{iI}M_{iI}} = \frac{\dfrac{\sigma_{\alpha\gamma}^2}{a'} + \sigma_\gamma^2}{\dfrac{\sigma_\epsilon^2}{a'n'} + \dfrac{\sigma_{\alpha\gamma}^2}{a'} + \sigma_\gamma^2}. \qquad (163)$$

To estimate $r_{M_{iI}M_{iI}}$, we substitute for the variances in (163) the estimates of them (160) secured from the sample. Thus,

$$\text{est'd } r_{M_{iI}M_{iI}} = \frac{\dfrac{ms_{AS} - ms_w}{a'n} + \dfrac{ms_S - ms_{AS}}{an}}{\dfrac{ms_w}{a'n'} + \dfrac{ms_{AS} - ms_w}{a'n} + \dfrac{ms_S - ms_{AS}}{an}}. \tag{164}$$

From (164) we can secure estimates of a number of more specific correlation coefficients. For example, if we wish to estimate the correlation between two observations of each subject by a single observer, we let $n' = 1$ and $a' = 1$ in (164). If we wish to estimate the correlation, for all subjects in the population, between the means of two groups of n' observations by the same observer, we let $a' = 1$ in (164). If, for a particular group of a' observers, we want the self-correlation of the mean of a single observation from each observer, we let $n' = 1$ in (164). This latter result would be more meaningful in the case in which A represents "items" in a test, in which case, by letting $n' = 1$ in (164), we secure the "test-retest" reliability coefficient of the mean score on the test. If we wish the self-correlation of the means obtained in our sample, we let $a' = a$ and $n' = n$ in (162). In the latter case, (164) reduces to

$$\text{est'd } r_{M_{iI}M_{iI}} = \frac{ms_S - ms_w}{ms_S} = 1 - \frac{1}{F_1},$$

in which $F_1 = ms_S/ms_w$. In this case, a confidence interval for $r_{M_{iI}M_{iI}}$ may be readily established by the method described on pages 361–362.

Another correlation coefficient of considerable general significance is that between the mean of n' observations in each of a' categories of A, and the mean of n' *independent* observations in each of a' *independent* categories of A. One of these means (that for subject i) may be represented by

$$M_{iI} = \frac{1}{a'}\sum_{j=1}^{a'} M_{ij},$$

and the second by

$$M_{iII} = \frac{1}{a'}\sum_{j=a'+1}^{2a'} M_{ij}.$$

The correlation coefficient is then represented by $r_{M_{iI}M_{iII}}$.

To estimate this reliability coefficient, we must first find an expression for the variance of M_{iI}. We first note that the corresponding true score is

$$\frac{1}{a'}\sum_{j=1}^{a'}\mu_{.j}[\text{when } a' \to \infty] = \mu.$$

What is needed, then, is the variance of M_{iI} about μ, or of

$$(M_{iI} - \mu) = \frac{1}{a'}\sum_{j=1}^{a'}(M_{ij} - \mu).$$

We must first write the identity

$$\frac{1}{a'} \sum_{j=1}^{a'} (M_{ij} - \mu) = \frac{1}{a'} \sum_{j=1}^{a'} (M_{ij} - \mu_{ij})$$

$$+ \frac{1}{a'} \sum_{j=1}^{a'} (\mu_{ij} - \mu_{i.} - \mu_{.j} + \mu)$$

$$+ \frac{1}{a'} \sum_{j=1}^{a'} (\mu_{i.} - \mu)$$

$$+ \frac{1}{a'} \sum_{j=1}^{a'} (\mu_{.j} - \mu).$$

(165)

Since the variance of the right-hand terms of (165) are independent, the variance of the left term, or of M_{iI}, is equal to the sum of the variances of these terms. The variance of the first right-hand term is $\frac{\sigma_\epsilon^2}{a'n'}$, of the second is $\frac{\sigma_{\alpha\gamma}^2}{a'}$, of the third is σ_γ^2, and of the last is zero, since $(\mu_{.j} - \mu)$ is the same for all subjects. Accordingly,[1]

$$\sigma_{M_{iI}}^2 = \frac{\sigma_\epsilon^2}{a'n'} + \frac{\sigma_{\alpha\gamma}^2}{a'} + \sigma_\gamma^2.$$

(166)

The variance of the corresponding true scores is found by letting $n' = \infty$ and $a' = \infty$ in (166) and the result is σ_γ^2. Thus,

$$r_{M_{iI}M_{iII}} = \frac{\sigma_\gamma^2}{\dfrac{\sigma_\epsilon^2}{a'n'} + \dfrac{\sigma_{\alpha\gamma}^2}{a'} + \sigma_\gamma^2}.$$

(167)

To estimate $r_{M_{iI}M_{iII}}$ we substitute from (159) in (167) and secure

$$\text{est'd } r_{M_{iI}M_{iII}} = \frac{\dfrac{ms_S - ms_{AS}}{an}}{\dfrac{ms_w}{a'n'} + \dfrac{ms_{AS} - ms_w}{a'n} + \dfrac{ms_S - ms_{AS}}{an}}.$$

(168)

Again we can secure several more specific reliability coefficients from (168) by letting a' and n' take different values. If we want the correlation of the

---

[1] To prove (156), we note that when $a' = a$ and $n' = n$, (166) becomes

$$an\sigma_{M_{i.}}^2 = an\sigma_\gamma^2 + n\sigma_{\alpha\gamma}^2 + \sigma_\epsilon^2.$$

But

$$an\sigma_{M_{i.}}^2 = an \cdot E[\Sigma(M_{i.} - M)^2/(s-1)]$$

$$= E\left[\frac{\Sigma an(M_{i.} - M)^2}{s-1}\right]$$

$$= E(ms_S).$$

Thus,

$$E(ms_S) = an\sigma_\gamma^2 + n\sigma_{\alpha\gamma}^2 + \sigma_\epsilon^2.$$

A similar proof can be provided for (155).

mean of n' observations by one observer with the mean of n' observations by another observer, $r_{M_{i1}M_{i2}}$, we let $a' = 1$ in (168). If we want the correlation of the mean of one observation from each of a' observers with the mean of a second observation from each of the same observers, we let $n' = 1$ in (168). (Again, this correlation is more meaningful when A represents "items" in a homogeneous test. In this case, by letting $n' = 1$ in (168), we secure the "equivalent forms" reliability coefficient of the mean score on the test.) If we want the correlation of a single observation by one observer with a single observation by another observer, $r_{x_{i1}x_{i2}}$, we let $a' = 1$ and $n' = 1$ in (168). If we want the reliability of the M_i's obtained in our sample, we let $a' = a$ and $n' = n$ in (168), which in this case reduces to

$$\text{est'd } r_{M_{iI}M_{iII}} = 1 - \frac{1}{F_2},$$

in which $F_2 = ms_S/ms_{AS}$. Again, a confidence interval for this r may be established by the method described on pages 361–362 .

If we want the reliability of an *observer* (A) *true score*, we let $a' = 1$ and $n' = \infty$ in (167), which then reduces to

$$r_{\mu_{i1}\mu_{i2}} = \frac{\sigma_\gamma^2}{\sigma_\gamma^2 + \sigma_{\alpha\gamma}^2}$$

and the estimated value of which is

$$\text{est'd } r_{\mu_{i1}\mu_{i2}} = \frac{\dfrac{ms_S - ms_{AS}}{an}}{\dfrac{ms_S - ms_{AS}}{an} + \dfrac{ms_{AS} - ms_w}{n}}$$

$$= \frac{ms_S - ms_{AS}}{ms_S + (a - 1)ms_{AS} - a \cdot ms_w}.$$

This may be regarded as an estimate of $r_{M_{i1}M_{i2}}$ corrected for attenuation due to variations in the observations of a single subject by a single observer. It is an estimate of the maximum reliability that can be secured in a mean score based on observations from a single observer. No matter how many observations are made of each subject by a single observer, the reliability of the mean of these estimates cannot exceed $r_{\mu_{i1}\mu_{i2}}$.

If there is no intrinsic AS interaction ($\sigma_{\alpha\gamma}^2 = 0$), $r_{\mu_{i1}\mu_{i2}}$ will equal 1.00. In the specific application here considered, in which the A categories correspond to observers, an $r_{\mu_{i1}\mu_{i2}}$ of less than 1.00, or an AS interaction other than zero, would imply that different observers are not really observing the same trait, or that each defines the trait differently than the other observers. In many applications of this design, one would expect $r_{\mu_{i1}\mu_{i2}}$ to be unity, but in some applications, as we shall see later, an intrinsic AS interaction may be quite plausible.

The discussion has thus far been based on a specific illustration in which $A_1, A_2, \ldots A_a$ correspond to different observers and in which X_{ij} represents a single observation or measurement by a single observer. There are many other interesting applications of this design, only a few of which can be suggested here. Suppose, for example, that in a study of the measurement of writing ability, each of a number of college freshmen is requested to write three different themes on comparable subjects, and each theme is read twice independently by the same reader. In this case, A_1, A_2, and A_3 represent the three themes, and X_{i2} represents a single rating of theme 2 for subject i. The coefficient $r_{x_{i1}x_{i1}}$ between the two ratings of the same theme may then be regarded as an index of the reliability of the reader, or might be described as the "objectivity" coefficient. The coefficient $r_{x_{i1}x_{i2}}$ would then represent the reliability of a single rating of a single theme for the particular reader involved, but would not take into consideration possible biases specific to individual subjects on the part of this reader. In this case, $r_{\mu_{i1}\mu_{i2}}$ would represent the maximum reliability that could be achieved in a score based on a single theme by averaging a number of independent ratings by the same reader. Since the same subject may reveal different aspects of his general writing ability in different themes, one would expect $r_{\mu_{i1}\mu_{i2}}$ to be less than unity: that is, one would expect an intrinsic AS interaction. Each theme might be regarded as representing a *sample* of the subject's writing performance, and $\sigma^2_{\alpha\gamma}$ is a measure of the variation in these samples from theme to theme.

Suppose, as another example, that each subject writes only one theme, but that the theme is read twice independently by each of two readers. In this case, we can compute a coefficient of reliability of a single rating of a single theme by a single reader $(r_{x_{i1}x_{i2}})$ which does take into consideration the effect of biases specific to individual subjects on the part of a single reader, but which does not take into consideration the effect of variations in the subjects' performance from theme to theme. If each subject wrote four themes, two of which were read by one reader and two by another, we would have a situation like the original illustration, in which $r_{x_{i1}x_{i2}}$ would take all important sources of error into consideration — the specific bias of the reader, the variations from theme to theme, and the "reading" error, but would not permit an independent estimate of the objectivity coefficient (the reader reliability), or of the component of the total variance associated with the reading error.

If A_1, A_2, ... A_a represent the items in a test, and if a single entry in each cell of the table represents the score made on a single item by a single subject, then $r_{M'_{iI}M'_{iI}}$ (with $a' = a$ and $n' = n = 1$) is equal to

$$r_{M_{iI}M'_{iII}} = 1 - \frac{1}{F_2},$$

in which $F_2 = ms_S/ms_{AS}$. Since the correlations between the sums of a number of variates is the same as the correlations between their means, $r_{M_{iI}M_{iII}}$ is also the reliability of the total score on the test of a items. This procedure [1]

[1] C. Hoyt, "Tests of Reliability Obtained by the Analysis of Variance," *Psychometrika*, vol. 6 (1941), pp. 153–160.

for computing the reliability of a test has been known as the "Hoyt procedure." A confidence interval may be established for the true r in the manner already suggested.

In other applications, $A_1 \ldots A_a$ might represent "equivalent forms" of a test of considerable length, so that variations from form to form due to sampling of content are negligible. These forms might be administered to the subjects on different days, in which case $\sigma^2_{\alpha\gamma}$ would be a measure of "diurnal variations" in the subject. If the forms were very short, and diurnal variations were negligible, $\sigma^2_{\alpha\gamma}$ would represent variations in the forms, rather than in the subjects, variations due to the sampling of content.

Although the reliability coefficients just considered are valuable for descriptive purposes, our major interest, for more constructive purposes, is in the estimates of the separate variance components. We may wish to answer such questions as "How many observations of a given trait must be made by each of five observers in order that the reliability of the mean of all observations for a subject may not be less than .90?" or "For a given total cost, what values of a' and n' will yield the maximum reliability in the mean of all observations for each subject, or will result in the smallest error variance?" To answer such questions, we must first analyze the results for a random sample of subjects from the population involved, in order to secure estimates of the variance components. From these estimates we can then determine the error variance for any specified values of a' and n', and can estimate the corresponding reliability coefficients. Suppose, for example, that we have secured two observations on each of 60 subjects from each of four observers. Suppose that an analysis of variance of the results yields

$$ms_A = 32.00$$
$$ms_S = 70.00$$
$$ms_{AS} = 30.00$$
$$ms_w = 20.00.$$

From these

$$\text{est'd } \sigma^2_\gamma = 5.00$$
$$\text{est'd } \sigma^2_{\alpha\gamma} = 5.00$$
$$\text{est'd } \sigma^2_\epsilon = 20.00$$

Suppose that we wish to secure measures of the given traits for a group of 200 subjects, and that we have just $1,000 to spend for this purpose. We find that for this amount we can have each of eight observers make one observation of each subject. Suppose, also, that for the same amount we could have each of five observers make two observations per subject, or each of four observers make three observations per subject, or each of three observers make five observations per subject. The question is "Which of these combinations will result in the smallest error variance in the obtained mean scores?"

We know that the error variance $(\sigma^2_{e_M})$ of the mean of n' observations by each of a' observers is given by

$$\sigma^2_{e_M} = \frac{\sigma^2_{\alpha\gamma}}{a'} + \frac{\sigma^2_{\epsilon}}{a'n'}.$$

Accordingly, we can construct a table as follows:

a'	n'	$a'n'$	$\sigma^2_{\alpha\gamma}/a' + \sigma^2_{\epsilon}/a'n' = \sigma^2_{e_M}$
8	1	8	$5/8 + 20/8 = 3.12$
5	2	10	$5/5 + 20/10 = 3.00$
4	3	12	$5/4 + 20/12 = 2.92$
3	5	15	$5/3 + 20/15 = 3.00$
2	10	20	$5/2 + 20/20 = 3.50$

from which it is evident that the most efficient procedure is to secure three observations of each subject from each of four observers. If this procedure is followed, the estimated reliability of the mean of the twelve observations for each subject is

$$\text{est'd } r_{M'_{iI}M'_{iII}} = \frac{\sigma^2_{\gamma}}{\sigma^2_{\gamma} + \sigma^2_{e_M}} = \frac{5}{5 + 2.92} = .63.$$

If we then wish to know what would be the cost of obtaining a mean score whose reliability is .90, (assuming that an increase in the number of observers is accompanied by a proportional increase in cost), we would substitute the known values in (167) and solve for a' to secure $a' = 21$ (rounded), which would mean that the estimated total cost would be $\frac{21}{4} \times \$1000 = \$5250.00$.

It will be apparent from this illustration that negative estimates of some of the variance components might sometimes be secured. For example, if in this illustration, ms_{AS} had been, say, 18.00, the estimated value of $\sigma^2_{\alpha\beta}$ would have been -1.00. Since negative variances are impossible, an estimate of zero must be substituted for the negative estimates in such cases. In such cases, biased estimates of σ^2_{γ} and σ^2_{α} will result. This is another reason why these techniques should not be employed in reliability studies when the degrees of freedom involved in the variance estimate are small. With large numbers of degrees of freedom, negative and biased estimates are less likely to occur, and, if they do occur, the bias introduced is less likely to be serious. This is equivalent to saying that these techniques should be employed in reliability studies only when s is large. In a case like that just considered, it would sometimes not matter if a were small, since ms_A might not be used in estimating any of the variance components in which we are interested. The component σ^2_{α} is usually of little interest since, in most applications, the same A-categories (for example, observers or equivalent forms of a test) are used with all observations, so that A is only a source of constant bias rather than of variable error.

The Three-Dimensional Design

We shall first discuss the three-dimensional design in general terms, and later consider some illustrative applications in more specific terms. In all applications, both A and B are presumably random effects. That is, the A-categories in the sample are presumably a random sample from a population consisting of an infinite number of A-categories, and similarly for B. The AB combinations (cells) in the sample are therefore also a random sample from a population of AB combinations. A constant number (n) of observations or scores is obtained for each of s subjects for each of a categories in the A classification within each of b categories in the B classification. Assuming that σ_ϵ^2 is the same for all subjects, and that the interaction variances are also homogeneous, the mean squares obtained from an analysis of variance of the $absn$ observations, and their expected values are as follows:

$$
\begin{array}{ll}
\textit{Mean} & \\
\textit{Squares} & \textit{Expected Values} \\[4pt]
ms_A & \sigma_\epsilon^2 + n\sigma_{\alpha\beta\gamma}^2 \quad + sn\sigma_{\alpha\beta}^2 \quad + bn\sigma_{\alpha\gamma}^2 \quad + bsn\sigma_\alpha^2 \\[4pt]
ms_B & \sigma_\epsilon^2 + n\sigma_{\alpha\beta\gamma}^2 \quad + sn\sigma_{\alpha\beta}^2 \quad + an\sigma_{\beta\gamma}^2 \quad + asn\sigma_\beta^2 \\[4pt]
ms_S & \sigma_\epsilon^2 + n\sigma_{\alpha\beta\gamma}^2 \quad + bn\sigma_{\alpha\gamma}^2 \quad + an\sigma_{\beta\gamma}^2 \quad + abn\sigma_\gamma^2 \\[4pt]
ms_{AB} & \sigma_\epsilon^2 + n\sigma_{\alpha\beta\gamma}^2 \quad + sn\sigma_{\alpha\beta}^2 \\[4pt]
ms_{AS} & \sigma_\epsilon^2 + n\sigma_{\alpha\beta\gamma}^2 \quad + bn\sigma_{\alpha\gamma}^2 \\[4pt]
ms_{BS} & \sigma_\epsilon^2 + n\sigma_{\alpha\beta\gamma}^2 \quad + an\sigma_{\beta\gamma}^2 \\[4pt]
ms_{ABS} & \sigma_\epsilon^2 + n\sigma_{\alpha\beta\gamma}^2 \\[4pt]
w & \sigma_\epsilon^2
\end{array}
\tag{169}
$$

From this it follows that estimates of these variance components may be obtained as follows:

$$
\text{est'd } \sigma_\epsilon^2 = ms_w
$$

$$
\sigma_{\alpha\beta\gamma}^2 = \frac{ms_{ABS} - ms_w}{n}
$$

$$
\sigma_{\beta\gamma}^2 = \frac{ms_{BS} - ms_{ABS}}{an}
$$

$$
\sigma_{\alpha\gamma}^2 = \frac{ms_{AS} - ms_{ABS}}{bn}
$$

$$
\sigma_{\alpha\beta}^2 = \frac{ms_{AB} - ms_{ABS}}{sn}
\tag{170}
$$

$$
\sigma_\gamma^2 = \frac{ms_S - ms_{AS} - ms_{BS} + ms_{ABS}}{abn}
$$

The estimated sampling variances of these variance estimates are given by

$$\text{est'd } \sigma^2_{\sigma^2_\epsilon} = \frac{2ms^2_w}{df_w}$$

$$\text{est'd } \sigma^2_{\sigma^2_{\alpha\beta\gamma}} = \frac{2}{n^2}\left(\frac{ms^2_{ABS}}{df_{ABS}} + \frac{ms^2_w}{df_w}\right)$$

$$\text{est'd } \sigma^2_{\sigma^2_{\beta\gamma}} = \frac{2}{a^2n^2}\left(\frac{ms^2_{BS}}{df_{BS}} + \frac{ms^2_{ABS}}{df_{ABS}}\right)$$

$$\text{est'd } \sigma^2_{\sigma^2_{\alpha\gamma}} = \frac{2}{b^2n^2}\left(\frac{ms^2_{AS}}{df_{AS}} + \frac{ms^2_{ABS}}{df_{ABS}}\right).$$

$$\text{est'd } \sigma^2_{\sigma^2_{\alpha\beta}} = \frac{2}{s^2n^2}\left(\frac{ms^2_{AB}}{df_{AB}} + \frac{ms^2_{ABS}}{df_{ABS}}\right)$$

$$\text{est'd } \sigma^2_{\sigma_\gamma} = \frac{2}{a^2b^2n^2}\left(\frac{ms^2_S}{df_S} + \frac{ms^2_{AS}}{df_{AS}} + \frac{ms^2_{BS}}{df_{BS}} + \frac{ms^2_{ABS}}{df_{ABS}}\right).$$

(171)

For large values of the numbers of degrees of freedom involved, the sampling distributions of these variance estimates are approximately normal, so that approximate confidence limits may readily be established for them. This method of estimating confidence limits should not be used when any number of degrees of freedom involved is small. Since in most applications df_A, df_B, and df_{AB} will be small, confidence limits for σ^2_α, σ^2_β, and $\sigma^2_{\alpha\beta}$ may not usually be established in this fashion. Since we are rarely interested in these components, however, this is not of much consequence.

To attach general meanings to these components, let us first write the identity

$$(X_{ijk} - \mu) = \overset{\gamma}{(\mu_{i..} - \mu)} + \overset{\alpha}{(\mu_{.j.} - \mu)} + \overset{\beta}{(\mu_{..k} - \mu)}$$

$$+ \overset{\alpha\beta}{(\mu_{.jk} - \mu_{.j.} - \mu_{..k} + \mu)} + \overset{\beta\gamma}{(\mu_{i.k} - \mu_{i..} - \mu_{..k} + \mu)}$$

$$+ \overset{\alpha\gamma}{(\mu_{ij.} - \mu_{i..} - \mu_{.j.} + \mu)} + \overset{\alpha\beta\gamma}{(\mu_{ijk} - \mu_{ij.} - \mu_{i.k} - \mu_{.jk} + \mu_{i..} + \mu_{.j.}}$$
$$+ \mu_{..k} - \mu)$$

(172)

$$+ \overset{\epsilon}{(X_{ijk} - \mu_{ijk})}.$$

In this expression, $a = (\mu_{.j.} - \mu)$ represents an "A effect," which may be regarded as the general bias which is associated with a given A-category. The term β similarly represents the general bias which is associated with a given B-category. The term γ represents the deviation of the subject's true score from the population mean, and its variance, σ^2_γ, is the trait variance for the population. The term $\alpha\beta$ represents the bias which is specific to a given

AB combination. Its variance, $\sigma^2_{\alpha\beta}$, is the variance of the true AB inter- action effects in the population. The term $\alpha\gamma$ represents the bias which is specific to a given A-category and a given subject. Its variance, $\sigma^2_{\alpha\gamma}$, is the variance of the true AS interaction effects in the population. The term $\beta\gamma$ is similarly defined, and its variance is the variance of the true BS inter- action effects in the population. The term $\alpha\beta\gamma$ represents the bias which is specific to a given AB combination and a given subject, and its variance, $\sigma^2_{\alpha\beta\gamma}$, is the variance of the true ABS interaction effects in the population. The last term, ϵ, is the deviation of a single obtained score from the mean of an infinite number of such scores for a given subject in a given AB-category, and its variance, σ^2_{ϵ}, may be called the basic error variance. All of these effects are independent of one another, so that the variance of all obtained measures for all subjects in the population, including an infinite number of A-categories and an infinite number of B-categories, is given by

$$\sigma^2_{X_{ijk}} = \sigma^2_{\alpha} + \sigma^2_{\beta} + \sigma^2_{\gamma} + \sigma^2_{\alpha\beta} + \sigma^2_{\alpha\gamma} + \sigma^2_{\beta\gamma} + \sigma^2_{\alpha\beta\gamma} + \sigma^2_{\epsilon}. \tag{173}$$

From the estimates of these variance components, (170), we can infer a number of correlation coefficients of considerable general significance. One of these is the correlation, for all subjects in the population, of the mean of n' measures in each of a' categories of A within each of b' categories of B, and the mean of n' independent measures in each of the *same* A and B cate- gories. We will let

$$M_{iII} = \frac{1}{a'b'}\sum_{j=1}^{a'}\sum_{k=1}^{b'}M_{ijk}$$

represent one of these means (that for subject i), in which case,

$$\mu_{iII} = \frac{1}{a'b'}\sum_{j=1}^{a'}\sum_{k=1}^{b'}\mu_{ijk}$$

is the corresponding true score for subject i, and

$$\mu_{\cdot II} = \frac{1}{a'b'}\sum_{j=1}^{a'}\sum_{k=1}^{b'}\mu_{\cdot jk}$$

is the population mean of these true scores.

We may now write the identity

$$\frac{1}{a'b'}\sum_{j=1}^{a'}\sum_{k=1}^{b'}(M_{ijk} - \mu_{\cdot jk}) \overset{①}{=} \frac{1}{a'b'}\sum_{j=1}^{a'}\sum_{k=1}^{b'}(M_{ijk} - \mu_{ijk})$$

$$\overset{③}{+} \frac{1}{a'b'}\sum_{j=1}^{a'}\sum_{k=1}^{b'}(\mu_{ijk} - \mu_{ij\cdot} - \mu_{i\cdot k} - \mu_{\cdot jk} + \mu_{i\cdot\cdot} + \mu_{\cdot j\cdot} + \mu_{\cdot\cdot k} - \mu)$$

$$\overset{④}{+} \frac{1}{a'b'}\sum_{j=1}^{a'}\sum_{k=1}^{b'}(\mu_{\cdot j\cdot} - \mu_{i\cdot\cdot} - \mu_{\cdot j\cdot} + \mu) \tag{174}$$

$$+ \frac{1}{a'b'} \overset{a'}{\underset{j=1}{\sum}} \overset{b'}{\underset{k=1}{\sum}} (\mu_{i.k} - \mu_{i..} - \mu_{..k} + \mu)$$

⑤

$$+ \frac{1}{a'b'} \overset{a'}{\underset{j=1}{\sum}} \overset{b'}{\underset{k=1}{\sum}} (\mu_{i..} - \mu) \cdot$$

⑥

For convenience, we will refer to the terms in this identity by the circled numbers above them. We may note then that

$$④ = \frac{1}{a'} \overset{a'}{\underset{j=1}{\sum}} \frac{1}{b'} \overset{b'}{\underset{k=1}{\sum}} (\mu_{ij.} - \mu_{i..} - \mu_{.j.} + \mu)$$

$$= \frac{1}{a'} \overset{a'}{\underset{j=1}{\sum}} (\mu_{ij.} - \mu_{i..} - \mu_{.j.} + \mu)$$

since the quantity in parentheses is the same for all values of k. We may note likewise that

$$⑤ = \frac{1}{b'} \overset{b'}{\underset{k=1}{\sum}} (\mu_{i.k} - \mu_{i..} - \mu_{..k} + \mu) \cdot$$

Now, since the terms in the right of (174) are independent of one another, the variance of the left-hand term is equal to the sum of the variances of the right-hand terms. That is,

$$\sigma_{①}^2 = \sigma_{②}^2 + \sigma_{③}^2 + \sigma_{④}^2 + \sigma_{⑤}^2 + \sigma_{⑥}^2.$$

But

$$\sigma_{②}^2 = \frac{1}{a'^2 b'^2} \overset{a'}{\underset{j=1}{\sum}} \overset{b'}{\underset{k=1}{\sum}} \frac{\sigma_\epsilon^2}{n'} = \frac{\sigma_\epsilon^2}{a'b'n'}.$$

Also,

$$\sigma_{③}^2 = \frac{1}{a'^2 b'^2} \overset{a'}{\underset{j=1}{\sum}} \overset{b'}{\underset{k=1}{\sum}} \sigma_{\alpha\beta\gamma} = \frac{\sigma_{\alpha\beta\gamma}^2}{a'b'},$$

$$\sigma_{④}^2 = \frac{\sigma_{\alpha\gamma}^2}{a'},$$

$$\sigma_{⑤}^2 = \frac{\sigma_{\beta\gamma}^2}{b'},$$

$$\sigma_{⑥}^2 = \sigma_\gamma^2.$$

Accordingly,

$$\sigma_{①}^2 = \sigma_{(M_{iII} - \mu_{.II})}^2$$

$$= \frac{\sigma_\epsilon^2}{a'b'n'} + \frac{\sigma_{\alpha\beta\gamma}^2}{a'b'} + \frac{\sigma_{\alpha\gamma}^2}{a'} + \frac{\sigma_{\beta\gamma}^2}{b'} + \sigma_\gamma^2.$$

The variance of the corresponding true scores is

$$\sigma^2_{\mu_{iII}} = \sigma^2_{M_{iII}} \, [\text{when } n' \to \infty]$$

$$= \frac{\sigma^2_{\alpha\beta\gamma}}{a'b'} + \frac{\sigma^2_{\alpha\gamma}}{a'} + \frac{\sigma^2_{\beta\gamma}}{b'} + \sigma^2_{\gamma}$$

from which it follows that

$$r_{M_{iII}M_{iII}} = \frac{\dfrac{\sigma^2_{\alpha\beta\gamma}}{a'b'} + \dfrac{\sigma^2_{\alpha\gamma}}{a'} + \dfrac{\sigma^2_{\beta\gamma}}{b'} + \sigma^2_{\gamma}}{\dfrac{\sigma^2_{\epsilon}}{a'b'n'} + \dfrac{\sigma^2_{\alpha\beta\gamma}}{a'b'} + \dfrac{\sigma^2_{\alpha\gamma}}{a'} + \dfrac{\sigma^2_{\beta\gamma}}{b'} + \sigma^2_{\gamma}}. \tag{175}$$

More specific correlation coefficients may then be secured by letting a', b', and n' take various combinations of values in (175). For example, if we wish the average correlation (for all B-categories) of the mean of n' measures in each of a' categories of A within a *single* B-category, with the mean of n' independent observations in each of the *same* A-categories within the same B-category, we let $b' = 1$ in (175). If we wish the correlation of the mean of n' observations in a given AB sub-category with the mean of n' independent measures in the *same* AB sub-category, we let $a' = 1$ and $b' = 1$ in (175). If we let $a' = 1$, $b' = 1$, and $n' = 1$, we have the correlation of a single measure in a given AB sub-category with a second measure in this same sub-category. To estimate any of these coefficients, we substitute the values obtained from (170) in (175) and give a', b', and n' their appropriate values. Again, in the case when $a' = a$, $b' = b$, and $n' = n$, the expression (175) reduces to one which can be written in terms of an F, so that a confidence interval may be established by the method of pages 361–362.

Another coefficient of general significance is that between the mean of n' measures in each of a' categories of A within each of b' categories of B, and the mean of n' *independent* measures in each of a' *independent* categories of A, within each of the *same* categories of B. We will represent one of these means by

$$M_{iII} = \frac{1}{a'b'} \sum_{j=1}^{a'} \sum_{k=1}^{b'} M_{ijk},$$

and a second such mean by

$$M_{iII\,I} = \frac{1}{a'b'} \sum_{j=a'+1}^{2a'} \sum_{k=b'+1}^{2b'} M_{ijk}.$$

The corresponding true score for subject i is

$$\mu_{iII} = \frac{1}{a'b'} \sum_{j=1}^{a'} \sum_{k=1}^{b'} \mu_{ijk} \, [\text{when } a' \to \infty]$$

$$= \frac{1}{b'} \sum_{j=1}^{b'} \frac{1}{a'} \sum_{k=1}^{\infty} \mu_{ijk}$$

$$= \frac{1}{b'} \sum_{k=1}^{b'} \mu_{i.k},$$

and the population mean of the true scores is

$$\mu_{\cdot II} = \frac{1}{b'}\sum_{k=1}^{b'}\mu_{\cdot\cdot k} = \frac{1}{a'b'}\sum_{j=1}^{a'}\sum_{k=1}^{b'}\mu_{\cdot\cdot k\cdot}$$

We may now write the identity

$$\frac{1}{a'b'}\sum_{j=1}^{a'}\sum_{k=1}^{b'}(M_{ijk}-\mu_{\cdot\cdot k}) \overset{①}{=} \frac{1}{a'b'}\sum_{j=1}^{a'}\sum_{k=1}^{b'}\overset{②}{(M_{ijk}-\mu_{ijk})}$$

$$+\frac{1}{a'b'}\sum_{j=1}^{a'}\sum_{k=1}^{b'}\overset{③}{(\mu_{ijk}-\mu_{ij\cdot}-\mu_{i\cdot k}-\mu_{\cdot jk}+\mu_{i\cdot\cdot}+\mu_{\cdot j\cdot}+\mu_{\cdot\cdot k}-\mu)}$$

$$+\frac{1}{a'b'}\sum_{j=1}^{a'}\sum_{k=1}^{b'}\overset{④}{(\mu_{ij\cdot}-\mu_{i\cdot\cdot}-\mu_{\cdot j\cdot}+\mu)}$$

$$+\frac{1}{a'b'}\sum_{j=1}^{a'}\sum_{k=1}^{b'}\overset{⑤}{(\mu_{i\cdot k}-\mu_{i\cdot\cdot}-\mu_{\cdot\cdot k}+\mu)} \quad (176)$$

$$+\frac{1}{a'b'}\sum_{j=1}^{a'}\sum_{k=1}^{b'}\overset{⑥}{(\mu_{\cdot jk}-\mu_{\cdot j\cdot}-\mu_{\cdot\cdot k}+\mu)}$$

$$+\frac{1}{a'b'}\sum_{j=1}^{a'}\sum_{k=1}^{b'}\overset{⑦}{(\mu_{i\cdot\cdot}-\mu)}$$

$$+\frac{1}{a'b'}\sum_{j=1}^{a'}\sum_{k=1}^{b'}\overset{⑧}{(\mu_{\cdot j\cdot}-\mu)}.$$

We may next note that

$$\sigma^2_{②}=\frac{\sigma^2_\epsilon}{a'b'n'},\ \sigma^2_{③}=\frac{\sigma^2_{\alpha\beta\gamma}}{a'b'},\ \sigma^2_{④}=\frac{\sigma^2_{\alpha\gamma}}{a'}$$

$$\sigma^2_{⑤}=\frac{\sigma^2_{\beta\gamma}}{b'},\ \sigma^2_{⑥}=0,\ \sigma^2_{⑦}=\sigma^2_\gamma,\ \text{and}\ \sigma^2_{⑧}=0.$$

Accordingly,

$$\sigma^2_{M_{iII}}=\frac{\sigma^2_\epsilon}{a'b'n'}+\frac{\sigma^2_{\alpha\beta\gamma}}{a'b'}+\frac{\sigma^2_{\alpha\gamma}}{a'}+\frac{\sigma^2_{\beta\gamma}}{b'}+\sigma^2_\gamma.$$

The variance of the corresponding true scores is

$$\sigma^2_{\mu\,iII}=\sigma^2_{M_{iII}}\ [\text{when}\ n'\to\infty\ \text{and}\ a'\to\infty]$$

$$=\frac{\sigma^2_{\beta\gamma}}{b'}+\sigma^2_\gamma.$$

The desired coefficient is then given by

$$r_{M_{iII}M_{iII I}}=\frac{\dfrac{\sigma^2_{\beta\gamma}}{b'}+\sigma^2_\gamma}{\dfrac{\sigma^2_\epsilon}{a'b'n'}+\dfrac{\sigma^2_{\alpha\beta\gamma}}{a'b'}+\dfrac{\sigma^2_{\alpha\gamma}}{a'}+\dfrac{\sigma^2_{\beta\gamma}}{b'}+\sigma^2_\gamma}. \quad (177)$$

Again we may secure more specific correlation coefficients by letting a', b', and n' take various values. For example, if we wish the average correlation (for all B-categories) of the mean of n' measures in each of a' categories of A within a single B-category, and the mean of n' independent measures in each of a' *independent* categories of A within the *same* B-category, we let $b'= 1$ in (177). If we wish the average correlation (for all AB sub-categories) of the mean of n' measures in one AB sub-category within a given B-category with the mean of n' measures in another AB sub-category within the same B-category, we let $a' = 1$ and $b' = 1$ in (177).

A correlation of particular significance is obtained by letting $a' = 1$ and $n' = 1$ in (177). The result is the correlation between the mean of a single measure within each of b' categories of B within a single A-category, and the mean of a single measure within each of the same B-categories but in a different A-category. If B represents "items" in a test and A represents "equivalent forms" of the test, this is the equivalent forms reliability of the mean score on the test.

$$r_{M_{i1I}M_{i2I}} = \frac{\dfrac{\sigma_{\beta\gamma}^2}{b'} + \sigma_{\gamma}^2}{\dfrac{\sigma_{\epsilon}^2}{b'} + \dfrac{\sigma_{\alpha\beta\gamma}^2}{b'} + \sigma_{\alpha\gamma}^2 + \dfrac{\sigma_{\beta\gamma}^2}{b'} + \sigma_{\gamma}^2}. \tag{178}$$

By reversing the roles of A and B in (177) we can obviously secure a similar expression for $r_{M_{iII}M_{iI\,II}}$.

Again we can estimate any of these correlation coefficients by substituting from (170) in (177) and letting a', b', and n' take the appropriate values. As in former instances, if we do this and let $a' = a$, $b' = b$, and $n' = n$ in (177), the result may be expressed in terms of an F, so that its confidence interval may be established.

Another coefficient of considerable general significance is that between the mean of n' measures in each of a' categories of A within each of b' categories of B, with the mean of n' independent measures in each of a' *independent* categories of A, within each of b' *independent* categories of B. We will represent one of these means by

$$M_{iII} = \frac{1}{a'b'} \sum_{j=1}^{a'} \sum_{k=1}^{b'} M_{ijk}$$

and a second similar mean by

$$M_{i\,II\,II} = \frac{1}{a'b'} \sum_{j=a'+1}^{2a'} \sum_{k=b'+1}^{2b'} M_{ijk\cdot}$$

The corresponding true score for subject i is

$$\mu_{iII} = \frac{1}{a'b'} \sum_{j=1}^{a'} \sum_{k=1}^{b'} \mu_{ijk} \quad [\text{when } a' \to \infty \text{ and } b' \to \infty]$$
$$= \mu_{i..}$$

and the population mean of these true scores is μ.

We may now write the identity

$$\frac{1}{a'b'}\sum_{j=1}^{a'}\sum_{k=1}^{b'}(M_{iII}-\mu) \overset{\text{①}}{=} \frac{1}{a'b'}\sum_{j=1}^{a'}\sum_{k=1}^{b'}(M_{ijk}-\mu_{ijk}) \overset{\text{②}}{}$$

$$+ \frac{1}{a'b'}\sum_{j=1}^{a'}\sum_{k=1}^{b'}(\mu_{ijk}-\mu_{ij.}-\mu_{i.k}+\mu_{i..}+\mu_{.j.}+\mu_{..k}-\mu) \overset{\text{③}}{}$$

$$+ \frac{1}{a'b'}\sum_{j=1}^{a'}\sum_{k=1}^{b'}(\mu_{ij.}-\mu_{i..}-\mu_{.j.}+\mu) \overset{\text{④}}{}$$

$$+ \frac{1}{a'b'}\sum_{j=1}^{a'}\sum_{k=1}^{b'}(\mu_{i.k}-\mu_{i..}-\mu_{..k}+\mu) \overset{\text{⑤}}{} \qquad (179)$$

$$+ \frac{1}{a'b'}\sum_{j=1}^{a'}\sum_{k=1}^{b'}(\mu_{.jk}-\mu_{.j.}-\mu_{..k}+\mu) \overset{\text{⑥}}{}$$

$$+ \frac{1}{a'b'}\sum_{j=1}^{a'}\sum_{k=1}^{b'}(\mu_{i..}-\mu) \overset{\text{⑦}}{}$$

$$+ \frac{1}{a'b'}\sum_{j=1}^{a'}\sum_{k=1}^{b'}(\mu_{.j.}-\mu) \overset{\text{⑧}}{}$$

$$+ \frac{1}{a'b'}\sum_{j=1}^{a'}\sum_{k=1}^{b'}(\mu_{..k}-\mu). \overset{\text{⑨}}{}$$

We next note that

$$\sigma_{②}^2 = \frac{\sigma_\epsilon^2}{a'b'n'}, \ \sigma_{③}^2 = \frac{\sigma_{\alpha\beta\gamma}^2}{a'b'}, \ \sigma_{④}^2 = \frac{\sigma_{\alpha\gamma}^2}{a'}, \ \sigma_{⑤}^2 = \frac{\sigma_{\beta\gamma}^2}{b'}.$$

$$\sigma_{⑥}^2 = 0, \ \sigma_{⑦}^2 = \sigma_\gamma^2, \ \sigma_{⑧}^2 = 0, \text{ and } \sigma_{⑨}^2 = 0.$$

Accordingly,

$$\sigma_{M_{iII}}^2 = \frac{\sigma_\epsilon^2}{a'b'n'} + \frac{\sigma_{\alpha\beta\gamma}^2}{a'b'} + \frac{\sigma_{\alpha\gamma}^2}{a'} + \frac{\sigma_{\beta\gamma}^2}{b'} + \sigma_\gamma^2.$$

The variance of the corresponding true scores is

$$\sigma_{\mu_{iII}}^2 = \sigma_{M_{iII}}^2 \ [\text{when } n' \to \infty, \ a' \to \infty, \text{ and } b' \to \infty]$$

$$= \sigma_\gamma^2.$$

The desired reliability coefficient is then given by

$$r_{M_{iII}M_{iIIII}} = \frac{\sigma_\gamma^2}{\dfrac{\sigma_\epsilon^2}{a'b'n'} + \dfrac{\sigma_{\alpha\beta\gamma}^2}{a'b'} + \dfrac{\sigma_{\alpha\gamma}^2}{a'} + \dfrac{\sigma_{\beta\gamma}^2}{b'} + \sigma_\gamma^2}. \tag{180}$$

Again we may secure more specific reliability coefficients by letting a', b', and n' take various values in (180). For example, if we let $a' = 1$, $b' = 1$, and $n' = 1$, we have the correlation between a single measure in a single A-category within a single B-category with a single measure from a different A-category and a different B-category. This coefficient, which may be denoted by $r_{X_{i11}X_{i22}}$, best deserves being described as "the" reliability coefficient of X_{ijk} for a specified population of subjects, since it takes into consideration all important sources of error identified in the analysis so far as the selected A and B categories are concerned.

We may in this situation distinguish several types of "true" scores. The mean of an infinite number of observations of a given subject in each of an infinite number of B-categories within the same A-category (Category 1), which has been denoted $\mu_{i1.}$, may be called an "A-true score." Similarly, $\mu_{i.1}$ represents a "B-true score," and μ_{i11} represents an "AB-true score." The mean of an infinite number of AB-true scores for an infinite number both of A-categories and B-categories is "the" true score, and has been denoted by $\mu_{i..}$.

The correlations between different A-true scores or different B-true scores, or between different AB-true scores in the same A-category, or different AB-true scores in the same B-category, or between AB-true scores from both different A and different B categories may all have considerable practical significance in planning a test or a measurement schedule. These may all be estimated from the estimated variance components.

The "reliability" of an A-true score, that is, the correlation between different A-true scores for the entire population of subjects is obtained by letting $a' = 1$, $b' = \infty$, and $n' = \infty$ in (178), which then reduces to

$$r_{\mu_{i1.}\mu_{i2.}} = \frac{\sigma_\gamma^2}{\sigma_{\beta\gamma}^2 + \sigma_\gamma^2}.$$

Similarly, the correlation between AB-true scores from different A and B categories is obtained by letting $a' = 1$ and $b' = 1$ and $n' = \infty$ in (178), which reduces to

$$r_{\mu_{i11}\mu_{i22}} = \frac{\sigma_\gamma^2}{\sigma_{\alpha\beta\gamma}^2 + \sigma_{\beta\gamma}^2 + \sigma_{\alpha\gamma}^2 + \sigma_\gamma^2}.$$

Expressions for $r_{\mu_{i11}\mu_{i12}}$, $r_{\mu_{i11}\mu_{i21}}$ $r_{\mu_{i.1}\mu_{i.2}}$, may be similarly obtained from (175), (177), and (178), in the last two cases by interchanging A and B.

Estimates of any of the preceding correlation coefficients may be obtained by substituting for the variance components in the right-hand side of the expression (180) the estimates of these components obtained from the sample

(170). It is left to the student to determine the simplest expression for each r in terms of the mean squares, and to show how these expressions simplify when $n' = n$ or $a' = a$ or $b' = b$, etc.

Possible applications of this design are suggested in the following paragraphs:

Each of the s subjects performs a task n times for each of a observers on each of b days, the observers and days being the same for each subject, and regarded as randomly selected from populations of observers and days.

Each of s workers produces a certain product on each of a machines on each of b days, the machines and days being randomly selected but the same for all workers.

Each of s pilots performs a certain maneuver a times on each of b' (random) airplane rides, being accompanied by a different observer on each ride, the same (random) observers being used for all pilots.

Each of s subjects responds to each of a' items on each of b' equivalent forms of a performance test. The items are not regarded as randomly selected, but the forms are a random sample from a population of forms.

Each of s randomly selected subjects responds n' times to each of a items in each of b parts of a performance test, neither A nor B being regarded as random effects.

It is left as an exercise for the student to suggest further applications and to discuss the meanings of the various variance components and of the possible reliability coefficients in each illustrative situation, as well as to suggest how the information may be employed in planning measurement schedules.

Groups (of Observations) Within Subjects

In some reliability studies, the design cmployed will be similar to the groups-within-treatments design discussed in Chapter 7. Suppose, for example, that each of s subjects performs a task n times independently on each of a occasions, the sample of "occasions" for each subject being regarded as independent of that for any other subject. The analysio of the total sum of squares will then be into between-subjects, between-occasions-within-subjects, and within-occasions. In more general terms, the analysis of the total sum of squares will be into between-subjects, between-groups-within-subjects, and within-groups.

We will let X_{ijk} represent the kth observation ($k = 1, 2, \ldots n$) in the jth group for the ith subject, M_{ij} represent the mean of the n observations in the jth group ($j = 1, 2, \ldots a$) for the ith subject, M_i represent the mean of the an observations for the ith subject $(i = 1, 2, \ldots s)$ and M represent the general mean of the ans observations. We will let μ_{ij}, μ_j, and μ represent the corresponding true means, respectively. We may then write the identity

$$X_{ijk} = \mu + (\mu_i - \mu) + (\mu_{ij} - \mu_i) + (X - \mu_{ij})$$

from which it follows that

$$\sigma_X^2 = \sigma_{(\mu_i - \mu)}^2 + \sigma_{(\mu_{ij} - \mu_i)}^2 + \sigma_{(x - \mu_{ij})}^2$$

$$= \sigma_\gamma^2 + \sigma_\alpha^2 + \sigma_\epsilon^2.$$

The expected values of the mean squares obtained from the sample are

$$E(ms_S) = \sigma_\epsilon^2 + n\sigma_\alpha^2 + an\sigma_\gamma^2$$

$$E(ms_{GwS}) = \sigma_\epsilon^2 + n\sigma_\alpha^2$$

$$E(ms_w) = \sigma_\epsilon^2.$$

From these it follows that

$$\text{est'd } \sigma_\epsilon^2 = ms_w$$

$$\text{est'd } \sigma_\alpha^2 = \frac{ms_{GwS} - ms_w}{n}$$

$$\text{est'd } \sigma_\gamma^2 = \frac{ms_S - ms_{GwS}}{an}.$$

From the preceding, it is obvious that the variance of the mean (M_i') of n' observations in each of a' groups is

$$\sigma_{M_i}^2 = \sigma_\gamma^2 + \frac{\sigma_\alpha^2}{a'} + \frac{\sigma_\epsilon^2}{a'n'}$$

and that the reliability of such a mean score is given by

$$r_{M_i M_i} = \frac{a'n'\sigma_\gamma^2}{n'\sigma_\alpha^2 + \sigma_\epsilon^2 + a'n'\sigma_\gamma^2} \qquad (181)$$

From (181) various reliability coefficients may be obtained by substituting various combinations of values for a' and n'.

It is again left as an exercise for the student to suggest various applications of this design and to discuss the meanings of the reliability coefficients that may be obtained with each, as well as to suggest how the information may be employed in the planning of a measurement schedule.

Appendix

TABLE OF RANDOM NUMBERS

How to Use the Table of Random Numbers. The basic operation in most uses of this table is the arrangement of a number (N) of serially-numbered items in random order. For example, if for a group of 120 subjects one wishes to assign 40 subjects at random to each of three treatment groups, one would first arrange the subjects in random order and then assign the first 40 in this order to treatment 1, the second 40 to treatment 2, etc. The simplest procedure, particularly when N is large, is to (1) enter the serial numbers on cards or slips of paper, (2) make a "blind" selection of a page of the table of random numbers and of an $(x + 2)$-digit row or column on this page (x being the number of digits in N), (3) enter the random numbers in this row or column on the cards in the order in which they appear in the table, going on to adjacent rows (or columns) if necessary, (4) arrange the cards in order of the random numbers. The cards will then be arranged in random order, except for those consecutive cards bearing the *same* random number. Since the random numbers contain two digits more than N, there will be very few such ties, but the cards within each "tied" set may be arranged in random order by assigning new random numbers to them and rearranging them in the order of these new random numbers.

APPENDIX

Table of Random Numbers [1]

	1	2	3	4	5	6	7	8	9	10	11	12	13	14	15	16	17	18	19	20
1	03	47	43	73	86	36	96	47	36	61	46	98	63	71	62	33	26	16	80	45
2	97	74	24	67	62	42	81	14	57	20	42	53	32	37	32	27	07	36	07	51
3	16	76	62	27	66	56	50	26	71	07	32	90	79	78	53	13	55	38	58	59
4	12	56	85	99	26	96	96	68	27	31	05	03	72	93	15	57	12	10	14	21
5	55	59	56	35	64	38	54	82	46	21	31	62	43	90	90	06	18	44	32	53
6	16	22	77	94	39	49	54	43	54	82	17	37	93	23	78	87	35	20	96	43
7	84	42	17	53	31	57	24	55	06	88	77	04	74	47	67	21	76	33	50	25
8	63	01	63	78	59	16	95	55	57	19	98	10	50	71	75	12	86	73	58	07
9	33	21	12	34	29	78	64	56	07	82	52	42	07	44	38	15	51	00	13	42
10	57	60	86	32	44	09	47	27	96	54	49	17	46	09	62	90	52	84	77	27
11	18	18	07	92	46	44	17	16	58	09	79	83	86	19	62	06	76	50	03	10
12	26	62	38	97	75	84	16	07	44	99	83	11	46	32	24	20	14	85	88	45
13	23	42	40	64	74	82	97	77	77	81	07	45	32	14	08	32	98	94	07	72
14	52	36	28	19	95	50	92	26	11	97	00	56	76	31	38	80	22	02	53	53
15	37	85	94	35	12	83	39	50	08	30	42	34	07	96	88	54	42	06	87	98
16	70	29	17	12	13	40	33	20	38	26	13	89	51	03	74	17	76	37	13	04
17	56	62	18	37	35	96	83	50	87	75	97	12	25	93	47	70	33	24	03	54
18	99	49	57	22	77	88	42	95	45	72	16	64	36	16	00	04	43	18	66	79
19	16	08	15	04	72	33	27	14	34	09	45	59	34	68	49	12	72	07	34	45
20	31	16	93	32	43	50	27	89	87	19	20	15	37	00	49	52	85	66	60	44
21	68	34	30	13	70	55	74	30	77	40	44	22	78	84	26	04	33	36	09	52
22	74	57	25	65	76	59	29	97	68	60	71	91	38	67	54	13	58	18	25	27
23	27	42	37	86	53	48	55	90	65	72	96	57	69	36	10	96	46	92	42	45
24	00	39	68	29	61	66	37	32	20	30	77	84	57	03	29	10	45	65	04	26
25	29	94	98	94	24	68	49	69	10	82	53	75	91	93	30	34	25	20	57	27
26	16	90	82	66	59	83	62	64	11	12	67	19	00	71	74	60	47	21	29	68
27	11	27	94	75	06	06	09	19	74	66	02	94	37	34	02	76	70	90	30	86
28	35	24	10	16	20	33	32	51	26	38	79	78	45	04	91	16	92	53	56	16
29	38	23	16	86	38	42	38	97	01	50	87	75	66	81	41	40	01	74	91	62
30	31	96	25	91	47	96	44	33	49	13	34	96	82	53	91	00	52	43	48	85
31	66	67	40	67	14	64	05	71	95	86	11	05	65	09	68	76	83	20	37	90
32	14	90	84	45	11	75	73	88	05	90	52	27	41	14	86	22	98	12	22	08
33	68	05	51	18	00	33	96	02	74	19	07	60	62	93	55	59	33	82	43	90
34	20	46	78	73	90	97	51	40	14	02	04	02	33	31	08	39	54	16	49	36
35	64	19	58	97	79	15	06	15	93	20	01	90	10	75	06	40	78	78	89	62
36	05	26	93	70	60	22	35	85	15	13	92	03	51	59	77	59	56	78	06	83
37	07	97	10	88	23	09	98	42	99	64	61	71	62	99	06	51	29	16	93	15
38	68	71	86	85	85	54	87	66	47	54	73	32	98	11	12	44	95	92	63	16
39	14	65	52	68	74	87	37	78	22	41	26	78	63	06	55	13	08	27	01	50
40	17	53	77	58	71	71	59	36	50	72	12	41	94	96	26	44	95	27	36	99
41	90	26	59	21	19	23	41	61	33	12	96	93	02	18	39	07	02	18	36	07
42	41	23	52	55	99	31	52	23	69	96	10	47	48	45	88	13	41	43	89	20
43	26	99	61	65	53	58	04	49	80	70	42	10	50	67	42	32	17	55	85	74

[1] Reprinted from Table 33 of R. A. Fisher and F. Yates, *Statistical Tables for Biological, Agricultural, and Medical Research*, published by Oliver and Boyd Ltd., by permission of the authors and publishers.

Table of Random Numbers (continued)

	1	2	3	4	5	6	7	8	9	10	11	12	13	14	15	16	17	18	19	20
1	53	74	23	99	67	61	32	28	69	84	94	62	67	86	24	98	33	41	19	95
2	63	38	06	86	54	99	00	65	26	94	02	82	90	23	07	79	62	67	80	60
3	35	30	68	21	46	06	72	17	10	94	25	21	31	74	96	49	28	24	00	49
4	63	43	36	92	69	65	51	18	37	88	61	38	44	12	45	32	92	84	88	65
5	98	25	37	55	26	01	91	82	81	46	74	71	12	94	97	24	02	71	37	07
6	02	63	31	17	69	71	50	80	39	56	38	15	40	11	48	43	40	45	86	98
7	64	55	22	21	82	48	22	28	06	00	61	64	13	54	91	82	78	12	23	29
8	85	07	26	13	89	01	10	07	82	04	59	63	69	36	03	69	11	15	83	80
9	58	54	16	24	15	51	54	44	82	00	62	61	65	04	69	38	18	65	18	97
10	34	85	27	84	87	61	48	64	56	26	90	18	48	13	26	37	70	15	42	57
11	03	92	18	27	46	57	99	16	96	56	30	33	72	85	22	84	64	38	56	98
12	95	30	27	59	37	62	75	41	66	48	86	97	80	61	45	23	53	04	01	63
13	08	45	93	15	22	60	21	75	46	91	98	77	27	85	42	28	88	61	08	84
14	07	08	55	18	40	45	44	74	13	90	24	94	96	61	02	57	55	66	83	15
15	01	85	89	95	66	51	10	19	34	88	15	84	97	19	75	12	76	39	43	78
16	72	84	71	14	35	19	11	58	49	26	50	11	17	17	76	86	31	57	20	18
17	88	78	28	16	84	13	52	53	94	53	75	45	69	30	96	73	89	65	70	31
18	45	17	75	65	57	28	40	19	72	12	25	12	74	75	67	60	40	60	81	19
19	96	76	28	12	54	22	01	11	94	25	71	96	16	16	88	68	64	36	74	45
20	43	31	67	72	30	24	02	94	08	63	38	32	36	66	02	69	36	38	25	39
21	50	44	66	44	21	66	06	58	04	62	68	15	54	35	02	42	36	48	96	32
22	22	66	22	15	86	26	63	74	41	99	58	42	36	62	24	58	37	52	18	51
23	96	24	40	14	51	23	22	30	88	57	95	67	47	29	83	94	69	40	06	07
24	31	73	91	61	19	60	20	72	93	48	98	57	07	23	69	65	95	39	69	58
25	78	60	73	99	84	43	89	94	36	34	56	69	47	07	41	90	22	91	07	12
26	84	37	90	61	56	70	10	23	98	05	85	11	34	76	60	76	48	45	34	60
27	36	67	10	08	23	98	93	35	08	86	99	29	76	29	81	33	34	91	58	93
28	07	28	59	07	48	89	64	58	89	75	83	85	62	27	89	30	14	78	56	27
29	10	15	83	87	60	79	24	31	66	56	21	48	24	06	93	91	98	94	05	49
30	55	19	68	97	65	03	73	52	16	56	00	53	55	90	27	33	42	29	38	87
31	53	81	29	13	39	35	01	20	71	34	62	33	74	82	14	53	73	19	09	03
32	51	86	32	68	92	33	98	74	66	99	40	14	71	94	58	35	94	19	38	81
33	35	91	70	29	13	80	03	54	07	27	96	94	78	32	66	50	95	52	74	33
34	37	71	67	95	13	20	02	77	95	94	64	85	04	05	72	01	32	90	76	14
35	93	66	13	83	27	92	79	64	64	72	28	54	96	53	84	48	14	52	98	94
36	02	96	08	45	64	13	05	00	41	84	93	07	54	72	59	21	45	57	09	77
37	49	83	43	48	36	92	88	33	69	96	72	36	04	19	76	47	45	15	18	60
38	84	60	71	62	46	40	80	81	30	37	34	39	23	04	38	25	15	35	71	30
39	18	17	30	88	71	44	91	14	88	47	89	23	30	63	15	56	34	20	47	89
40	79	69	10	61	78	71	32	76	95	62	87	00	22	58	40	92	54	01	75	25
41	75	93	36	47	83	56	20	14	82	11	74	21	97	90	65	96	42	68	63	96
42	38	30	92	29	03	06	28	81	39	38	62	25	06	84	63	61	29	08	93	67
43	51	29	50	10	34	31	57	75	95	80	51	97	02	74	77	76	15	58	49	44
44	21	31	38	86	24	37	79	81	53	74	73	24	16	10	33	52	83	90	94	76
45	29	01	23	87	88	58	02	39	37	67	42	10	14	20	92	16	55	23	42	45
46	95	33	95	22	00	18	74	92	00	18	38	79	58	69	32	81	76	80	26	92
47	90	84	60	79	80	24	36	59	87	38	82	07	53	89	35	96	35	23	79	18
48	46	40	62	98	82	54	97	20	45	95	15	74	80	08	32	16	46	70	50	80
49	20	31	89	03	43	38	36	92	68	72	32	14	82	99	70	80	60	47	18	97
50	71	59	73	05	50	08	22	23	71	77	91	01	93	20	49	82	96	59	26	94

Table of Random Numbers (continued)

	1	2	3	4	5	6	7	8	9	10	11	12	13	14	15	16	17	18	19	20
1	22	17	68	65	84	68	94	23	92	35	86	02	22	57	51	61	09	43	95	06
2	19	36	27	69	46	13	79	93	37	55	39	77	32	77	09	85	52	05	30	62
3	16	77	23	02	77	09	61	87	25	21	28	06	25	24	93	16	71	13	59	78
4	03	28	28	26	08	73	37	32	04	05	69	30	16	90	05	88	69	58	29	99
5	78	43	76	71	61	20	44	90	32	64	97	67	63	99	61	46	38	03	93	22
6	93	22	53	64	39	07	10	63	76	35	87	03	04	79	88	08	13	13	85	51
7	78	76	58	54	74	92	38	70	96	92	52	06	79	79	45	82	63	18	27	44
8	23	68	35	26	00	99	53	93	61	28	52	70	05	48	34	56	64	04	61	86
9	15	39	24	70	99	93	86	52	77	64	15	33	59	05	28	22	87	26	07	47
10	58	71	96	30	24	18	46	23	34	27	85	13	99	24	44	49	18	09	79	49
11	57	35	27	33	72	24	53	63	94	09	41	10	76	47	91	44	04	95	49	66
12	48	50	86	54	48	22	06	34	72	52	82	21	15	65	20	33	29	94	71	11
13	61	96	48	95	03	07	16	39	33	66	98	56	10	56	79	77	21	30	27	12
14	36	93	89	41	26	29	70	83	63	51	99	74	20	52	36	87	09	41	15	09
15	18	87	00	42	31	57	90	12	02	07	23	47	37	17	31	54	08	01	88	63
16	88	56	53	27	59	33	35	72	67	47	77	34	55	45	70	08	18	27	38	90
17	09	72	95	84	29	49	41	31	06	70	42	38	06	45	18	64	84	73	31	65
18	12	96	88	17	31	65	19	69	02	83	60	74	86	90	68	24	64	19	35	51
19	85	94	57	24	16	92	09	94	38	76	22	00	27	69	95	29	81	94	78	70
20	38	64	43	59	98	98	77	87	68	07	91	51	78	62	44	40	98	05	93	78
21	53	44	09	42	72	00	41	86	79	79	68	47	22	00	20	35	55	31	51	51
22	40	76	66	26	84	57	99	99	90	37	36	63	32	08	58	37	40	13	68	97
23	02	17	79	18	05	12	59	52	57	02	22	07	90	47	03	28	14	11	30	79
24	95	17	82	06	53	31	51	10	96	46	92	06	88	07	77	56	11	50	81	69
25	35	76	22	42	92	96	11	83	44	80	34	68	35	48	77	33	42	40	90	60
26	26	29	13	46	41	85	47	04	66	08	34	72	47	59	13	82	43	80	46	15
27	77	80	20	75	82	72	82	32	99	90	63	95	73	76	63	89	73	44	99	05
28	46	40	66	44	52	91	36	74	43	53	30	82	13	53	00	78	45	63	98	35
29	37	56	08	18	90	77	53	85	46	47	31	91	18	95	59	24	16	74	11	53
30	61	65	61	68	66	37	27	47	39	19	84	83	70	07	38	53	21	40	06	71
31	93	43	69	96	07	34	18	04	52	35	56	27	09	24	86	61	85	53	83	45
32	21	96	60	12	99	11	20	99	45	18	48	13	93	55	34	18	37	79	49	90
33	95	20	47	97	97	27	37	83	28	71	00	06	41	41	74	45	89	09	39	84
34	97	86	21	78	73	10	64	81	92	59	58	76	17	14	97	04	76	62	16	17
35	69	92	06	34	13	59	71	74	17	32	27	55	10	24	19	23	71	82	13	74
36	04	31	17	21	56	33	73	99	19	87	26	72	39	27	67	53	77	57	68	93
37	61	06	98	03	91	87	14	77	43	96	43	00	65	98	50	45	60	33	01	07
38	85	93	85	86	88	72	87	08	62	40	16	06	10	89	20	23	21	34	74	97
39	21	74	32	47	45	73	96	07	94	52	09	65	90	77	47	25	76	16	19	33
40	15	69	53	92	80	79	96	23	53	10	64	39	07	16	29	45	33	02	43	70
41	02	89	08	04	49	20	21	14	68	86	87	63	93	95	17	11	29	01	95	80
42	87	18	15	89	79	85	43	01	72	73	08	61	74	51	69	89	74	39	82	15
43	98	83	71	94	22	59	97	50	99	52	08	52	85	08	40	87	80	61	65	31
44	10	08	58	21	66	72	68	49	29	31	89	85	84	46	06	59	73	19	85	23
45	47	90	56	10	08	88	02	84	27	83	42	29	72	23	19	66	56	45	65	79
46	22	85	61	68	80	49	64	92	85	44	16	40	12	89	88	50	14	49	81	06
47	67	80	43	79	33	12	83	11	41	16	25	58	19	36	70	77	02	43	00	52
48	27	62	40	96	72	79	44	61	40	15	14	53	40	64	39	27	31	59	50	28
49	33	78	80	87	15	38	30	06	38	21	14	47	47	07	26	54	96	87	53	32
50	13	13	92	66	99	47	24	49	57	74	32	25	43	62	17	10	97	11	69	84

Index

389

$$\frac{800}{2.5 \overline{)2000}}$$